Mildred
the Crazy
Cat Lady

Mildred the Crazy Cat Lady

K. S. Horak

First published in the United Kingdom in 2019 by Wolf House Publishing Ltd.

Copyright © K S Horak 2019

FIRST EDITION

A catalogue record for this book is available from the British Library.

ISBN: 978-0-9557769-6-0

Wolf House Publishing Ltd
8 Shoplatch
Shrewsbury
Shropshire
SY1 1HF
United Kingdom

kshorak.com
wolfhousepublishing.com

Cover Art by Lyndon White who has granted exclusive license for perpetuity to K S Horak.

Printed and bound in Great Britain by Bell & Bain Ltd.

CONTENTS

For Lauren

Chapter One:

EVERY CAT HAS A NAME

Missy was a lonely cat and the only cat of Mildred.

Missy did not like being called Missy as she preferred to be called by her 'real' name of Nahla; other cats in the neighbourhood would call her that and she addressed them by their proper names as well.

Humans for some reason called cats stupid names like Fluffy, Mr Jinks, Bumpkin and other ridiculous names that made absolutely no sense at all.

It is for this reason that Nahla does her best to ignore Mildred when she stands outside the house, whether it be in her slippers and nightgown or her usual choice of 'ladies fashion', shouting 'MISSSSYYYYY' as loud as she can while banging the lid of a tin of horrible cat food with a spoon.

The neighbours were used to this of course; they could even set their clocks by Mildred as every day without fail at 7am and 7pm she would scream the 'Missy' name as loud as she could for prolonged periods of time.

In fact Mr Jenkins who lives next door uses Mildred's voice as his alarm clock to wake him before he goes to work. There are many things certain in life and Mildred's morning cat call would be one of them.

Overall the neighbours didn't speak with Mildred regularly and she was okay with that as she didn't really want to talk to them much either. Mildred was a very private person, a single person and more of a cat person you may say.

She would speak to Nahla all day long even when she was sleeping or pretending to be. It was a useful relationship of convenience staying with the human and the constant drone of her voice was helpful background noise to fall asleep to.

But Mildred loved cats; in fact all Mildreds loved cats and that was a fact.

Most of Mildred's friends were also called Mildred or Daphne or Jessica; Nahla had no idea why this was and for some reason she didn't have friends called Suzie, Louise or other more common names as most people do.

Mildred's friends would never come to the house and they would always call her on the phone. Whilst other humans used computers to speak with each other, Mildred grew up in a different time a long time ago, when the telephone was used for people to speak with each other, there was no hint of a computer or any form of 'technology' in Mildred's home.

Mildred was probably quite ancient Nahla considered and at least over the age of 40.

Mildred's phone was also shaped like a cat. She would speak to the other Mildreds with her ear pressed firmly against the face of the cat and after the person had finished talking at the other end, she would then speak back to them through the cat's bottom.

She had many pictures of cats on the walls as well as a framed certificate that she polished most days; it was the only thing in the house that was regularly cleaned. Her mug for drinking tea had a picture of a cat on it, Mildred's bedspread had lots of pictures of cats on it and a rug outside the front door said 'beware of the cat'; what people had to be beware of Nahla did not know but that was the way it was in Mildred's house.

Mildred's day was the same nearly every day:

- 7am find Missy
- Talk to Missy all morning
- Go to the shop to see Mr Franks to buy cat food and a newspaper (on Wednesday she would also buy the weekly television magazine)
- Talk to Missy in the afternoon
- 7pm find Missy
- Watch television game shows
- 9pm go to bed

Nahla also had her daily routine:

- 7am ignore Mildred
- Sleep all morning when Mildred tried to talk to her
- Make a mess of the house when Mildred went to the shops
- Watch Mildred on occasion attempt to clean up the mess
- 7pm ignore Mildred
- 9pm playtime!

Once a month however Mildred would leave the house and sometimes not return all day, often arriving back late in the evening. Nahla never knew where she went but she always returned with a smile; dragging her oversized bag behind her and often walking faster than usual resembling something like a waddling penguin with a hat on.

Nahla had a jet black coat with big round eyes and in summer time she would lie outside, usually on her side, with her black tail with a white tip swinging to and fro sometimes swatting away flies. Summer was good, summer was fun and the world around Nahla seemed happier. There were more flowers than winter and there were bees that she could chase. Young children would drop sweets on the floor and Nahla was happy to pick them up afterwards. This made a wonderful change from the same tinned cat food Mildred would attempt to feed her every day. Quite why she would serve up food that contained meat (that was fish flavoured) with broccoli and carrots only Mildred knew; Mr Franks whom she bought almost everything from clearly owned a most peculiar shop.

Sometimes often through sheer boredom Nahla liked to play tricks on Mildred and therefore Mildred was very well known to the fire brigade. Mr Watkins was the fire chief "What is it this time Mildred, where is the cat now?" in what seemed to be a regular monthly phone call.

Nahla liked to climb up trees and as she got older she decided to climb bigger trees, the bigger the better! The biggest tree Nahla and the other cats in the neighbourhood would call 'Stan'. Stan was a very old tree and around October time Stan would grow conkers. This was the only time of the year that Nahla and the others would not climb up Stan as boys in the area would throw sticks up at Stan to knock his conkers off as the boys liked playing conkers at school apparently. Nahla was yet to be able to climb to the very top of Stan and the furthest she had got was 10 branches from the top, but she would get to the top soon as her climbing skills were forever improving.

However Nahla had climbed all of the other trees within the three roads where she lived. Nahla like many other cats had her own territory and hers was Rocke Road, Benbow Street and Darwin Road. One time on a very, very rare occasion Nahla decided to pay some attention to Mildred and as she talked away she informed her there were many Mildreds, Daphnes and Jessicas and that you could usually find one in every town, village or city. Humans appeared to have larger territories.

Mr Watkins was not very happy with Mildred as for some reason Mr Watkins would 'rescue' Nahla from trees on a regular basis. Nahla had no idea why he did this as resting at the top of a tree is perfect for a nap after exercise even more so if the sun is out. Mr Watkins had also appeared on the roofs of houses and shops; in fact wherever Nahla decided to climb Mr Watkins would appear as regular as clockwork. She and others always knew when Mr Watkins was due to make an appearance as you could hear his fire engine coming around the corner as he always had his siren on; Mr Watkins always liked to make a grand entrance so everyone in the surrounding three streets knew when he and his team were in the area and more often than not it was on some form of 'cat rescue'.

One time she heard Mr Watkins approaching in his fire truck and he drove straight past her as on this occasion he was putting out an actual fire in Mr Ablett's garden shed. Mr Ablett liked to hide away in there for long periods of time playing with his very expensive train set. Nahla upset with this and not receiving her regular attention from Mr Watkins climbed a tree and waited for him afterwards. She did not need Mr Watkins' help of course but some days were busy days and some days were lazy days and for Nahla that was a very lazy day indeed. Sometime soon she would eventually climb to the top of Stan and when done she would wait for him; he should be giving her a medal of achievement for completing such an outstanding feets instead of complaining all of the time, he probably couldn't do it after all!

Nahla would be very happy to share the house with another cat friend but Mildred only had one cat unlike others she knew that had two cats, three cats or more so Mildred kept informing her anyway. As such she often found herself short of company and sought out some other friends. Although Sam the Squirrel would make appearances during the day, Bungle the badger would only come out after dark along with Freddie the fox. They slept during the day and did not like the noise of busy street life and the comings and goings of people. People were a nuisance when there were plenty of things to be getting on with and that included sleep.

And that was why after Mildred went to bed at 9pm it was playtime for her and pretty well everyone else within the three streets that mattered.

Bungle was always in a hurry, looking for something to eat and loved to dig up people's gardens. Mr Jenkins next door could sometimes be heard early in the morning shouting 'oh no, look what the badger has done' (or words to that effect) with his head in his hands and he would point at his garden and his prize rose bushes where Bungle had been sniffing around looking for food; quite why he was pointing and whom he was talking to no-one quite knew. He would also gesticulate at his bins as they could often be found on their sides and mess would be scattered all over the floor around them – although Nahla knew Freddie did this of course but Freddie did not mind that Bungle took the blame for the mess; Freddie could usually be found in someone's bin at some point of the evening.

Harry was quite nervous of Bungle and although he had never meant him any harm he was a large badger and when his white stripes shone in the moonlight Harry found this somewhat intimidating. Harry was a hedgehog with a little black nose that would twitch constantly; however Bungle was very clumsy and made a lot of noise often snorting like a little piglet when he was rummaging for food. This snorting noise and the crack of twigs as Bungle stumbled around everywhere let everyone know he was out to play and out to forage. Being a hedgehog Harry would protect himself by rolling up into a ball. He would do this regularly when he was nervous and would hide away inside his prickly coat protecting him from the outside world and the intimidating badger.

In the house next door to where Nahla stayed there were a family of mice and mice like to sleep during the day keeping warm but they too liked to play at night. Mice were friendly creatures for some and incredibly fast when they ran but Nahla did not like them. Nahla did not like mice at all as well as rats for that matter, unlike peas and carrots that go together cats and mice do not. Head of the mouse family Mike would constantly be chased by Nahla but he was too fast, way too fast and could never be caught, it was like he had lightning bolts on his tiny little feet.

Nahla took pride in her name as all cats did – that's their real name of course and not the 'Missy' human made up name that Nahla had been 'given'. Dogs however were a mystery and there were many of them, more than cats within the three streets actually. Dogs however had only the names given to them by their owners unlike cats and Nahla considered herself and all other cats as superior to dogs. Dogs could be bigger – yes, much bigger in fact but when their owner calls for them they go running back to them. Nahla did not understand this at all as although Nahla kept warm in Mildred's house and although Mildred would feed her (albeit it awful food), she considered herself not to be owned by anyone and she would come and go as she pleased – never would she respond to Mildred first thing in the morning and later in the evening to the 'Missy' name at full volume. Humans can be strange and as daft as dogs sometimes.

Playtime took place every night when the world had gone to sleep, the human world that is. Nahla loved peace and quiet and when the sound of motor cars and televisions from people's houses had faded away it was time for her to catch up with her friends. Nahla was fascinated by Freddie's tail, it was much longer and vibrant than her own. She loved to follow Freddie around on his adventures although on occasion Freddie would go beyond the three streets and be gone for some time. Nahla would always stop at the corner of Darwin Road; she knew that beyond there were other cats and sometimes they would not play nicely. Sometimes like people, cats had disagreements with each other especially where territory was concerned. Freddie had no such fear of this and Freddie did what Freddie wanted to do. For him, every night was a search for as much food as he could find as well as causing the usual mischief along the way, much to Mr Jenkins' annoyance. Freddie could be quite greedy at times and along with a big tail he also had a very big ginger coloured belly. Although he did not make as much noise as Bungle as he had finer stealth skills, he did burp and trump quite a bit due to a mixture of diet of whatever he found in everyone's bins. At times he could be quite unpleasant to be around especially for prolonged periods.

Nahla would often play around the streets in the peace and quiet of darkness and it was a welcome break from Mildred talking all of the time especially about cats. It wasn't jealousy or anything like that as apparently she was not allowed to have another quite yet for some reason; it just got boring to hear about after a little while.

Mildred, along with providing food and a warm and safe place to sleep, also did provide something else that none of Nahla's friends could do and that was tummy tickling. Lots of cats love having their tummy tickled and Nahla was no exception to this. Sometimes if Nahla decided to return home early from her evening's excursions she would gently slip in through her own private doorway (humans called this a cat flap) and make her way up into Mildred's room. Mildred would snore a lot like a chuffing train in a rush to get somewhere, so if Nahla wanted attention sometimes she would put a paw on the end of Mildred's nose as she slept. Mildred knew that a cat's paw on the end of her nose meant that Nahla wanted her tummy stroked and tickled, it did not matter what time of the night it was; Nahla was in charge of her own decisions and when she wanted tickle attention she made sure she got tickle attention. Anything up to 30 minutes or so of tickling would be enough for her depending on her mood. This of course would often lead to purring and when done she would gently bite Mildred who would usually stroke her in her sleep and thus informing her that she had had enough of that for today, well for now anyway. She would then jump off the bed away from Mildred who was probably snoring again and then it was her turn to have a nap; it can be a hard life for a cat on occasions.

Nahla knew that Bungle, Freddie, Mike, Harry and Sam the squirrel did not have their own personal Mildred as they had to look after themselves, Nahla knew she was a special cat, in fact all cats were special but some were more special than others…

The Cat Family Of Benbow Street, Rocke Road and Darwin Road

So we know that all cats are special but Nahla was very special indeed as she had Mildred and only Mildred. The other cats within the three roads (with the exception of Scamper) had other humans in their lives; some big and some little. Humans could be quite demanding often wanting attention from their cats and at times that could be quite time consuming.

On Benbow Street lived Sikari although the humans called him Tom (he preferred to be called Sikari as that was his real cat name). Sikari was a Persian white cat with blue eyes and he had a very similar daily routine as Nahla. Except Sikari stayed with Jack and Susan who were grownups and they had their own children who were called Jack Junior and Melissa. Jack Junior was 5 and Melissa was 8 human years old.

Jack Junior was at an age when he liked to play and he would tease Sikari quite a lot, he would often try to pull his tail and chase him around the house. Sikari would get very tired of this and as such could often be found on top of the wall at the end of their garden out of reach of little Jack. Melissa was a very happy and outgoing young girl and loved dressing up and playing with Sikari. Sikari preferred Melissa to Jack Junior, Melissa would also feed him when her mother was not looking but with all of that said Sikari preferred his own company and a lot of cats can be like that.

On Darwin Road you may find Scamper and that is only a maybe, as you would have to look for her as Scamper had far more energy than was necessary and at times even being in her company could be exhausting. Never staying in one place for very long she would leap over walls, chase cars, bounce over people's sheds and with very long claws she could climb anything. She often appeared in other people's homes by climbing through their windows especially when she was not invited. She once claimed that she had climbed to the very top of Stan; however Nahla somehow doubted this as although she liked Scamper she had a mischievous streak in her and could be unreliable about a great many things. Scamper unusually for a cat actually quite liked being called Scamper and she was the only one in the three streets that did not use her real cat name and to the others that made little sense.

The polar opposite to Scamper was Bernard who also lived in Darwin Road.

Although Bernard is a strong name it was very old fashioned and cats get very embarrassed when their 'owners' call out their names in public; it is for this reason that humans calling out cat names in your very own street go largely ignored.

Mrs Meacher loved Bernard but she had been a little unwell recently so it was Mr Meacher who took over official duties of calling out for Bernard when it was feeding time. In a gruff voice Mr Meacher would stand by the gate of the front garden and bellow "BERNARDDDDD, DINNER TIME." However unlike Mildred who would yell MISSYYYYY for ages and ages at the top of her voice while banging a tin of cat food with a spoon, Mr Meacher was really quite embarrassed about doing this. Mr Meacher has an important job as he is the head teacher for Beaverwood School at the end of Darwin Road and every time he would shout out for Bernard everyone in the street would watch and the local children would make fun of him. Bernard much preferred to be addressed by his real name of Said and if other cats wanted to get Said's attention they would have to address him by his REAL name.

And so that was the cat family of the three streets, along with dogs of different shapes and sizes, a pet ferret, a gerbil, 3 goldfish and Mr Ryan who owned a lizard called Barney it was quite a happy but largely uneventful place and that suited everyone just fine.

Chapter Two:

Mr. ABLETT'S SHED

MONDAY

Mildred's phone rang; it was 11 o'clock in the morning when she picked up the phone. Her phone shaped like a cat did not ring like other phones; it made a meow noise instead. Initially this would momentarily confuse Nahla as it sounded like another cat was in the house but she shook that off quickly and would usually just roll her eyes. Although Nahla would like a playmate to live with, an uninvited cat would not be welcome in Nahla's home.

"Hello Daphne" said Mildred, "How are things?"
"Well I'm looking forward to the forthcoming gathering, it will be lovely for us to get together again, plenty of cat talk I'm sure" Daphne answered in complete happiness.
"Oh really, I'm so excited, I've just knitted a lovely new cardigan just for this special occasion." Mildred spoke in the same equal measures of excitement as Daphne although at the last two gatherings she had been to she felt she had been largely ignored by everyone.

Mildred liked to sew and create things with her hands; just cat things of course as nothing else really mattered in the grand scheme of things. She had also recently made a cushion with a picture of a cat on it that rested pride of place on her very dishevelled old sofa, a white cat though and not a black cat like Nahla.

Nahla had noticed this of course but did not care; in fact she left what Mildred called a special 'present' on it. Presents really were supposed to be left outside or in the cat litter tray but Nahla, like many cats, chose not to use it all of the time as sometimes when you have to go, well you have to go.

"On this occasion Mildred I think there will be over 50 of us attending, nearly all from our region have confirmed so far."

"Well, that's a lot of sandwiches" Mildred said somewhat concerned that someone would have to make them. Mildred knew that as she was fairly new to the club, chores were for new members to do (she had only been a member for coming up to 3 years). Daphne had been a member for 7 years and she had two cats called Aziza and Binky.

"I will call you back with the exact numbers Mildred once I'm told. Mildred from Merewood Close in Coningsby and Mildred from Alpine Grove in Stratford-Upon-Avon will also be providing food."

"That's good to know and I would appreciate the help" said Mildred the 'owner' of Nahla.

"Daphne, do you happen to know if there will be an awards ceremony?" Mildred said quite anxiously whilst biting at the ends of her nails.

"I'm not sure as yet Mildred, I haven't been told, these things are always last minute arrangements."

"I understand" Mildred replied but she didn't really understand why these things would always be so disorganised.

"Look I must go Mildred as I have others to speak to on the phone today, much to do!"

"That's okay Daphne, thank you for taking the time to call me."

"You are most welcome, goodbye for now Mildred and may peace be with you and Nahla."

"Thank you Daphne" said Mildred and put the phone down. Her mind was ticking like a clock with so much to do and less than a week to prepare. She paused further in thought wondering if Daphne was starting to go funny in her age; who exactly was Nahla?

The letterbox at the front door chattered into life. Mildred almost skipping to her feet from her comfy old chair let out an excited "Weeeee" noise upon seeing what had arrived in the post. "Oh Missy it's here" as she held Cats Quarterly Magazine aloft beaming with pride. Nahla was not impressed with this revelation having been awoken with this most uninteresting of news.

"Missy, oh look there are pictures of Savannah cats, Minx cats and Birman cats" she announced with glee clutching at the magazine like it was a priceless artwork. "Oh, what a beautiful Siamese Missy, one day I would love to own a..." Mildred's words faded away as Nahla drifted off back to sleep again.

It was approaching 9pm and Nahla was wide awake and primed for this evening's escapades; although curled up in a ball on the home made cat cushion pretending to be asleep she waited, 'any moment now'...'any moment now'...and as regular as clockwork Mildred switched her bedroom light off.

Here we go as Nahla raced towards the cat flap out into the night air. She strutted off into the night seeing what was going on in Rocke Road this evening before following her usual routine of seeing what was happening on Benbow Street and Darwin Road.

She could see that Barney's light was on in his tank; Mr Ryan would leave Barney's light on for him as he was a lizard and needed the warmth that came from it. She would often stare at Barney perched on his tree stump inside his tank and he would rarely move even if she pawed at the window trying to get his attention. He would win any staring contest Nahla thought to herself. He had a couple of crickets hoping around in his tank to keep him company but Barney seemed to ignore those as well. Strange company he kept, Nahla considered, and she hopped off the windowsill to find out what else what going on in the road this evening as frankly Barney was not very interesting.

Jumping over other people's fences was not a problem in the latter hours of the evening as the humans would often take their dogs inside with them to tuck up for the evening; some apparently would even take their dogs to bed with them as well she had heard. During the day however it would be a completely different story and it would have to be a mad dash running from one garden to another before one of the local dogs tried to spring a surprise. There were a couple of quite big dogs and a few small yappy ones within the three streets. The yappy ones were not a problem as they yap on sight as soon as they see a cat so Nahla had plenty of time to escape or, of course, climb up somewhere and allegedly tease them. However the bigger ones had more stealth skills and cunning and one in particular would lie in wait. Nahla did not know the names of the dogs that lived close by to her as she was largely disinterested but she knew the names for all of the other animals she would encounter. But dogs were dogs and their names were just not important to her; probably Mutley, Titan or Dave or other daft names that the humans seemed to call all animals they claimed to keep.

She popped up on top of the fence that overlooked Mr Ablett's garden. A small light was flickering from underneath the door in Mr Ablett's new garden shed. It had been recently replaced following the fire that Mr. Watkins put out. Nahla cocked her head back and forth straining to listen to the noises coming from within it; she recognised a familiar sound much like Mildred's snoring, the sound of a train on tracks going round and round. Mr. Ablett was not allowed to keep his train set in the house according to local gossip. She had overheard this as she was sitting on top of the shelter at the local bus stop on Rocke Road. As such he spent many hours in his shed by himself painting miniature figures of people and adding new train tracks and locomotives to his collection.

"Andyyyyyyyyyyyy, are you coming to bed soon?" was the shrill that could be heard coming from the inside of the Ablett household.
"Yes dear, I will be just 5 more minutes" he responded and Nahla could hear some other indiscernible mutterings coming from Mr Ablett.

Mrs Ablett's voice or yell (as some would say) made far more noise than Mildred's ever could even when she stood out in rain calling out the 'Missy' name.
He appeared at the shed door, switched the light off and then secured what must have been at least 5 padlocks to the shed door. Muttering to himself and kicking the ground with hands in pockets he headed back to his home leaving the shed and his prized possession train set in darkness.

Nahla jumped onto the shed roof looking back towards Mr Ablett's home, her tail twitching back and forth. Mr Ablett turned around upon hearing the familiar sound of cat's claws on his shed roof. Unimpressed with this repetitive cycle of events he asserted "Shooo, go away" he yelled.
Nahla not always receptive to human instructions just kept looking at him and

her tail curled a little more and moved back and forth a little more hastily.

"Shooo I say" and he stepped forward in a very feeble attempt to assert his ownership of the shed.

"What's all the noise?" The familiar voice at some volume could be heard tumbling down the street again from Mrs Ablett.

"Oh, it's nothing; just the damn cat again, go away cat!" he said with more authority in his tone.

"Just leave it; it won't do anything, it's just a cat" retorted Mrs Ablett.

"Yes dear" he grumbled looking down at the floor and kicking a couple of weeds that had grown through his patio flooring.

Mr. Ablett retreated and upon opening the sliding doors to go back into his home he turned around giving Nahla quite the stare of unpleasantness.

"I'm sure that cat was responsible for the fire" he muttered under his breath albeit not as quietly as he should have said it.

"The fire started because grown men should not play with toy trains!" was the unhelpful response that came from his wife. "Now come to bed."

He rolled his eyes and whilst still muttering to himself he closed his sliding doors and pulled the curtains closed not before staring at Nahla one more time.

"I see what you are doing."

Nahla spun around to see Freddie staring up at her, surprised that she could understand anything he was saying with the remainder of a hamburger hanging out of his mouth.

"Its harmless fun" she explained trying to justify her actions to a fox that destroys everyone's dustbin probably within a mile radius.

"Indeed" muttered Freddie with an unconcerned deep tone.

"Found much this evening Freddie?" Nahla asked in what was an all too familiar question (much like adults asking taxi drivers if they are having a busy night).

"Not really, slim pickings tonight Nahla; one hamburger that was half eaten (now fully), 2 pieces of pizza but I had to remove the pineapple (Freddie did not care for pineapple on pizza), a third of a tin of tuna and I took some dog food out of the bowl at number 13."

"It's no wonder your belly is getting bigger Freddie if that is slim pickings" retorted Nahla.

Freddie scoffed upon hearing this.

"Have you seen Barney this evening?" asked Nahla.

"I've not bothered looking as yet" replied Freddie.

"I don't think he's moved in a week" offered Nahla as much as a question as a statement.

"I don't know what's going on with him, strange creature that lizard, it's like he sunbathes all day and night."

No wonder his skin was so hard thought Nahla.

"You think we should try and free him from his tank sometime?" Nahla questioned.

"Not especially" said Freddie, "I think he'd be really boring to hang around with."

"Oh" said Nahla surprised at Freddie's bluntness.

"Anyway, I must make my rounds" said Freddie and stretched his back legs as if he were priming himself for action, "see you later."

"See you later then" and she watched Freddie's big tail disappear back into the darkness.

Still perched on Mr Ablett's shed roof she glanced back towards the house and watched him appear at the bedroom window and her tail started twitching again. Mr Ablett now in pyjamas with pictures of trains on them stared back at her; there was only ever going to be one winner of this staring contest. Mr Ablett distracted at clearly being told off from the shrill coming from behind him broke away and Nahla could read his lips that said something like 'Yes, dear' and he snatched at the curtains bringing them to a close and in that very moment playtime with Mr Ablett was over for today.

It was only a short hop down to go from the shed roof onto the back fence and back into Rocke Road.

All was calm within the street just a few bedroom lights were on and the occasional front rooms lit up where adults were playing their children's video games.

Rocke Road had 54 houses on it, quite a big road for the area; but with exception to the likes of where Nahla stayed at number one on the far corner and Mr Jenkins, Mr Ablett and Barney's house not a lot went on other than the comings and goings of people. Benbow Street on the other hand had Mr Frank's shop, The Tudor House Café and the Futility public house. Although the shop and café were closed at this hour there was always something to find or see in Benbow Street. The peace and serenity of Rocke Road becomes a distant memory when getting close to the Futility pub. If it wasn't quiz night or bingo night it would probably be Karaoke night where the worst singers in the land seemed to descend. Like some cats, these vocally challenged humans only seemed to come out after the hours of darkness as well.

She could see Sikari sitting on one of the tables outside the pub with his eyes fixed on what was going on inside. Nahla upon seeing him quickened up her pace and bounced along the road past the shop and café and hopped up on the table next to him.

"I find this all very confusing" purred Sikari upon seeing Nahla taking her place alongside him.
Nahla turned her head to look at him and gave a puzzled expression.
"Listen to them all making that racket" said Sikari and nodded his head towards the noise coming from inside the pub.
Nahla could hear plenty of raised voices singing in unison and badly singing it had to be said.

"Who is this Sweet Caroline then? They keep singing about her this time every week, is this someone important?"
"I have no idea" replied Nahla, "last week they were also singing about someone called Vindaloo."
They both paused for a short but not uncomfortable silence.
"Very odd" grunted Sikari.

"You look tired" said Nahla.
"I feel tired; have a look at the state of my tail."
Nahla observed that Sikari's usually plush tail looked a little worn at the end.
"I got told off and was sent outside early this evening."

"Why, what happened?" Nahla asked with some curiosity.

"Little Jack Junior kept pulling my tail" Sikari stopped talking to pause in thought. "So I bit him. It wasn't a hard bite or anything it's just that he was doing it to me all day."

They both sat in silence for the second time.

"I bit him, he cried and I got told off and sent out with no tea; that's why I'm here waiting for this place to close to see what I can find."

At least you have nice tea Nahla thought to herself unlike what she was fed, "All will be forgotten tomorrow."

"Do you ever bite your master?" asked Sikari.

"Master?" Nahla Laughed, "I don't have a master, never have and never will" she stated in a very confident and firm tone.

"Where I stay the woman who calls herself Mildred I nip on occasions when I've had enough of her tickling my tummy."

"I don't like tummy tickles" said Sikari, "it's not natural."

"That's as may be but it helps me sleep, my mind is always so busy with so many things" she said.

"Really, what sort of things?"

"I don't know...I can't explain, purpose I guess?"

"Purpose?" Sikari enquired questioning this statement whilst raising one eye.

"Mmm; like I should be doing more than going out every night roaming the three streets, doing the same thing over and over, do you understand what I mean?"

"Not really" he said quite bluntly.

They sat in silence again now for the third time.

"Like I have something more to offer, like I'm being prepared for something, I can't explain it."

"Well if you can explain to me how I'm going to get some tea tonight that would be most helpful."

Nahla looked at Sikari and pondered; maybe not all cats were the same after all.

Chapter Three:

FISH PASTE SANDWICHES

TUESDAY

"MISSSSYYYYYY" the familiar noise rang out across Rocke Road at 7am. "MISSSSYYYYYY" and now the clattering of a spoon on a cat tin was added as an early morning wake up call for everyone.

Nahla was at the end of the back garden having had an uneventful night overall. After seeing Sikari rummaging around the back of the pub she had seen Harry the hedgehog briefly who spent most of his time in a ball, so she couldn't understand a muffled word he was saying. She also looked in on Freddie again who was unmoved as usual.

Jumping over the gate she headed to the side door, unnoticed by Mildred, and went through her private entrance to the house and sat and waited for the owner of the house and the keeper of bad food.

"MISSSSYYYYY"...Upon hearing the cat flap close at the side door Mildred walked back into the house.

"You ignoring me Missy?" she was staring at her cat with an inquisitive smile. "I've got you herring in cod roe today; I know how much you love that." Oh joy Nahla thought wondering if she could take it to Sikari instead just in case he hadn't eaten last night after all.

"I have a busy day of sandwich making today Missy, it's only three days before I meet with everyone" she spoke with some excitement.

Making sandwiches three days beforehand? Do any of them actually get eaten Nahla considered? Well at least if there are any leftovers and she brings them home it will keep Freddie happy in the bins for a little while.

"I also need to speak with the two other Mildreds Missy, Mildred from Alpine Grove and Mildred from Merewood Close; you've heard me talk about those I know you have." She was shaking her head to herself. "They only have one cat each as well." She then looked towards the ceiling; cat daydreaming.

Shaking her head and quickly snapping out of her daze, there was much to do. Everything must be perfect for Friday. She was faffing with her hands with over excited emotions when she paused and a strained look appeared across her face. "They never really talk to me much" she said very gently, "and some ignore me" she bit her lip in pensive thoughts. "I need to make a good impression" although she was at a loss why she may not have done so before. "First impressions are the most important impressions Missy" and she bent down towards her cat with an index finger aloft as if she were a politician making an important point, not that many paid attention to politicians these days.

She turned back around looking out of the kitchen window deep in thought. "I have my new jumper, I've shined my shoes, well kind of and my hat is ready, well I think it is, I really can't make my mind up which one to wear" she pondered on this most important of points; "oh it's so exciting I can't tell you Missy" as she put her hands together in a tight clench with gleeful expressions all over her face.

Ever since Daphne had come into Mildred's life things had changed for the better; very much the better in fact. "The day Daphne brought you to me Missy, it was my happiest and..." she spun around to talk to Missy directly and noticed she had gone. "Missy...Missy?" she left the kitchen and walked into the living room and as ever predictable Missy was curled up in a ball on the couch. "Oh, Missy, I was talking to you!" she said with quite some emotion. "I'm sure you don't care for me sometimes, I really do..."

And off she walked returning to the kitchen with much to consider regarding sandwiches.

"Fish paste; everyone loves fish paste" Mildred said to Mr Franks.
"We don't sell as much of it as we used to Mildred, not by a long margin; fish paste is part of a dying art of food, not all developments are progress" Mr Franks rasped. "It's all microwave meals and Pop Tarts and the suchlike these days" Mr Franks owner of the Franks Convenience Shop asserted.

Mildred having no idea what a Pop Tart is chose to ignore this advice; ladies love fish paste she thought to herself.

"How much do you need Mildred?" Mr Franks enquired and typically rasped his breath at the end of every sentence – he was not a figure of fitness.

"I think about 10 pots of the Salmon and 10 pots of the Sardine and Tomato please."

"20 pots Mildred!! That's big spending, I'll have none left" as he put his hands on his hips in amazement at the scale of the fish paste order.
"Well if it's not selling then it shouldn't worry you too much" Mildred asserted.
"I'd better check the sell by dates Mildred" something he clearly didn't do very often.

Deep in thought she had found out that the other two Mildreds were providing cheese and ham sandwiches and cakes; Mildred from Merewood Close was quite nifty in the kitchen with her cakes; alas our Mildred was not and sandwiches it would have to be.

"I'll need around 20 loaves of bread as well please."
"Right you are." Mr Franks' hands were back on his hips again as he surveyed the bread shelf to see if he had enough, he frowned that he may be a little short.
"White or brown?"
"A mixture will be fine please."
It was going to be difficult to impress when Merewood Mildred could make such good cakes.

"Mildred"...Hello Mildred?" Mr Franks said her name for a second time and added a cough noticing that Mildred had drifted off somewhere deep in thought. "Oh sorry, my mind drifted somewhere else" she turned her head to the side with fluttering blinky eyes and smiled at Mr Franks.

"Do you need anything else?" he asked.

"A couple of pots of butter please."

"So what's going on then Mildred, why you need so much fish paste?" he spoke in his gruff voice.

Stunned by the question Mildred's eyes widened, think, think, think as she wrestled with her thoughts. "Oh I'm donating sandwiches to the Church for their fete."

"I didn't know you went to Church Mildred?" he politely responded.

"Well you don't really know me Mr Franks" Mildred retorted in a snap so much so that Mr Franks realised that questioning and curiosity would have to wait for another time.

"I meant no offence Mildred."

"None taken Mr Franks" she smiled but she was very happy to stop answering his questions. "I'll probably be back tomorrow for some more supplies."

"No problems Mildred, I'm open most hours you know that, and your TV magazine is here on Wednesdays as per the usual" he said.

If it's usual I'm not sure why he told me Mildred considered with some paranoia let alone this open all hours type of talk.

She offered him some money as Mr Franks bagged up the bread, butter and pots of fish paste.

"I'll have to charge you for the bags I'm afraid, as I say, not everything in life is progress."

It certainly wasn't as Mildred remembered that she probably had over 50 empty carrier bags at home gathering dust all bearing the 'Franks' name.

Gathering her newly purchased carrier bags and placing her purse into what can only be described as a 'Nan bag' she turned to go.

"Goodbye for now Mr Franks."

"Goodbye Mildred" he responded as she left the shop.

Upon seeing her exiting the door, Mr Franks looked up puzzled. "I'm sure the church fete isn't until next month," and without giving it a second thought he returned to reading his newspaper.

Mildred was deep in thought as she often was; you need to be much more prepared for questions Mildred, this just won't do as she mentally berated herself following the brief exchange that she had had with Mr Franks. Why does he want to know what I'm doing anyway she pondered with a tinge of suspicion? For reasons that she was yet to understand, the Kat Club was private, very private. Daphne had explained this to her a few years ago when she came to her on the first and only occasion that she had visited Mildred's home.

'You were chosen Mildred' Daphne said looking her straight in the eye; her well kept blond hair could not shield the ageing lines across her face. *'You've always known you were different from others, you must have felt it?'*

'I'm not sure what you mean?' Mildred had responded as confused as someone who decides to pursue juggling as a meaningful career.

'As a youngster you didn't have pets did you?' she spoke very softly and clearly.

'No, I didn't, my parents would not allow it, and my father had an allergy to animals and a temperament that would not suit.'

'It upset your mother though didn't it?' Daphne said with a smile and nodded her head towards Mildred that she already knew the answer.

'How could you possibly know that?' Mildred responded her voice breaking a little with emotion, the statement clearly upsetting her.

'All will be revealed in time, we are not so dissimilar,' she smiled and stepped forward to Mildred and lowered her chin to make direct eye contact *'but you are special Mildred, more than you know, you have an affinity with animals.'*

Mildred's eyes widened in utter disbelief at what she was hearing *'All animals?'* she enquired.

'No, just cats' was the matter of fact and chirped response *'but it's only cats that matter Mildred, everything else is secondary.'* She spoke with a knowing expression and touched Mildred on the hand as if offering reassurance that what she had said was fact.

'There are many others like us Mildred; yes people keep cats in every few streets and every

town the breadth of the land over, but some are more enlightened than others and you are enlightened Mildred.'

Aghast with what she was hearing and not understanding a word of it Mildred took a step back.

'I know this is a lot to take in, it was the same for me when I was visited by my elder.' Daphne smiled trying to offer further reassurance that she was not a complete crackpot although she was failing miserably.

'And I have something for you Mildred something very precious, please do look after her.'

As Daphne left Mildred was stunned in silence, the cogs of her brain whirring with 100 questions that offered zero answers. Irrespective of the beautiful new kitten she was holding she did know one thing for certain and she was very sure of it...she would never let complete strangers into her home again.

Mildred's house had changed somewhat following that meeting nearly 3 years ago. There had been the addition of the cat flap – yes; but her front and rear garden had fallen almost into a state of disrepair as gardening takes time and there was never enough time when there was much to consider and TV game shows to watch of course.

Paintwork around the windows of the house was beginning to flake and the glass in the window frames had taken on a misty and dusty sheen. So much so that the net curtains in her front room could not be seen at all in direct sunlight, the dust colour they had changed to had seen to that.

In the warmer months of the year the hedge in her front garden would grow out of control and would be left hanging over the pathway. Mr Jenkins would not put up with it any further and he would cut it back himself as the road sign for Rocke Road on the wall below was often hidden. Tutting under his breath and shaking his head upon seeing the ever decreasing state of Mildred's garden and her weedy paths he often wondered what had happened to her, she used to be so house proud. In fact he could not recall the last conversation that he had had with her.

Mr Jenkins' front garden by comparison was a picture postcard of gardening perfection, with exception to the occasional holes in the grass and borders left by Bungle of course. His bird feeding table had been void of birds for quite some time largely thanks to Sam devouring whatever type of feed he would put out. "Vermin!!!" he would yell at the squirrel. Such offensive terms however do not affect the determination of the will of squirrels, as well as cats, foxes, badgers, hedgehogs and well, pretty well everything really. Animals have the ability to take these things in their stride and could chose to ignore humans if they so wished.

A dog was at the top of his list of considerations to keep unwanted animals away; Mr Jenkins had pondered on this in the past. But due to the 'presents' they leave about the place the idea was dismissed quickly from his mind as he didn't want his garden serenity fouled any further. I'm guessing that's what she means anyway he thought having heard Mildred use the term 'presents' on numerous occasions whilst talking to her cat running around the garden after her with kitchen roll. I do hope she washes her hands before tea thought Mr. Jenkins glancing towards Mildred's unkempt home. He would regularly return back to his thoughts about squirrels and badgers and how his life was inconvenienced by them.
He pondered looking at Mildred's household and shook his head; he greatly suspected it would not be the last time his garden sheers would be making an appearance at Mildred's garden.

If she were honest Mildred could not bear the sight of fish paste any further.

With having Missy in her life for the best part of 3 years her nostrils had become accustomed to the smell of fish related foods. Knowing that Missy loved them so much she had been feeding her tins of luxury fish related cat food for all of that time, well as luxurious as the Franks' shop had to offer anyway.

But sometimes in life the line can be drawn and Mildred's line had run right out as far as fish paste was concerned for today.

She sat down wearily on the stool next to the kitchen table and surveyed what can only be described as the Mount Everest of fish paste sandwiches. In some doubt she not so much questioned whether she had made enough, rather should she have added cucumber to them? Fish and cucumber goes together she considered.

The very thought of going to see Mr Franks to buy 10 or 12 cucumbers and risk him asking more questions she really wanted to avoid right now.

So fish paste sandwiches it was and that would have to do without any fancy cucumber trimmings.

She stared back at her three plates of stacked sandwiches that towered reasonably high and they were now wrapped in cling film – 'would it be enough?' she thought to herself, how much had the other two Mildreds made?

With Merewood Mildred no doubt focused on cake detail it was a reasonable presumption the other Mildred from Alpine Grove would be providing the ham and cheese sandwiches. Suddenly with a momentary brain freeze Mildred paused and her body became rigid...was it ham and cheese together or ham and cheese separately? 'On no, I never thought to ask; maybe I should make some more just in case.'

Mildred from Merewood Close took enormous pride in her cakes and whilst it was not a competition the club needed to see that new members took their roles seriously to ensure they would be good positive role models for the future. Mildred didn't really understand this, yes she was asked to join but her interests were in cats, a positive role model; a positive role model for what?

'Oh this is no good', Mildred's mind chattered to herself...'I better call the other Mildreds and see what is going on' and without further ado and with no time to waste the cat's bottom was pressed firmly to her mouth.

"Hello Mildred, its Mildred!"
"Hello Mildred" said Mildred from Alpine Grove followed by a brief pause "I'm sorry, which Mildred is this?" asked Mildred.

"It's Mildred from Rocke Road" said Mildred.
"Oh good afternoon Mildred, lovely to hear from you, there are so many Mildreds you can never be too sure" Mildred asserted with a little laugh.

Mildred joined her in laughter "Well the only Mildreds I know are you and Mildred from Merewood Close" she said as a clear statement.

"Mmm" was the response.

Mildred pulled the phone away from her face in shock and stared incredulously at the cat's bottom at what she had just heard. 'Mmm' she thought, 'mmm' what could that possibly mean? This would suggest that Mildred from Alpine Grove may know other Mildreds and that would be somewhat disconcerting.

"Err….um, well" she stumbled with her words.
"Whatever is the matter Mildred?" Mildred enquired.
"Well…..I was just thinking about the meeting on Friday."
"The gathering" Mildred interrupted.
"Yes, that's right, the gathering. I'm not fully aware of how many may be going. Can I ask how many sandwiches have you made?"
"Well I think everyone is coming from across the region so at least 45" Mildred responded.
'How could she possibly know that?' Mildred asked her own mind and a little scowl appeared across her face; a couple of things were now starting to concern her. "I see, and how many sandwiches have you made?" she added.

"Three plates" Mildred responded.
Mildred breathed a sigh of relief, 'I've probably done more than her, that's good!' she thought.
"Yes, three plates of cheese, three plates of ham and three plates of cheese and ham."

Damn it!! Thought Mildred as she waved a frustrated fist in the air; her victory was short lived and concern was now starting to creep in.

"I see" said Mildred as she bowed her head towards the floor and composed herself. "That's good" she added quietly down the telephone trying to think what to do next.
"And what have you done Mildred?"
"I've done three plates of fish paste" she responded proudly holding her chin aloft.
"Fish paste Mildred, fish paste you say?" She scoffed with a little shrill of

laughter……..“I didn't know anyone ate that any more let alone that you could buy it; honestly Mildred that local shop of yours and the strange man type who runs it….ha ha, you could have at least added cucumber.”

Mildred's facial scowl deepened with teeth clenched. She could visualise Mildred on the other end of the phone shaking her head in right royal disapproval and laughing at her expense. Feeling very protective of Mr Franks and his little shop of culinary delights she reacted “It's very much the thought that counts Mildred!”

There was silence at the other end...

“Yes of course; you are completely right Mildred and besides if there are left overs you could always feed them to your cat.”
She scowled and it was at that very moment that Mildred realised that she really didn't like Mildred too much.

Sat in silence in her kitchen Mildred had decided not to call Merewood Close Mildred after all. She was staring at the floor and had been for some time. 'Other Mildreds?...She knew the exact number going to the gathering?...she knew that fish paste was not very popular anymore confirming what Mr Franks had said.

How does she know all of these things? Mildred was biting at her nails in a state of worry.

The sound of ticking fluttered into her ears breaking the mental deadlock that she had found herself in.

She looked up at the old clock on her kitchen wall, it was approaching 7pm. She stretched her arms above her head, best go and find Missy. I do hope she comes in quickly this time she thought as her favourite programme was coming up on television.

Pushing her toes out in her scuffed brown shoes and wrinkled stockings she got up and walked through to the front room and switched the television on and turned the volume up.

With the sound loud enough that she could hear she returned to the kitchen and opened the door of a very sparse larder and took out a tin of cat food. Reaching out for a spoon it was now time to find Missy.

In the background she could hear the music starting of her favourite game show; she glanced up in panic and looked at the clock and could see that the seconds hand was moving too slowly. "Oh no the clock must be slow!" Now in a quandary flapping her arms like an insane penguin she was torn between watching the show and finding Missy.

"MISSY!!!!!" she yelled from inside the house banging the cat food tin as loud as she could. "MISSSSYYYY!! She practically screamed at volume hitting the cat tin as if it were the drum of an army marching into battle. Eyes still firmly fixed on the television "MISSSSSSSSSSSSSSSYYYYYYYYYY" she hollered and brought her knees together like she was desperate for the toilet to try and get more lift from her voice. "MISS..." She was immediately drawn to the television as the presenter came forward onto the screen; with his usual beaming and cheesy smile and outstretched hands he proclaimed "Welcome to Bang Goes Your Money!!" and the television audience roared with approval.

Mildred was smiling, she had stopped yelling, she had stopped banging the cat food tin, transfixed she listened to the presenter and focused on the words coming out of his mouth, the very same words he says every time he is on television.

She liked him; he was okay and almost acceptable...well for a man anyway.

Chapter Four:

Mr. FRANKS TARDIS EMPORIUM

WEDNESDAY

It was 8am; not that Nahla really would have cared as she watched with occasional and casual interest at Mildred and her rapidly over excitable behaviour. Mildred looked upon her plates of sandwiches that she had just taken out of the fridge. Lifting up a corner of the cling film from one of them she prodded a fish paste sandwich, not so much that she was hungry more like checking their suitability of excellence.

"Well Wednesday is here and the day I collect my TV magazine Missy," she turned to look at her black cat whom as standard was curled up in a ball with her white tipped tail resting on her body.

However, this was not a regular Wednesday, the gathering was in two days time and she would be able to celebrate three years of membership. The longer she was a member of the club the more she felt she was one of them and part of them.

Poking her head into the living room she stared at the certificate on her wall (one of the cleanest objects within her house) chewing her lower lip and occasionally biting one of her nails.

"What to wear Missy, what to wear?" she said in a concerned tone, "I need to be sure that everything is in order." She raised both hands to her head, fully outstretching her fingers as if they had the answers and with that she moved absurdly quickly to the stairs to go through her wardrobe....for about the tenth time this week.

Upon seeing Mildred disappear upstairs, Nahla got up, stretched her back and extended her tail as part of her stretching routine. 'Oh why not...I could do with the exercise' hearing Mildred taking apart her wardrobe upstairs and she proceeded towards the cat flap with a swagger. Catching a casual glance at her food bowl which was mostly full of the usual inedible offerings she headed out of the Mildred house.

Nahla sat on the wall outside number 1 Rocke Road now that she could after Mr Jenkins had cut the hedge back. Surveying all that she could see the road was awash with traffic, cars going back and forth, people pushing prams as well as the occasional dog on a lead with its master.

Jumping down onto the pathway she headed towards Benbow Street but not before checking in on Barney. That took all of one minute and he was still perched on his log in the same position as last time she saw him.

From the corner of Rocke Road she looked down Benbow Street and she could see bushes twitching behind the wall at number 19; intrigued and on impulse she darted over to investigate. Suddenly the loud noise of car brakes could be heard followed very quickly with the sound of tires skidding to a halt.

Freezing in the middle of the road she stared at the driver of the car who was firmly gripping the steering wheel. The driver did not appear to be in any momentary shock and stepped calmly out of the car. Nahla looked upon the dark suited figure as he moved towards her. She tilted her head to the side with her eyes still firmly fixed upon the driver and what he was wearing as her tail began to twitch. The driver looked down at her "You should not be in the road; this is a dangerous place for you." The statement was spoken quite firmly and she noticed some saliva run down his chin from bad dental work. Nahla took a step forward towards the driver and in return he bent down to look at her and took off one of his gloves and outstretched his right arm towards her. "I mean it, this is no place for you." The driver's voice was softer now and very calm as he extended his hand towards Nahla's head.

Nahla took a further step forward towards him, his hand now just above her head, when she jumped distracted by a sudden noise behind the driver's car and took a couple of paces backwards. The driver, still crouched down, turned around and hissed in displeasure now looking at Mr Watkins whose siren had suddenly rung out. "Can you get out of the road please?" Mr Watkins also hit the horn on his fire truck "I'm in a rush."

"Honestly, some people" Mr Watkins was grumbling under his breath "the road is not a place to play on" he was saying to himself whilst looking at the figure as he stood up and the peculiar glasses he was wearing.

Nahla moved to the kerb with her eyes fixed upon the driver who wiped saliva from his chin as he stared at Mr Watkins before very slowly getting back into his car.

As the car moved away the driver never once averted its gaze from her and she felt strangely drawn towards him. As soon as the car turned around the corner and out of sight she hopped up onto the wall to where the bushes had initially been twitching. Mr Watkins sped by and just as Nahla was about to peer over the wall she froze gathering her thoughts about the stranger; something seemed oddly familiar about him.

"Good morning" Mildred said striding through the doorway of Franks' Convenience Store. She was mentally prepared for any questions that Mr Franks would throw her way today; she had rehearsed them all in her mind beforehand.

"Well good morning Mildred" was the response that quickly headed her way. "And what can I do you for today?" he followed up with and lifted his head from reading his paper.
"My TV magazine please and I need a few more supplies."
"Supplies, supplies for what then Mildred?" he politely enquired "Ha, ha, you creating an army?" he carried on chuckling away to himself whilst shaking

his head.

Oh, I wasn't prepared for a simple question like that Mildred thought to herself...she brushed her chin gently.

"Err, just for home...That's all" and she nodded her head smiling politely.

"Well okey dokie I'm guessing you will not be needing any more fish paste, now will you?" He smiled and continued to giggle to himself, with rasping breath he looked up in thought.

"Have you ever given thought to having cucumber with your fish paste sandwiches Mildred?"

His question was met by a long and vacant expression.

"No, I hadn't" she said whilst gently clenching her teeth. His thoughts on all things sandwiches were not appreciated.

"Oh, right you are then" Mr Franks responded; he had stop giggling and just had the slightest of well meant smiles on his face realising that once again he may have offended his most regular customer; he returned to reading his newspaper.

Mildred turned her gaze away from him and returned to her thoughts. She knew that Merewood Mildred would be cake ready, Alpine Mildred was ham and cheese ready so what else could she add to being fish paste with no cucumber ready...?

Having a look through Mr Franks' convenience store was like stepping back in time; the shop that time forgot, Mildred amused herself with this thought. Somewhat musty with postcards on the walls of old Shropshire that had faded, remnants of Christmas decorations from celebrations of years gone past and creaky floorboards and sticky lino on the floor in places, it was not a plush shopping experience. But it was comfortable and safe with no unexpected surprises. Mildred was happy in knowing that she had routine and was a creature of habit.

Mildred worked her way past the toy aisle of old children's trikes with their garish yellow seats, bright orange snowboards (even though it was summer) and build your own tree house sets complete with hammer and nails – all of which was no doubt a health hazard to anyone who may care to use it, probably circa 1980's or something.

Making her way to the back of the store where even the cleaning products had passed their use by date she moved on quickly to jams, marmalades and peanut butters. The very thought of spending the rest of the day making sandwiches filled her with dread. She wanted to excel and impress but there is a limit even to Mildred's usual very calm demeanour.

"Do you have little sausages on sticks Mr Franks?" she shouted across the shop without even looking at him.
"I have some sausages yes but not on sticks"...he paused before resuming "However, I've got a woodcutter out the back and I have some wooden tent pegs that I can cut up for you if you would like?" he said very loudly.

She stared at him at this clearly absurd suggestion and realised that he was being quite serious. "No, I think I may pass on that, thank you" Mildred responded with a frown across her face at the very thought of spending the afternoon putting shards of wood into little sausages. The Franks man was difficult to fathom.

"I'm glad to hear you are not prescribing to modern day living Mildred" he went on to add.
"Whatever do you mean Mr. Franks?"
"Well this veganarisum or whatever this newfangled thing is called. I just don't understand youngsters anymore; as I say not everything in life is progress" he asserted, returning to his newspaper that he was probably reading for the second time today.

Leaving Mr. Franks to his thoughts Mildred was starting to get a little frustrated as she continued to work her way through the tardis of the Franks Convenience Store, rummaging through all the nooks and crannies. Nothing was jumping out at her that was going to make a clear and memorable statement for the gathering. That was until she saw a rack of very old cards; birthday cards, anniversary cards, congratulations on your new born type of cards, the list of buy a card for everything went on. The cards had clearly been on display for some time and the plastic wallets that were meant to protect them were looking somewhat old and shrivelled. But poking from the top of a *'sorry you've lost your job'* card. She could see what looked to be a pair of black ears sticking up behind old cellophane. She pulled it out from the rack and they were indeed what she hoped they were; cat's ears!

"Mr Franks, do you have any more of these please?" and she held the card aloft with the little black cat on the front.

Mr Franks lifted his head from his paper "No Mildred, some of those cards are quite old if I'm honest, but you are welcome to buy it all the same."

"Would you be able to get any more...for tomorrow?" she gave Mr Franks a pleading look.

"Well I would need to speak to my supplier if they are still in business that is, been a while since I called them." He pulled up his trousers "don't sell many cards you see" he considered "it may be a tall order in this time frame Mildred" he replied, shaking his head slightly in unison with his over regular rasping noise.

"I just need a card with a beautiful black cat on it just like this," she walked over to Mr. Franks thrusting the card in his face.

"Well why don't I make a phone call and you go for a nice cup of tea in the café next door and come back in 10 minutes or so?" he smiled. "I'll see what I can do for my best customer" and gave a nod of the head trying to get back into Mildred's good books.

"Oh I need some more of your batteries, my clock is slow again."

"Really, you only bought some last week Mildred?"

"Yes quite."

"When you come back I'll have those ready for you."

"Can I take my TV magazine with me?" she asked.

"Yes of course Mildred, pay me when you come back, if I can't trust someone like you who can I trust?" He smiled as he passed her the magazine.

She put the TV magazine into her bag "Well thank you Mr. Franks." Mildred's smile of glee was much like the young girl who had just found a chocolate in her pocket as she turned towards the door. The shop bell tinkled as the door was opened.

"Oh, Mildred, sorry, how many cards exactly do you want?"

"44" responded Mildred.

Mr. Franks' mouth fell open, "How many?" he quivered.

"I like cats you see," and with that the cat lady was gone.

She was quickly able to assess there were around 12 people in The Tudor House Café as she opened the door to the quaint tea shop.

Holding her usual oversized bag she took a seat next to the front window. Waiting to be served she enjoyed these moments of just watching the world go by and it was a welcome break taking her mind off the forthcoming gathering.

Chloe came over to her; not that Mildred knew her name of course, but her shinny badge with her name on it also stating *'here to serve you'* was all the introduction she needed.

"Hello and welcome to The Tudor House, how may I help you today?" Chloe asked whilst looking curiously up and down at what Mildred was wearing.
"I would like a cup of Earl Grey please" Mildred requested.
"Would you like cream with that?"
"Heavens above no" Mildred recoiled in horror.
Chloe almost took a step back.
"But some lemon if you have it would be fine please" she said giving Chloe a little smile.
"That's no problem at all, I'll just be a jiffy" and she headed off behind the serving counter.
Earl Grey with cream, what on earth is happening to modern society? Not everything in life is progress she said to herself and quickly snapped that out of her mind realising she sounded like a clone of Mr Franks.

She dived into her TV magazine quickly skipping the features at the start of the magazine and went straight to the programme listings – she needed to be sure that 'Bang Goes Your Money' would be on again for the forthcoming week. Relieved to find that it was she lowered the magazine down and looked at other people in the café. A couple of people were sat by themselves, there was one group of four and there were three couples and almost all of them were tapping away on phones. Laughter would occasionally erupt inevitably followed by someone reading a quote aloud for the others to hear or they would show a picture of something they had seen that seemed to be absurdly funny.

Plenty of noise but very little conversation about natural things Mildred considered as one of her eyebrows rose.

On the café wall was a sign that said 'Our WIFI code is Freye13n2dys'; Mildred read this having no idea what that could possibly mean and equally she had no idea what a 'WIFI' is; but as she had gotten older there were many things in her life that just didn't seem to add up.

A white poster with a red border was to the right of this and she noticed that it was an advert for the church fete, the forthcoming church fete, the very same church fete she had claimed to be making sandwiches for. She gulped upon reading that it wasn't until next month.

She shook her head in annoyance that she really must get her stories straight and prepared for when others ask questions of her.

She really didn't understand the need for all of the secrecy about the club but Daphne had explained this to her, not long after they had first met.

"One simply doesn't join this organisation Mildred; it is not for everyone, you needed to be invited and you were." She recalled that Daphne had put a 'reassuring' hand on hers *(as she often did when making important points that often made no sense at all)*. *"We take pride that we are the invited and that pride extends to our commitment and above all complete discretion."* Mildred recalled seeing Daphne's head nodding enthusiastically as she made this point. At the time, and still to this day, she found all of this behaviour a little odd in being a member of this cat club; but she didn't ask questions, didn't make waves and guessed that this was just the way it had to be, as strange as it all sounded.

A very traditional white china cup was placed in front of her and she could see a thin slice of lemon was floating in her Earl Grey; Chloe had listened and thankfully it was without cream.

"Here we go" added Chloe "Can I get you anything else?"
"No thank you, that will be fine for now" and with that Chloe turned around to head back to the counter.

Bowing her head to take a sip of her Earl Grey she enjoyed the warm and smooth taste of the tea leaves. Letting out a satisfied puff of air she straightened her head back up and found herself drawn towards an advert on the wall that had a photograph of a dog on it.

'Do you understand your pets; do you know what they are thinking? No, well you should because they understand you!' was written across the top of the advert.

What a bizarre statement thought Mildred as she stood up and walked over to the wall so she could read the small print of the advert.

Her vision was not as good as it used to be as she strained her eyes to read 'I'm Doctor Bethany Birks, animal psychologist and I would like to introduce you to my human training programmes where you will be able to understand your pet and communicate with them.' There was a small picture of a smiling woman with a stethoscope wrapped around her neck who presumably was the doctor in question.

A curious Mildred decided to read more about these absurd statements.

'My one to one programmes will enable you to understand your pets more and in doing so they will understand you more.'

All of a sudden Mildred found herself quite fascinated by this as it had occurred to her that Missy may ignore her on occasions, she mentally wrestled with this for the briefest of moments. Well I'm sure Missy does not ignore me she just has a funny way of showing it she pondered. That's part of her character, she reassured herself accepting there were no flaws in the way she tended to her cat.

She carried on reading with interest. 'Whether you own a dog, a budgie, a hamster or a CAT call me today, I will change your life forever or your money back!' *

She was drawn to this final paragraph on the advert upon reading the word 'cat' and saw a phone number to call.

She looked around the café; no-one was watching her or paying her the slightest bit of attention as they were engrossed in their various phone technologies. Turning her back towards everyone she quickly pulled the advert off the wall and placed it into her jacket pocket and sat back down.

It was at that moment, having a momentary wobble of guilt that she may have just stolen something that she glanced out of the window and smiled upon seeing Missy perched on a wall next to a ginger looking cat. They were looking at each other and looked comfortable with each other like they had met before. She leaned her head forward to the window with a perfect smile on her face looking at her beloved cat and tilted her head to one side. They were not moving and kept staring at each other. It's almost like they were having a conversation with each other. Mildred smiled and shook her head at the absurdity of her own thoughts.

subject to status and mental health assessment

"I went up the top of Stan again earlier this morning" proclaimed Scamper.
Here we go again thought Nahla looking directly into Scamper's eyes.
"Really? You'll be getting up him with one leg tied behind your back soon!" Nahla interjected.
"Ha ha, I'm good but not that good Nahla" Scamper laughed…"Oh wait, are you making fun of me?"
"Me?" replied Nahla, "wouldn't ever dream of it, although I do always seem to miss your climbing exploits."
"You have to be up early to catch me Nahla" said Scamper beaming with pride, "you know that" and her tail began to swing back and forth. "You spend too much time with that human, it's making you lazy!"

Nahla frowned but knew that Scamper kept the most peculiar hours and always seemed to be at 100 miles per hour in anything she did.

Scamper lived alone in an old abandoned house on Darwin Road and like many cats did not seek out the need to have human company all of the time; so if that was a positive it was most definitely a negative that she needed to feed herself all of the time and as such was completely self reliant.

"Have you seen that fox about?" Scamper asked.
"Not so far today but Freddie often sleeps at this hour of the day; you should know that by now." "I'm not surprised with the amount he eats; I need to speak to that fox he isn't leaving a thing."
"He's a big eater alright" said Nahla.
"It's not on, he's greedy and I keep getting things thrown at me if I go through people's bins during the day. I don't see people throwing things at him."

"Maybe that's why he sleeps during the day."

"He sleeps all day because he eats too much! I don't like things being thrown at me Nahla, the shouting is okay I can just ignore that."

"It's a risky life being a cat; the humans will never understand us."

"This is true but I have no intention of trying to understand them either; strange breed" Scamper retorted.

"Mmm" was the sound that came from Nahla as if in some form of agreement. "The keeper of food where I stay is getting very excited with herself, her behaviour is quite odd at the moment, even more so than usual."

Scamper turned her head towards Missy upon hearing this.

"She keeps going on about a gathering she needs to go to and she won't stop fussing."

"Humans; can't live with them, can't eat them" Scamper said and turned her head away to face the café opposite.

"Humans" Nahla added as if in mutual agreement, well except for the last bit as that was kinda odd but in keeping with Scamper's regular attempts at humour.

After both of them had stared at the café for a little while Nahla gave a little sigh, "I'm bored" she said "Let's go and see Stan, I can watch you climb to the top!"

Scamper bolted her head around to look at Nahla again upon hearing this.

"You know, I'd love to but I'm a little tired from climbing up him from earlier, maybe next time."

Scamper prepared to move herself off the wall.

"Hey Nahla what do you call a cat that steals a lot?"

Nahla looked at Scamper "eh? Don't we all kinda take a bit?"

"No, no, that's not what I mean! What do you call a cat that steals a lot?"

"I really have no idea"

"A cat burglar! Ha ha – get it?"

Nahla looked at Scamper completely unmoved "that is not even in the slightest bit funny."

"Well I thought it was; you are so serious all of the time Nahla you need to lighten up." Scamper adopted the getting ready to move position. "Oh well, catch you later lazy Nahla."

And with that Scamper leaped off the wall and trotted down the road.

Nahla turned her head towards the café and could see the Mildred woman staring at her...

Humans she thought and jumped off the wall and walked away.

Chapter Five:

THE NOOK AT THE
COACH AND HORSES

WEDNESDAY

It was a rare occasion for Daphne to meet with her elder away from the monthly meetings or the yearly regional gathering. As such she was looking forward to seeing her again in person; in fact she was surprised when she called asking for her time, it must be quite important.

There were no hard and fast rules about this. It's just gathering business takes place at gatherings and more generalised topics take place at the monthly meet ups, it was a simple as that; there was always the phone if needed.

The monthly meet up would be very informal and members within the local district would attend; in this case that being the shire of Shropshire where Daphne lived also alongside Jessica, her elder. The Shropshire meetings were very popular as it is a reasonably large county in England close to the Welsh border. At times there could be a crossover of accents as well as the occasional musings of the Welsh language. The Shropshire group also had Mildred from Rocke Road and 1 other Jessica who were part of the new intake. New members were considered as such if they had been a member for anything up to three years.

However, within the Shropshire local area there were some who had been members for much longer than Daphne and for that reason the monthly meetings were usually fairly well attended.

The forthcoming yearly gathering was a lot different however and members across the region are invited. Unless due to ill heath every member is requested to attend and this is the same as it has always been. In total (including the new intake) within the region of the middle sector of England and Wales there were 8 Mildreds, 5 Daphnes, 11 Jessicas and 21 other elders that went by different names.

Daphne was preparing herself in anticipation of this unscheduled meeting. Unlike Mildred she had two cat food bowls in her kitchen and one water bowl that Aziza and Binky could share. She was due to meet with Jessica at 3pm at the Coach and Horses on Castle Street, Shrewsbury. It was also unusual to meet in a public house but she had been advised by her that there was a quiet area towards the back of the pub. There they would be able to drink tea and talk privately. The tea houses throughout the county and the country for that matter may have others listening in and Jessica explained that she needed to speak with her most privately about gathering business.

Looking at the pendulum swinging back and forth on her grandmother clock next to her certificates she re-read the familiar words engraved upon it 'Tempus Fugit', indeed time does fly, much too quickly she considered and that was as much of the Latin language that she knew. Some of the other elders, those who were much more senior to her, spoke many of the old languages and followed many old traditions passed down through generations of enlightenment.

As an 8th degree elder Daphne had her responsibilities and she took those very seriously. This included assisting other elders of the same level as her with whatever their needs may be but she also had to liaise with the new intake as well; especially Mildred, Mildred was her direct responsibility. But there were also responsibilities to the club that elders often referred to as the 'Order' and those responsibilities were to ensure that rules were followed – after all anarchy will prevail and the system will fall apart without discipline within the membership. Daphne had been informed of this by Jessica some time ago; anyway, I wonder what this meeting could be about she continued to ponder?

The Coach and Horses consisted of two bars, one was for recreation with a dart board and sports on the television, the other was in a restaurant area and within that restaurant was a little nook. Here hidden from prying eyes it was this little nook where Daphne was now sitting at a grand old oak table waiting for her elder to arrive.

Surveying her surrounds in this public house she could see old posters from a bygone era framed on the walls. The posters were proudly promoting the health benefits of drinking beer and were of a design and colouration that was from probably just after the war; the second that is.

Within the nook itself were images and paintings of old lawyers and references to law and acts of law that probably didn't pose much use to society at all these days. There was a huge green plaque that had names of lawyers inscribed into it going back as far as 1860. She decided to read a few lines of one of the acts of law on the wall in front of her whilst she was waiting and in doing so a couple of minutes of her life had just passed by forever, something that she never would be able to reclaim back – tempus fugit indeed she muttered to herself.

When you are 7th degree elder (or higher) certain privileges are afforded to you or generalised lifestyle changes are offered and these can take many different forms. The higher your status the more privileges you had as well as more access to information, it was quite simple really.

One of the notable differences or benefits (some elders may say) is that you are allowed the use of a motor car.

New members and 8th degree elders do not have motor vehicles and other such mobile movement contraptions. Televisions are commonplace as they are good vessels for assimilating information and messages but computers, mobile telephones, electric tin openers and the internet were not encouraged, owning some social media?? – Well what was that anyway? New members lead a simplistic life and they do not require the complications of modern day living.

A car became necessary as there would be a larger area to be covered and people of influence have to be seen. Sitting on buses and other forms of public transport prompts complete strangers to ask questions and they may try to make random conversation about the weather and the suchlike and well let's face it, no one wants to be bothered with any of that. Members of the Order lead private and quiet lives and keep themselves to themselves.

Jessica who holds a 7th degree elder status had just got out of her little black car; it was fair and reasonable to say that she was not very 'car proud'. However, that's not to say there was anything wrong with the car she was driving; sure she did have a picture of a cat stuck to one of her windows, but the inside of the car, well that was a different story altogether. Sweet wrappers, empty chocolate boxes and receipts and carrier bags from expensive clothing stores were just a few items that could be spotted in Jessica's car if you were so inclined to check. It didn't smell too good either would be another nasal observation, the perfume from her cat shaped air fresher that hung from her rear view mirror had expired some time ago.

Staring at the front door of the Coach and Horses she composed herself and straightened the tartan design of the long skirt she was wearing. Lifting up her right leg she removed a piece of dirt that had attached itself to the front of her new high heels and brushed herself down leaving bread crumbs and the remnants of her lunch on the floor below.

She locked her car and dropped the keys into her expensive clutch bag and checked her little box was inside and turned around to survey the place she was about to enter to meet Daphne. Two security cameras were above the front door to the pub and she could see another down the side road. Ignoring them but noting their presence she wobbled on the street cobbles and went inside.

Daphne was overjoyed to see her elder walk in. Beaming with a smile that represented a dental TV commercial *(without the pristine teeth of course)* she stood up to greet her friend and elder.

"Good afternoon Lady Jessica" Daphne bestowed.
"Good afternoon my friend."

Both had checked that no-one was listening before they addressed each other and hugged like old friends do.

"Can I get you anything?" Daphne enquired.

"Tea please, mint tea if they have it."

"Of course please take a seat" Daphne politely requested, "would you like something to eat?" she added..."fish paste sandwiches?"

"Oh no thank you I've already eaten a little something" although she did momentarily consider it.

Daphne nodded and headed towards the bar area to place the order. Turning around she could see Jessica surveying the pictures of lawyers long passed and reading the same legal language that she had herself only moments beforehand. It had been some years now since she came into my life she smiled to herself at the thought of it and she turned to place her order at the bar.

Jessica having gotten bored reading the old legal language on the wall in front of her had turned her attention to the inside of the pub. There were a few small security cameras in domes fixed around the ceiling and above the bar areas nestled as discreetly as they could be between the painted black beams that wove their way around the ceilings as many buildings did in this area. Upon seeing Daphne paying at the bar she quickly gathered her thoughts and was pleased to see her return with a cup of mint tea.

"It's very quiet in here" Daphne said and placed the cup with hot steam rising from it on the table in front of Jessica.

"I thought this would be a good place to meet at this hour of the day" she smiled.

After the briefest of pauses Jessica was itching to talk.

"I have news" she proclaimed "and it's exciting, very exciting Daphne" she grinned, "although somewhat sad at the same time." She softened her voice and her face became simultaneously sad and serious.

"You wouldn't have known her but Lady Tempest from Cheshire *(whose former name was also Jessica)* who was a 6th degree elder has passed over."

"Gosh, I'm sorry to hear that Jessica" Daphne recoiled upon hearing this sad and uncomfortable news.

"I know, I only met her the once; it has come as such a shock to everyone and the elders especially...she was a perfect role model and most respected."

"Oh this is very sad news, I'm shocked; was it ill health and could she not have been healed?"

"No, I'm afraid not; her health was quite perfect; unfortunately the world of men did for her."

"Oh, that sounds most terrible" Daphne added.

"Yes, she was hit by a bus."

They both fell silent for a few moments.

"This is terrible to hear, what became of her cats Jessica?"

"Not surprisingly at her degree level she had 4 cats. I'm guessing they have joined her now or been returned to the Keeper; I'm not knowledgeable on these things I'm afraid."

Jessica's eyes had strayed and in this awkward silence and almost without her knowledge had started reading the legal posters in front of her again.

"And that's why I wanted to meet with you" she said as if almost leaping back into life. "At the forthcoming gathering I have been selected and I will be presented with my real name!"

"Oh Jessica that is amazing news!" Daphne grinned and put her hands together and started gently clapping them like a crazed windup chimpanzee toy.

"It's more responsibility of course and there are many perks and benefits, most of which have not been explained to me quite yet." Jessica was shaking her head and speaking with speed and excitement as she reflected upon becoming a 6th degree elder.

An elder moving up a degree level only ever takes place when another has passed over, so this is not a commonplace event. A naming ceremony would have to be prescribed by an elder at least 2 degrees higher than the one being appointed. The forthcoming meet was a yearly one but on occasions, just sometimes, it can be as long as 13-14 months before the collective regional gathering would meet, such is the way of things.

"I long for my real name" Daphne mused.

"It will come...in time my friend" Jessica added and placed a supporting hand on Daphne's although never once looking her in the eyes.

Jessica was deep in thought when she gave out a little nervous cough almost for attention.

"Tell me, how is Mildred progressing?" Jessica asked.

Daphne who was lifting her cup to her mouth paused "fine" she said and then took a sip of tea before stopping at such a random question. "Wait, which Mildred?"

"Mildred from Rocke Road, your Mildred" Jessica gave a nervous smile, took a sip of her tea and quickly returned her gaze to her cup.

"All three of the new Mildreds are fine across the region; well to the best to my knowledge" she was now looking at Jessica with some curiosity. "You've never asked after the Mildreds before, or after any of the others from the new members the other Jessicas or Daphnes for that matter, is everything okay?"

"Oh yes, just doing my 'elderly' bit" she offered a wide smile with this statement and widened her eyes. "I just thought with this new level of responsibility that Mildred, who is right on my doorstep, I should get to know more; as I do you."

"I see," Daphne commented, "that's very nice of you" she added with some suspicion after this new revelation. Surely it was her role to look after the local Mildred after all she was Mildred's direct elder.

Jessica was holding her cup in her hands and stirring her tea.

"Nothing strange going on or you need to confide in me about at all?" she muttered quietly.

Daphne now had a confused expression on her face and her eyebrows had lifted at hearing this most strange of questions. "No, everything is well Lady Jessica" and she gave a gentle nod of her head to support what she had said, along with an awkward smile stemming from the left hand side of her mouth.

"Oh, that's good then" Jessica lifted her cup up again and took a sip of tea. "You will tell me if something is not right or if you need to share any concerns won't you Daphne?"

Daphne quickly turned her head towards her "Of course Lady Jessica" she paused for a little, "are you quite sure that everything is okay?"

"Oh yes, of course my dear, I'm just tired please ignore me, much to do and not enough time." She looked at Daphne with a tired smile, "there never is" she offered in support of her previous comment.

"There is never enough of what Lady Jessica?" Daphne said looking at her with further curiosity.

"Time my friend."

Jessica's eyes were now firmly fixed looking ponderously into her cup.

"I may offer Mildred a lift to the gathering" she said; before looking up, "just part of the getting to know everyone more type of thing."

Daphne, whom to that point had not averted her eyes from looking at Jessica, was now looking at the pictures on the wall in contemplation of how odd the conversation had just turned. In all of the time she had known Jessica she had never once offered her a lift anywhere.

After 20 seconds or so of silence had passed Daphne cleared her throat.

"It really is amazing news for you Jessica and it's always wonderful to see you of course, but you decided not to tell me these things on the phone?"

"No...the watchers Daphne, the watchers."

"But the watchers see Jessica?"

Jessica turned her head towards Daphne "No my friend, they hear as well."

They both resumed looking at the wall and Daphne knew that something was seriously wrong.

Pleased and somewhat surprised Mildred had made her way home fresh with the knowledge that 44 cards with the lovely black cat on the front would be at Mr. Franks' shop the very next day for her to collect. Incredible service she thought and even more so that the picture on the card looked just like her Missy. I do hope they all arrive exactly the same she thought to herself. How amazed the group are going be that she had arranged a card for all of the members from across the district; she doubted that anyone else would have gone to such a personal effort. She would have to address most of the cards 'with best wishes' as she didn't know the names of most of the members from the whole of her district even after all of this time; the monthly meetings were far more intimate and everyone had got to know each other but when everyone comes together for a gathering it was a completely different thing. Those who had been members of the club for longer would usually sit by themselves in their own groups and even the local members from Shropshire who were mostly older than her would peel away to sit with others of their own rank or however it was that it worked.

There was a mutual respect between the members who had been involved for longer, pleasantries were exchanged of course but newer members knew their place; quite odd for a cat members club Mildred had considered in the past but had not dwelled upon it. But this time she would make an effort and do something that at least all of them will remember her by.

Quite pleased with today's progress and efforts she was sat on the end of her bed facing her wardrobe now almost knowing what she would wear on Friday. She pushed one of her shoes on the heel of her other foot and shook both of her shoes off where they fell on their sides on the floor. She noticed that her shoes were looking somewhat tired but so were her other three pairs of exactly the same colour and design.

Standing up and stretching she turned around and flattened out the creases on the bed where she had been sat and made sure that the pictures of cats printed on her bedspread were all perfectly in line.

Approaching her wardrobe she opened the doors; on the left side is where jackets and pullovers would hang and on the right hand side on the shelves were her stockings and her undercrackers *(as she sometimes referred to them)*. At the top of the wardrobe were hats and neck accessories and on the floor were her other three pairs of shoes.

The wardrobe doors would always make moaning sounds when they were opened as they were built of a time much before she was born, not too dissimilar to most of the furniture within her home. Creature comforts were minimal.

So, let's work from top to bottom Mildred thought whilst displaying a big beaming smile.

Head and neckwear to start...

She looked at her rather small selection of cloche hats; they were all grey of course but that was not the problem, the consideration had to be all about the accompanying design. The right hand side of all of her hats had some form of flower pattern, either as a single rose or as a mixed variety of flowers, with exception to one - the special one and the one that she was yet to wear in public. The special one cost her quite a lot more money than she would usually spend and she debated with herself about spending so much within a charity shop, even though the profits were being donated to the local cat rescue charity. The special hat featured a woven bright red outline of a cat on it and she loved it as soon as she saw it. Sometimes in life you need to take the initiative Mildred had thought to herself and she purchased it on impulse, it was a material thing, yes, but a lovely thing all the same.

Settled then; the cat hat it would be.

She then picked up her burgundy fake fur stole that would keep her neck warm just in case there was a chill in the evening *(even though it was the height of summer)* and she laid that out on the bed next to the hat.

Turning back to her wardrobe she took her new homemade cardigan off the hanger and laid that out on the bed next to the hat and stole.
She was most impressed with her knitting skills as she marvelled at her creation of this 6 button cardigan masterpiece; blue in colour with a black cat chasing a ball of string woven into it, it would have the ladies talking she thought. She smiled assessing her work and clapping her hands together in glee although she contemplated that in all of the time she had owned Missy never once had she seen her chase a ball of string...

Her floral white shirt that buttoned to the top and her brown pencil skirt that went just below the knee she collected next. All that remained were her quite large stockings and brown shoes and with the exception to her gloves and handbag she was ready.

She looked forward to the evening of everything cat related.

Chapter Six:

DRIVE OF THE NAVIGATOR

TUESDAY – APPROACHING MIDDAY

Jessica felt quite lost as her car had stopped at a grass verge; with some concern she looked at her watch confirming what she already suspected - that she was behind schedule.

It had only been two days before that there had been a knock at her front door and when it came she was a little in shock as it was rare for anyone to knock on her door, even more so on a Sunday. A notice hung in her front porch that said quite clearly *'No salespeople, no leaflets and no politicians'* and as such she was left alone in peace for the best part of the day. Scrambling with her dressing gown and trying to put her bright red fluffy slippers on she tripped on one of her three cat bowls and scowled hoping that she hadn't chipped her nail polish. She opened her front door to discover that no-one was there. Stepping out of her porch on Porthill Crescent she looked left and then looked right, there was not a soul in sight.

Frowning and reasonably positive that she hadn't imagined it she turned around to go back inside when she looked down and saw a small package on her doorstep.

Not distinctive in any way or bearing any postmarks she bent down and picked up the clearly hand wrapped square package and took it inside. Filling her kettle with water she stared at the box now on her kitchen table wrapped in brown paper and fastened with string.

Switching on the gas on the hob and igniting the flame into life she placed the kettle gently upon it and pulled up a stool and sat down at her kitchen table to consider what it could possibly be.

No stamps and no delivery company sticker it just said 'Jessica' Number 13 Porthill Crescent.

Whoever had dropped it off clearly didn't want to wait around and that alone had her intrigued.

Jumping slightly at suddenly feeling a cat's tail on her ankles she looked down to see that Khepri her eldest cat was looking up at her. Their eyes met momentarily, she whispered to her "shall I open it?" Her cat kept staring at her and without breaking eye contact Jessica started nodding her head. "Okay..."

She pulled at one of the ends of the string and the package started to unfold. She removed a hand written note, a shiny metal badge and another smaller black box that equally bore no marking of any distinction.

Picking up the badge she could see that it had a symbol on it that she did not fully recognise but for some reason it did have a feel of familiarity about it. She had observed at gatherings in the past that some of the other elders who were of a higher degree than her wore badges but she did not wish to appear to be rude by staring at them but it did occur to her that this may be one of them.

'Staring is very rude!' her mother used to remind her regularly *(her adopted mother that is)* and as such to this day she was very self conscious about looking at people directly.

Putting the badge down she picked up the handwritten note that she had to unfold to read. The handwriting was immaculate and pleasing to the eye. Every single word was equally spaced and every written line was millimetre perfect in line with each other, quite a feat on unlined paper.

Dear Jessica

Following your selection and forthcoming appointment to degree level 6 you are required to attend an informal meeting this coming Tuesday at 14.00 hours. The contents of the box enclosed will help you to find our national headquarters. It is paramount that you do not discuss your appointment with anyone else and the contents of the box are to remain on your person at all times day and night hereafter.

In order not to be late you should leave Porthill Crescent at midday using your motor vehicle; it is advised that you have an appropriate amount of fuel for the journey.

Do not switch on the navigator until that time.

Thank you for your cooperation.

The box itself you can throw away'

Jessica put her hands together behind her head and leaned back before remembering she was on a kitchen stool so she bolted herself upright again with a start.

Her elder had only very recently given her the amazing news that she was to become a degree level 6 but this was the first 'official' communication she had seen confirming this. Initially smiling upon receiving this clarification there also could be no doubt that the note was very 'to the point', not just that she was clearly being told what to do but she had no idea where she was heading.

Taking the small black box into her hands she lifted it up and lowered her head to look underneath it and started turning it around in her fingers. All that she could see was one tiny gold dot which presumably was an indicator to open here.

Pulling at the side with the gold dot on it she lifted the flap back and could see there was a compartment inside that was very well padded. In the centre of the padding was a silver coloured object not much bigger than the size of her palm. Taking it out and studying it carefully she could see one push button on the side, she froze and then with her right arm picked up the note again. *'Do not switch on the navigator until that time.'*

With the navigator in her left hand and the note in her right she was frozen ridged in a perplexed state. What happens if I push the button now she considered. It was something that she would have to keep considering for the next two days.

During the ten minutes or so that had just passed during the box opening ceremony Kherpri stared at her constantly and was unmoved throughout.

Jessica stepped out from her car and wobbled slightly on the uneven road and rested both of her arms on top of the open car door. Looking up and down the road all she could see were masses of huge cedar trees and all she could feel was the gentle summer breeze passing over her. Stepping out fully and moving away from the car she turned around now standing in the middle of the road completely confused at the dead end road she had just driven down or rather where the car had chauffeured her to.

Putting one hand on her hip and the other to her head and pushing it through her long hair as if for some sort of inspiration, she felt that she was forced to consider what sort of clueless place she had been brought to. She had known that she had passed over the Welsh border some 30-40 minutes ago in what initially seemed like a great motoring adventure as it was rare that she travelled very far; after her nerves had calmed down that is. She had passed by wonderful landscapes and mountains in order to get to here, here in this not so much lifeless but very quiet place in the middle of nowhere.

She looked up and noted there were no birds singing from the very well maintained trees that stretched in a perfect line on both sides of the road possibly for a least half a mile; were it not for the noise of the gentle breeze that blew through them she could have heard a pin drop.

She could see a rabbit staring at her towards the end of the road that simply just ended in a semicircular 180 degree curve of trees. Nose twitching with some greenery in its mouth it was unmoved and curious that its day had been disturbed by the presence of another. Markings on the tarmac at the end of the road directly in front of the staring rabbit suggested that others had driven down this road to nowhere in the past and had abruptly turned around. She looked away before returning her gaze back to the end of the road and noticed the rabbit had disappeared. The only disturbance she could now hear was from the bleeping noise coming from the inside of her car - it was then she realised that she had left the door open with the engine running.

Retuning back to her car to switch the engine off and closing the door to silence the beeping noise she walked the short distance to where she had seen the rabbit. The greenery below the trees was as neat and tidy as the trees themselves. Someone had gone to a lot of trouble to maintain this dead end road. She stepped onto the grass verge towards the trees on the right hand side of the semicircle and attempted to peer through them in what was a fruitless attempt to see if anything lay beyond. The trees had immense depth and viewing anything further than a few feet in front of her was impossible. Somewhat nervously glancing at her watch it was now 5 minutes to 2 and she felt a wave of anxiety come up through her tummy. She was definitely going to be late.

For two days she had stared at the box that had been referred to as a *'navigator'* and to say she was excited to switch it on was an understatement. She knew that rules had to be followed, as all members of every degree level did, as rules ensured balance and stability *(this was constantly being reminded)*. It would not be the last time that day that she would feel waves of anxiety but the time for switching on the device was finally upon her. Nervous at first she picked it up and stared at it for a little while; taking a deep breath she pressed the single button on its side. The matt blackness of the 'navigator' was immediately lit up with a clear white screen that said one word at the top left hand side 'Videmus'.

What could that possibly mean she thought to herself?

Turning it in her fingers like it was a type of puzzle and touching the screen yielded nothing of any interest, just the blinking dot after the word 'Videmus' remained.

Clearly she had to input something but there were no other buttons to press and no keyboard had appeared on the screen. Switching it off and on again three times yielded no further clues either.

Khepri had come into the kitchen and sat at her feet looking up at her as she had a couple of days beforehand.

"What is it Khepri?" she said aloud realising that she had just asked her cat a question. Unsurprisingly no response was forthcoming and Khepri just continued to stare back at her.

Frustrated she continued to press at the mysterious device.

Khepri turned her head to the left upon realising that she had been joined by Neith and Tabby at her sides.
Jessica looked down at her cats to see that three pairs of eyes were now firmly fixed on her.

"What do you all want?" she questioned in a stern voice in what was quite a rare display of ill-patience.

Clutching the navigator firmly she looked directly into the cats eyes; something that she was free to do without fear unlike her nervousness of direct eye contact towards humans.
"Why are you all staring at me?" Her voice had now softened but her frown had not as she etched a hint of a smile from the left corner of her mouth. All four pairs of eyes were now locked together.

Jessica did not realise that she had done it but her chin had lowered so her head slightly bowed towards her cats, she hadn't blinked for some time. Khepri lifted her head up to break the deadlock and Jessica blinked and jolted and returned her gaze to the navigator. Looking at the white screen and re-reading the word she glanced back down at her cats. Khepri's head was still slightly aloft whilst Neith and Tabby to either side of her head were still slightly bowed.

She quickly turned her head back to the machine; 'enlightened', 'to see'; 'illumination' were some of the words bouncing in her head. 'To see'...'To see'...'TO SEE!" she said out aloud and she lifted the navigator to her face and brought it up closely to her eyes and speaking loud and firmly "I have the ability to see!" she said with confidence. Instantly the white screen disappeared and was immediately replaced by the same symbol that was on the badge. She snatched at the badge on the table and affixed it to her jacket and as she looked back at the screen a message had appeared:

'Time for you to leave, make haste Jessica.'

A huge beaming smile had stretched all the way across her face "ha ha" she exclaimed out load and stamped her feet up and down. Excitedly she peered over the kitchen table and looked down ready to speak to the cats when she noticed that all three of them had disappeared. "That's odd" but without hesitation she reached out for her car keys.

It was time to depart, to where she had no idea.

The breeze had picked up a little as she looked back down the eerie and overly quiet road. Her little car parked on the right hand side almost seemed a place of refuge despite what had happened earlier. The navigator had brought her here but she had no idea why.

After she had cracked the entry code to activate the navigator she had gone directly to her car without any hesitation and got inside. Sitting behind the steering wheel she placed the keys into the ignition whilst mentally preparing herself for what may well be a long drive *(well, long for her)*. She turned the key clockwise and the engine fired into life. It was at that very moment the air vents in front of her came forward slightly and then turned around back into the dashboard revealing a new panel that had been hidden behind them. She froze in shock as this had never happened before and she could see the new panel had a cradle in it as well as a small screen to the right. Making sure the handbrake was on she picked up the navigator and could now see directly below the screen that a small entry port had appeared. Looking back at the panel and its cradle she assessed to see if this were to be a perfect fit. It was!

The navigator fitted perfectly into the cradle and she immediately felt the footbrake beneath her right foot move and the accelerator pedal moved forward as the car began jumping. Nervously she released the handbrake. As she did, she had let go of the steering wheel and the words 'auto-drive' had appeared on the screen next to the navigator and the car immediately moved forward towards the end of her drive.

In a panic she re-grabbed the wheel again and put her foot on the brake but the car kept moving as well as gaining speed. She was now heading out of her drive into the main road.

Squealing she shielded her eyes with her hands as the car rushed straight out of her drive and turned right. Puffing and panting she pressed one hand on the window glass next to her and the other over her heart in a complete panic as she realised that she had no control of the car. The forthcoming pedestrian crossing was ahead as she recognised an elderly gentleman with a walking stick in hand waiting at the side of the road ready to cross. The car was not slowing down as the lights changed from green to amber to red.

"GET OUT THE WAY!!!" she yelled and screamed as loud as she could whilst in a panic pressing the button for the window to come down. Head now cocked out of the window with her hair flailing behind her "GET OUT OF THE ROAD!!!! she screamed with an arm waving sounding and looking like a crazy person, but it was all too late as the man had already started slowly walking across the crossing.
"AHHHHHH" she yelled stamping on the break and covering her eyes when the car suddenly came to an abrupt stop. Heart racing at 150 miles per hour she was still gasping for breath as she slowly removed her hands from her eyes; the car had stopped directly at the stop sign.
The man stopped in the middle of the crossing looking directly at her in a state of shock having been yelled at whilst he was minding his own business. As soon as her eyes met his she looked away.
"What's the matter with you crazy woman?" he gesticulated with his stick.
"Sorry, sorry" she repeated with much sincerity and embarrassment whilst flapping her hands in the air and her eyes partially weeping with tears of shock.

He finished crossing, the lights changed back to green and the car lunged forward again. Without holding the steering wheel Jessica turned around and could see through the rear windscreen that the man was still staring at her and waving his stick.

Oh heavens, what on earth is happening she thought to herself and with that the car made its way in the direction of the Welsh border.

Perplexed she stared at the car in what had been quite a terrifying journey and rubbed her chin. Taking yet another glance at her designer watch she walked quickly back to the car and opened the door. The navigator was still in place and the display that had said auto-drive had now disappeared. She got in and sat in the front seat and considered her options, she had no number to call and no-one she could speak with as the instructions were quite clear. She pondered; the instructions? She took the note out of her pocket that had been delivered with the navigator and reread it. '....do not discuss your appointment...box to remain on your person at all times...'

'At all times...' She considered. Pulling the navigator from the cradle the panel immediately turned back around revealing the air vents. She looked at it; it was still lit but offered nothing else so she placed it towards her mouth.
"Navigator help" she spoke into it and then pulled it away from her mouth looking longingly at it for guidance.
"Navigator...err...navigate?" Nothing; all that could be heard was the breeze outside and the cursor light still flashed on the screen.

Scratching her head she stepped outside from the car again to notice that the rabbit had reappeared. She stared at it still munching something in its mouth. Looking back down at the navigation device that offered no navigation whatsoever she walked towards the rabbit, it didn't move. She quickened her pace up to the semicircle of trees and walked right up to the rabbit. It swallowed whatever it had be eating and then disappeared into the undergrowth.

She stepped forward to the trees now in the centre of the semicircle and saw something that she hadn't noticed before. The tarmac ended at the semicircle but there was a dip in the grassed area towards the right of the centre, exactly where the rabbit had disappeared into almost as if it were an entry point to somewhere.
Stepping forward she walked up to the trees and only when she was completely parallel with them she could see further to the right of her a camouflaged green post that would not have been visible from where she was standing before.

Crouching down and peering very closely at the post she could see a tiny symbol was on it. She recognised it instantly. She held her navigator next to the post and leaned down so her pin badge was level with it and immediately she heard a loud clicking noise followed by the sound of grinding metal coming from the ground below. She was unsure if the ground beneath her feet were moving or not such was her confusion as she stared at the trees shaking in front of her. Further sounds of movement were coming up from below where she stood and she took a couple of steps backwards in panic. The trees directly in front of her started to part and move backwards, she could see twigs and foliage that had been loose on the ground falling into the gap that had now appeared as the trees gave way either side of her. The mechanical rumblings from below became louder as the gap that had appeared was now being refilled by a huge slab of tarmac that was being pushed upright from below. The twigs and dirt that had fallen into the gap only moments before were now resting directly on top of what was an unblemished tarmac driveway.

There was a loud crunching noise of metal and she was sure that she felt the ground shake as everything came to a standstill. The peace and quiet of before had returned as she looked around to see if anybody else had seen this unbelievable event that had just happened right in front of her.

Stumbling a couple of steps to her right with adrenaline racing through her veins the trees had given way revealing what Jessica had been summoned to see. Astounded and letting out a noise of shock, her hand shaking she straightened herself up although shuffling awkwardly; she gulped and swallowed deeply before her mouth fell open.

"Oh my" were the only words that could be heard drifting down the eerie road.

Chapter Seven:

WORD OF THE ORDER

WEDNESDAY AFTERNOON

Mildred tilted her head towards the stairs, she had only just finished putting her clothing away in the wardrobe when she heard the not too familiar noise of her phone ringing downstairs; or meowing if the truth be told.

Not due a call from Daphne, or the other Mildreds, it was a reasonable assumption that it was probably someone trying to sell something; she had no idea why as her house was immaculate as it was.

All the same she dived down the stairs to answer it just in case.

Although not unhappy in the slightest about her quiet and virtually solitary life with her cat, since her membership of the club in the period she refers to now as her *'former life'* she had been a reasonably sociable person. Nowadays people asking very personal questions like *'How is your day going'*, *'have you ever considered...'* are just plain awkward questions. Why on earth do they want to know anyway she would often consider, after all she didn't ring strangers asking them personal questions. But all the same one thing she was not was rude, there is no place for rudeness and etiquette must prevail.

"Hello, number 1 Rocke Road" she answered, never fully knowing why

sometimes she would answer the phone informing the caller of where she lived.
"Oh hello Mildred, it's Jessica."
"Oh hello, Jessica"...the cogs of her brain turned, "I'm sorry, which Jessica is this?"
"Oh, yes you are right, sorry Mildred, its Jessica, you met me at last year's gathering when I was speaking with Daphne, do you remember?"
Mildred pulled the cat's bottom away from her mouth staring at the phone in quite some disbelief, yes of course I remember, what would Daphne's 'elder' be doing ringing me she thought?

Composing herself with a little cough to clear her throat "Yes of course Lady Jessica, I remember you very well, how are you, how are the cats? I'm very sorry I do not recall their names."
"That's okay Mildred, my cats are fine, thank you for asking; I wanted..."
"I can't remember, how many do you have?" interrupted an overexcited Mildred.

Jessica had to remind herself that Mildred was still new to the Order and there were a great many things that she was yet to understand.

"Well I have three Mildred; a person of my degree level always has three."
"Oh how wonderful, I just have Missy, she's my company, Daphne has two cats you know, Binky and Aziza."

Jessica smiled to herself hearing Mildred speaking at motormouth speed and knowing all too well that Daphne has two cats and that Binky was not her real name.

"Yes, I am aware of this Mildred."
"I've been thinking about getting another cat; company for Missy as well as for myself, I can afford to keep another one. In cats monthly I've seen some beautiful..."
Jessica's eyes widened upon hearing this.
"No, Mildred, you do not need another cat at this time!" she interjected very quickly then realising that she had snapped her answer and interrupted Mildred at the very same time. With renewed composure she closed her eyes and gathered her words.
"I'm quite sure in the future this will not be a problem, not a problem in the slightest and I'm sure that we can work that...something...out for you."

Mildred saddened upon hearing this, she had heard it mentioned before that she should only own one cat; why it was such a problem in this club that celebrated cats she really did not know, surely the more cats the better after all.

Breaking the momentary silence Jessica composed herself remembering further that it was only five years ago that she had been at the same point of membership within the Order that Mildred was currently at. She knew that she would need patience for the rest of the duration of this phone call.

"I wanted to call you to see how you are and if you are keeping well Mildred?" "I'm fine thank you" Mildred said in a soft and saddened voice still somewhat curious as to why Jessica had called her in the first place; so far all she had gleaned from this call was that she was being told that she couldn't have another cat. She removed that from her mind and picked up the tone of her voice "I'm better now that I've finally settled on what to wear for Friday."

"Oh good, so you are looking forward to Friday then are you? It should be a very good night and well attended." Jessica smiled to herself realising that she had got the conversation back on track, and part of that smile was due to her knowledge that Friday would be her naming ceremony of course.

"Oh yes, I have my new handmade cardigan and my hat! And it's always exciting to meet other members in the region; many of the older members I've never had a chance to speak with as yet."

Jessica sensed Mildred's curiosity, "That may well be the case right now but that will most certainly change Mildred; the longer you are a member of the Order the much more valued you become." Jessica was nodding at the same time with a smile of contentment across her face.

"I'm sorry, the Order?"

Jessica froze and the smile had disappeared as quickly as it had arrived. Putting one hand to her face as if berating herself she had to remind herself yet again that Mildred did not know these things yet, thinking quickly...

"Er, yes, the order... I'm so sorry, I was reading a takeaway menu at the same time, I was thinking of ordering something to eat later. How very rude of me, I do apologise, I meant to say the 'club'."

"Oh that's okay Lady Jessica; I've done it before when speaking to the other Mildreds. Mildred from Merewood Close likes to talk about her cakes. Now I'm not much of a cake person, but she is and she does make a wonderful jam sponge…"

Jessica was pleased that she had gotten out of that one but had to pinch herself as a reminder that she needed patience; she mentally tried to rejoin the conversation whilst Mildred was still talking away at 100 miles per hour.

"Yes she really is quite remarkable with her baking skills; anyway I did the same thing to her recently. As she was talking away I was flicking through Cats Quarterly and she asked me a question and I didn't even hear what she said, ha ha – can you believe it, I felt so silly!" Mildred was still laughing but seemed to be the only one doing so.

Silence was at the other end of the phone.

"Jessica, Lady Jessica?"
"Oh yes, Mildred I am here" she responded upon realising that she had drifted off for the second time during the phone call. The thought of takeaway food now had her searching through a kitchen draw looking for a menu.
"That is a very amusing story."
"Yes, isn't it" Mildred said with a frowned expression as she was rapidly coming to the conclusion that Jessica didn't appear to be paying much attention.

Upon finding the take away menu she had now regained her concentration.

"Well I guess I had better get to the reason as to why I called you today Mildred. As part of my new and expanding role within the Or…, the club I wanted to spend more time with our members and get to know them more on a personal level and this very much includes you, so I wondered if you would like a lift to the gathering on Friday?"

"Oh, do you have a new role then Lady Jessica?"

She raised her eyebrows and put a hand to her head again upon realising that for the second time she had spoken out of turn. Her promotion was supposed to be kept quiet for now; she had informed Daphne of her move up the ranks earlier in the day at the Coach and Horses but she had used that as an excuse to meet with her to find out how Mildred was doing. She contemplated that she was not particularly good at this sneaky kind of behaviour but she had been asked to do it and it was for the benefit of the Order after all.

"Yes, apparently so I'll find out more on Friday, it's still a little vague to be honest." But she was not being especially honest at all.
"Well I'd be delighted to accept a lift from you. I would also like to spend more time with you, you must know a great deal about cats."
"Well, yes, I guess I do really Mildred," but then Jessica knew a great deal more about other things as well as cats. "Well I guess that I'd better run so I'll see you on Friday."

"I understand Lady Jessica; do you know where I live so you can collect me?"

"Oh yes, we know where you live."

Mildred was staring at her phone yet again.

Said was not happy; once again he knew he was going to lose.

Perched on the window sill of number 13 Rocke Road he peered as hard as he could, his eyes were starting to sting...any moment now...blink...he sighed and looked at the floor shaking his head in disappointment.
With probable bloodshot eyes he looked back up at Barney who was unmoved and his eyes were still focused on him.
"How do you do that Lizard?" Said muttered out loud.
"Because that lizard has no eyelids dummy!" Said *(who as far as he was concerned was top cat in the three streets)* spun around.
"I might have known" he said almost in disgust to see Scamper looking up at him.

He turned his head back to look at Barney now quizzically looking to see if there were any merits in what Scamper had to say - Scamper was more of a fountain of lies than truths.

Upon the realisation that Scamper may be right he looked back at her. "How could a filthy and unkempt cat like you know that?"

"Simple really" she said and jumped up onto the sill next to Said and turned to look at Barney.

"Yes, how so?" snorted Said in his usual deep gruff voice.

"Well I let myself in the other day, the window up there was open" and she nodded her head to an upstairs window next to the drain pipe. The window had since been closed.

"So you've been right up to Barney's tank?"

"No, I was going through their drawers upstairs and I could hear Mr. Ryan talking to a girl downstairs called Chloe and he was telling her about it."

"Mmm, I see." Said paused and looked across hearing a banging noise coming from a few doors down. "The humans don't like it when you go into their house uninvited."

"I know" said Scamper "whatever."

Said looked at her, not impressed with this usual display of a lack of decorum from Scamper.

"When you don't have a proper home, every home is your own" she smiled in her usual hyperactive don't care type of manner.

Said turned his head back to the other side to concentrate on the banging again. "You are not welcome where I stay, just so as you know that."

"Duly note note noted" were the words Said heard reverberating in his ears in response to his very clear statement.

He jumped down from the sill and walked off. "I want to see what that noise is all about" he said.

"I'll come too."

"If you must" was about all that Said could think of what to say in response to this with a shrug of his shoulders.

They both hopped up onto the fence and two doors down they could see Mr. Ablett doing something with his shed roof.

There was another bang as Mr Ablett hit something with a hammer.

"There you see?" Said looked at Scamper.

"What?" questioned Said.

"Case in point, you see old Ablett up there?"

"Yes I can see him."

"A few weeks back a window was open in his shed, I had a bit of a look around, couldn't find much to eat but there was a nice little heater in there."

"A heater at this time of year?" asked Said.

"Yep, I curled up and fell asleep next to it but it got too hot and half asleep I kicked out at it and knocked it over. Not sure what happened but his shed wasn't there the next day."

Said tilted his head to look at Scamper "You really are a brainless idiot sometimes."

I don't know what you mean." said Scamper quizzically looking at Said.

"That really is not news to me" Said muttered and they both kept watching what the Ablett man was doing.

"ANDYYYYYYYYY" reverberated around the neighbourhood.

Andy paused and wiped his brow not appreciating his concentration being disturbed. Offering the most unspectacular of smiles he turned around from his step ladders looking back at the house "Yes dear, what is it?"

"Well what on ever are you up to now?" Mrs Ablett said with her usual ill-patience.

Sighing he looked at his wife "I'm putting up a CCTV camera dear, for security." Some sort of raspberry sound came from his wife's mouth "For what Andy" she said putting her hands on her hips "that damn expensive train set?"

"Yes that's right my damned expensive train set!" he said quickly and without thought and regretted it instantly.

"Don't you raise your voice at me!" she said sternly.

Andy looked towards the floor, "Sorry dear."

"Wait; wait a second, you are putting a camera up to watch the outside of the shed?"

"Yes?" He said.

"For security?"

"Yes...and."

"And you are fixing it towards the back of the shed roof?"

Andy turned around to see where he had been hammering the screws into the roof and froze.

"Well all it will see is the shed roof then and the top of the house!" she scoffed "it won't see any of the garden at all."

He looked at where he was positioning the camera and closed his eyes in disbelief.

"Honestly Andrew Ablett you are such a halfwit sometimes" Mrs Ablett said as she walked off laughing.

Andy screwed up his face in disgust; "58 people who watch my train set broadcasts on YouTube would disagree with you" he said out loud and without caring...well as long as she couldn't hear obviously.

"Strange lives humans lead" said Scamper.
Nodding his head having watched all of this, for once on this very rare occasion Said was in total agreement.

Chapter Eight:

THE CURATOR AND
THE WATCHED GARDEN

TUESDAY

Standing at the front of a very imposing driveway Jessica could see that it was a short distance to walk to a very elaborately decorated archway with huge gates. Stepping forward beyond the tree line the walls that ran from either side of the archway stretched for as far as she could see. They had to be at least ten feet tall keeping the uninvited and prying eyes at bay. Looking back at the tree lines to her left and right looked like an immense never ending long forest, secluded and peaceful.

Turning her attention back in front of her and lifting her head up she could see that the archway was made of huge pieces of sandstone that were a combination of white and dark colours no doubt from weather exposure over many years. She could see that triangular like turrets pointed towards the sky from the very top of the arch and in the centre lay a huge crest, no doubt of some significance to the owner and a small decorative shape lay below that. She was unable to work out what it was or meant an old family crest presumably.

The trees that had moved allowing her to view this stunningly huge archway sat motionless behind her save the breeze that passed over them. She guessed they would resume their position as soon as she had entered or been allowed to. Set in the worn stone beneath her lay metal tracks that guided the trees back and forth.

Not knowing what to do next she heard the sound of moving metal in front of her as she took a couple of steps backwards as the gates underneath the archway started to open inwards. The tranquillity of the surroundings were abruptly halted from the noise of the sheer weight of the solid gates that slowly opened as the gardens that lay beyond came into view. It was a reasonable presumption on her part that this was her invitation allowing her right of entry as there was a loud crash of metal against metal as the gates found their resting place and drew to a halt.

Nervously taking a couple of steps forward the open gates had now revealed what they had been protecting and she was amazed at the stunning beauty of such an old mansion house that lay peacefully hidden away from the eyes of others. The building that lay beyond was impressive and intimidating from the sheer enormity of its scale. She had to strain her eyes a little to see the finer details as it must have been at least half a mile away at the end of the driveway. There looked to be a grand entrance and there were dozens of windows and rooms and huge chimneys broke up the skyline and were far too many for her to count. The detail of the gardens in front of her and how well they were maintained either side of the main driveway was equally impressive.

She looked down at her clean and expensive heels that were not especially practical for walking such distances and considered her options.

The trees behind her had not closed back on themselves as she looked at her little black car sitting alone in the road with no name. Scratching her chin looking at her car, then looking back at the house she made the decision that the car would take her the length of the driveway thus preserving her heels and that she was already late for her meeting.

Positive her decision was the right one she turned her back on the house and starting moving quickly towards her car. Puffing a little by the time she got to it, she got in, turned the keys over, saw the hidden panel behind her vents reappear and heard the engine start. She placed the navigator in the cradle and felt the car move forward all within a very short space of time. I'm getting good at this she thought, although nerves were starting to get the better of her.

Her car headed directly for the centre of the semicircle and drove straight over the dip in the grass verges towards the main gates. As it did so she could hear the sounds of moving metal again. Turning around looking out of the rear windscreen she could see the trees shaking as they moved back into place. They had to be at least 10 trees deep, how on earth could that be possible? She quickly knocked the thought out of her mind as she was now being auto driven towards a place that she did not know to meet whom she had no idea – sometimes it was best to keep focused on the present situation.

As she passed under the main gates they immediately started to close and she turned her head to resume her focus on the mansion house directly in front of her.

The gardens on both sides of the driveway were stunningly impressive; she had never seen grass so green and cared for. Hedges were trimmed; bushes had been carved into shapes or possibly symbols that meant something to someone and they all looked like they were directly in line with themselves. Between some of the carved topiaries there were occasional statues that sat almost within their own gardens. She spotted one huge statue in the distance to her right that held one arm aloft and possibly a cat was being held in the other but at that distance she couldn't really be sure.

The car must have been moving at 30 miles per hour down the driveway as the imposing size of the grand mansion house came more into view. Bowing her head down so she could see the roof of the mansion she supported herself by placing one hand on the dashboard of the car. She smiled, this was indeed a spectacle and she giggled a little to herself that she had received a personal invitation to this most grandest of places.

Still smiling she looked over to the gardens on the right and could see multiple lines of perfectly trimmed pyramid shaped bushes when something moved that caught her eye heading towards the large statue. She pressed her face closer to the glass positive that she had seen something; she craned her head to try and see more and swivelled around in the driving seat.
"Car stop, car stop!!!" she yelled.
"Navigator, stop car!!" she issued the order with authority in her tone that was duly ignored.
Passing by the lines of pyramids she saw a single cloaked figure. Without even thinking about what she was doing she hit the car horn for attention. The black cloaked figure spun its head around looking at where the sound of the horn had

K. S. HORAK

come from and stared directly at the car and Jessica. She was frozen to her seat seeing this singular stationary figure and remained frozen as the car kept moving until the cloaked figure disappeared from view.

The car was rapidly approaching the grand main entrance doors as Jessica tried to gather herself and her thoughts whilst still occasionally looking over her shoulder in case the hooded figure reappeared.
Preparing herself for exit she ran one hand through her hair and then using the same hand pressed it down the length of her jacket as if it were a portable iron. She was nervous, very nervous and could hear her heart beating as well as feeling it.

She quickly practised a smile as the car veered to the left and kept going. "Wait, what, car where are we going?" she exclaimed with some panic upon seeing the main entrance disappear over her right shoulder. The car kept moving and as she looked out of her window she could see the enormity of the mansion house as she moved at speed down the driveway to the side of it. House on right, more gardens on the left; her hands were starting to shake as her adrenaline was spiralling out of control.

She could see a lake on the left hand side with a boathouse and more stunning gardens but there are only so many gardens you can take into account when you are in a state of panic. The length of the width of the building was drawing to a close when the car made an abrupt turn to the right and Jessica could see a series of doors and as she did so the car immediately stopped and she was lunged forward in her seat as the engine switched off. Peering out of the side window small plumes of dust were distracting her view. The braking of the car so suddenly on the gravel had seen to that and she waiting briefly for the dust to clear unsure what to do next.

It had served little purpose but she had had both hands on the steering wheel for the last few moments of the drive and her knuckles had turned white in colour. As she released them she looked at what she guessed to be the rear of the house.

"So is this it, do I get out now?" she said to the car not expecting or receiving some form of response.
"So do I have automatic doors as well now do I?" She did not and sat gathering her thoughts attempting a cool demeanour when she took a deep breath and

82

opened the car door. Whilst stepping out she looked up at the grand old house and its stone construction and cornices. She could see huge windows some that were probably 12 feet high and there were many of them. She presumed that each tier indicated a floor so she guessed the building must be at least 4 or 5 storeys high. There were many busts on their own plinths, carvings with their own shields and gargoyles on each tier of the house. She leaned back into the car and took out her bag that had been resting on the passenger seat and closed the car door.

She was drawn to an arched doorway that was inset at the centre of the rear of the building. No-one had appeared to greet her so she went to investigate for herself albeit it if somewhat perturbed by the cloaked intimidating figure that she had seen only moments before.

She was walking towards the building when she turned around to look at her car; it was 'parked' quite abruptly at an angle. Turning her head around she couldn't see any other vehicles, quite odd for such a huge place, it almost looked abandoned. But she knew that couldn't be the case as someone must have controlled the gates as well as looking after these immaculate gardens.

She was considering leaving the car where it was when she remembered *'the navigator must remain on your person at all times'*. Realising that she had left it in the car she reopened the door and snatched the navigator out of the cradle and dropped it into her bag. As she walked back towards the house she heard her car start from behind her and she witnessed it drive off by itself and it passed by her before it dipped out of view turning around the other side of the house. Without giving it another thought Jessica shook her head as she was clearly adapting to all things new on this strangest of days.

She walked up to the archway and looked at the incredibly strong oak doors that lay before her. Stepping inside the arch and now being only a few feet away from the doors she noticed on the wall on the right hand side the familiar symbol that had opened doors for her all day thus far.

She leaned towards the symbol with her badge and waited. A loud click was heard followed by the sound of huge wooden doors moaning as if being disturbed from their resting place of some hundreds of years. As the doors moved inwards her eyes opened as wide as they could go and she tilted her head to one side to survey what she could see inside; not surprisingly it appeared to be a very old room and had no-one in it, "Well done!" she muttered to herself whilst shaking her head in making these two most obvious of observations.

Taking the initiative in this new found courage Jessica stepped through onto wooden flooring that creaked under her weight and continued to creak the further she stepped forward. She could see dozens of mahogany coloured wooden panels all over the walls. There were flickering candles that were being supported on wall mounted silver holders that just about offered enough light to brighten the room. Reflections could still be seen from the sheen of the mahogany panelled walls and there were shadows in this eerie place. She looked up and could see multiple black wooden beams running the whole length of the ceiling and it was cool, very cool for the time of year. The whole room felt unnerving and unlived in.

She abruptly turned around upon hearing the groaning of the wooden doors moving behind her. As they came to a close with a loud bang an echo could be heard reverberating around the room and her pulse increased again as she swallowed with her dry throat.

She returned her gaze forward and jumped as she was startled by a figure looking at her. The figure that was short in stature had its hands behind its back and was partially silhouetted from the candle light.
"Oh don't worry about the car; it has a beacon when on the grounds of the Order" the figure said looking directly at Jessica.
Jessica froze in fear.
The figure took a step forward and Jessica could now see that the figure was a she.
"It's good to see you again Jessica, it's been quite some time. I'm Nubia, the curator, welcome to the Great Manor Of Loxley and thank you enormously for bringing it to our attention that you had arrived by banging your car horn, quite the entrance you choose to make" as she beamed an enormous smile that bordered on the line of terrifying.

The smile had disappeared from Nubia's face as they stood in silence.
Still with her hands behind her back Nubia quietly spoke "Look at me Jessica."

Jessica who was facing Nubia but not looking directly at her shifted her body weight awkwardly and stuttered a little cough under her breath, she reluctantly turned her eyes towards Nubia. Upon receiving Jessica's slightly nervous watery gaze Nubia bowed her head slightly and lifted her eyes up to look directly at her. A couple of seconds passed by. "There, that wasn't so bad was it now?" the smile had returned "much to discuss, follow me" and with that she quickly turned around.

The sound of old floorboards being disturbed and the sound of Jessica's heels on wood echoed around the unfurnished room as they headed towards an old door.

"I am taking you to the long walk which is the main corridor and the heart of the house, from there you can access anywhere." She stopped abruptly and paused and turned her head to the left of her shoulder, "well, where permitted that is of course." No eye contact was made between them but the briefest of a shallow smile had appeared on Nubia's face and just as quickly as it had appeared it disappeared and she started walking again.

Closing the door behind her the next room was comprised of very old furniture and seats, with an unlit fireplace that took centre place in the room. Jessica also noticed there was a viewing balcony above with an immaculately carved banister rail. A couple of old artworks hung on the wall depicting scenes and events from days past by she guessed. She would have liked more time to view these but the ever quickening pace of her house guide did not allow time for that.

Moving forward rapidly and exiting this room Jessica left the door open behind her as she found herself in a carpeted corridor that displayed many artworks on the walls of older distinguished ladies. Their poise was upright, confident and authoritive clearly having posed for an artist to paint their portraiture; many had similar decorative chains around their neck or emblems or badges that displayed some form of common order.

The corridor had an old musty smell to it, whether through damp or just a lack of use over many years she could not possibly know. She could only imagine the generations that had passed through these corridors at some point in time.

Despite the noise of their footsteps on carpet over a solid floor the surroundings were incredibly quiet with the only exception being the sound of ticking coming from multiple clocks placed throughout this reasonably long corridor. She paused to look at an extremely old looking clock and she could see the pendulum swaying back and forth steadily when the clock seemed to come alive and chimed into action. Within that fraction of a second other chiming sounds were echoing throughout the corridor around her from the multitude of clocks. At the volume of these synchronised clocks the sound reverberated around her almost bringing this silent corridor to life. She paused spinning her head around in every direction and found herself now staring at a portrait of what she guessed to be an elder. She looked deeply at the face and the old eyes as if it had reminded her of someone from her past. The sound of the clocks became more unnerving than reassuring; she did glance at one informing her that it was now quarter past two.

The clocks silenced in unison as Jessica froze.
"Keep up! Time doth tick by" Nubia asserted trying to disrupt her gaze from the portrait. Nubia's pace was considerable for someone of such small stature.

Even moving at pace Jessica could see that she had passed by what looked to be a study, a library, a weapons room...a what? She stopped abruptly looking to the room on the right and peered through the slightly open door where she could see swords, shields and a few other items that were antique in their appearance but looked consistent with items of battle. Why they were here and what their possible use was unnerved her further.

Staring at a shield that proudly displayed some form of damaged crest she could see a plaque directly beneath it with a statement inscribed. She leaned her head closer to the door and began to read it.

'The Gate Of Souls...' the door suddenly slammed shut before she could finish reading it. Hastily recoiling backwards with a jump having felt a draft of air hit her in the face from the door closing so hard and close to her face, she looked to her left and could see Nubia had stopped and was staring at her again. Bolt upright with chin aloft and her hands behind her back she wore a frowned expression "You'll find nothing of use to you in there I assure you." As she said this immediately all of the other open doors within the corridor slammed shut with a loud thud; there was no smile on her face this time. "Come, we are nearly at the long walk."

Jessica resumed following and made a mental note to keep looking forwards from now on.

Approaching the end of the corridor Jessica could see there was a huge tapestry on the wall that depicted what looked like a mountain scene with a lady with long grey hair holding her arms in the air with some form of spear in one hand and something that was not especially clear in the other. She had a cat at her feet and dark cloaked shapes were coming up the mountain towards her.
Before assessing it further Nubia had turned the corner to the left and stopped. She turned around and looked at Jessica and proclaimed most proudly.

"Welcome to the long walk of Loxley."
Jessica's mouth fell open letting out a small audible gasp upon seeing the most elaborate corridor she had ever seen. Nubia was now motionless having stopped her overzealous pace, her feet were together and her hands had resumed their normal place behind her back allowing time for Jessica to take everything in. In what must be a well rehearsed routine for when the invited get to see this architectural spectacle for the very first time Nubia had a pleasant smile across her face that looked rich in contentment and pride.

Jessica edged a few paces in front of Nubia and she could see that the corridor ran the whole length of the house. There were multiple grand arches with each arch indicating that other corridors lay to their left with much shorter passages or doorways to the right. Halfway down she could see there was a considerable opening as the archway beyond was of a much further distance than the others and with exception to that one all of the arches were separated out in equal proportions throughout the length of the corridor. There were doorways to her left and right and she could see two staircases directly in front of her and she suspected that many more lay beyond.

The staircases were opulent in style with the most glorious of carvings cut into the wooden panelling that surrounded almost every square inch of where she could see. The ceiling was also of the same mahogany panelling she had seen on the walls in the other rooms and they were only disrupted by the presence of chandeliers that hung down from long black chains. Looking up she studied one of the chandeliers and observed that the candle lights did not flicker as they had in the first room that she had come into, these were powered. She also noticed how incredibly clean everywhere appeared to look for a place clearly so old.

The musty smell of the corridor of clocks had long since dissipated and this corridor that Nubia called the long walk was clearly more lived in or had purpose. Carpet deep red in colour ran along the floor for as far as she could see; only the larger spacing ahead differed with tiled flooring presumably next to the main entrance doors. Jessica was shaking her head in disbelief; it must cost a fortune to maintain this place but thought it wise to keep this to herself.

"Come, let me show you to my quarters" said Nubia resuming the lead again. Jessica almost did not know where to look. The further they travelled the more fascinated she became with the enormity of the place and the elaborate display of wealth. Looking up at the ceiling as much as she did everywhere else she marvelled at the opulence of it all, this was not a manor house, it was a palace.

Looking ahead she could see that all of the forthcoming doorways were closed. She looked to her left and right whilst passing doorways and could see the familiar symbol of the Order to the right hand side of every single door. Upon seeing this it instantly told her that these were not turn the handle to enter doors for just anyone, a passcode or similar was clearly needed to enter. Whether her pin badge would open any of these doors she guessed with Nubia watching her every move that it was unlikely that she would find out.

As they drew up to the large lobby area, the centre of the house, she could not help but smile as she looked up to the glass skylight dome high above her and the balconies that lay below that. Everything was so grand in scale it was almost unprecedented, the carvings in wood, the opulence of the archways and the four hooded people sitting at a huge old oak desk. She paused and looked at the white cloaks they wore and there was a symbol etched in black on the top of their hoods. She could not see their faces as all four heads were bowed down busy working away at something. Jessica swallowed not knowing what to say, if anything at all, as she turned to Nubia who was stood by a flight of stairs with her hands behind her back.

Directly to the left of this stairway Jessica noticed a metal sliding gate with a lit compartment right behind it with push buttons inside. "Follow me" Nubia started to walk up the stairs.
"Do we have far to go?" questioned Jessica.
Nubia stopped climbing up the stairs and turned around looking quite perplexed "Why ever would you ask?"

"Oh it's just; it looks like there is a lift here." Jessica shrugged her shoulders and gave a half hearted attempt at pointing at the lift. "I was just curious" and she offered a smile.

Nubia descended a couple of steps towards her and for the first time today they were at the same height as each other.
"Why would you want to go in there Jessica, the lifts only go down?" she said and presented a very quick and fake smile.
"Oh, that's unusual" there was a short pause..."For such a large building I mean" Jessica nervously added and offered an ill attempt at a smile exposing more teeth than she meant to.

Nubia was unmoved and once again was looking her in the eyes with one eyebrow slightly raised as Jessica averted her gaze.

Very firmly and composed she responded.

"We only go down when we choose to go down; if we choose to go down we are carried down. We are always supported when entering the lower places and that is the way it has been for a very, very long time. When we ascend we do it on our own terms"..."We are ascending, so we walk" she flashed the fake smile again and turned around and proceeded up the stairs.

Chapter Nine:

THE LONG HAIRED
MAN ON BENBOW

WEDNESDAY EVENING

Roy Jenkins was tapping his watch staring at it quizzically; he then took it off his left wrist and held it to his ear. He didn't have to strain to hear as the ticking from it was quite clear. According to the watch it was 6.45 pm. He got out of his seat and walked into his kitchen to check his kitchen clock that said 6.46. Lifting an eyebrow he returned to his front room and pulled back his net curtain to look next door.

He could see Mildred in her front garden holding a tin can and standing on her tip toes craning her neck looking up and down the street. As standard she had a pair of brown shoes on, crumpled stockings with a plain skirt, a blouse, a baggy cardigan and a knitted woollen hat with some sort of flower pattern on it. What was not standard was that it was not 7 o'clock and she was already banging the cat food tin; he checked his watch again to make sure.

"What on earth is that woman up to now?" he said out aloud knowing this was the first time he could ever recall her being out looking for the cat ahead of schedule.

He sat back down and mentally prepared himself for anything up to ten minutes of noise.

"MISSYYYYYY" could be heard up and down the length of Rocke Road followed by a combination of bangs and clattering noises.

"MISSSYYYYYYYYY."

Mildred walked to the end of her path and poked her head over her gate looking up and down the road. Nothing, Missy was nowhere to be seen. Having now opened her gate she stepped onto the pavement still surveying everything to her left and right, noticing for the first time that her hedge had been cut back. She knew it was rare that Missy would show up straight away but just in case Mildred always made a point of looking at people's garage roofs, looking up trees, including the one above her, and bending down to see if she was sitting under a parked car. She really wished Missy wouldn't do that.

She looked down the road towards the bus stop and could see some youths were playing around there, they usually were these days. One had a skateboard, a couple had bikes and a further three were sitting down. She was fairly sure they were not waiting for a bus.

She started banging the tin with a spoon again 'MISSY'; she looked over and could see the youths were laughing and making fun of her. Mildred who was becoming quite used to this did not like it; she did not like it at all.

"Mildreddddd" one of them yelled in her direction and as usual she chose to ignore it.
"Oh Mildredddddd, are you the crazy cat lady?"
"Crazy cat, crazy cat" a couple of them were now jeering in unison.

She could see they were all laughing at her now. Quite what she had done to receive this regular abuse she did not know, it was most unpleasant and she had no idea who they were or how they knew her name. She went to bang the tin again and stopped and looked over and could see they were still laughing. This was becoming her least favourite part of the day, whenever they were around that is, it always made her feel quite sad. All she wanted to do was feed Missy, her only friend.

"THAT'S ENOUGH!!" was shouted somewhere from behind where the boys were standing. "Leave her alone, she's done nothing to you..."

Some other words were said that were out of her earshot. She strained her eyes rather than her ears to try and listen but she could not hear whatever was being said as much as she tried. The young boy who owned a skateboard threw it down onto the floor and the others who were sitting down started to get up. And with that they moved away in the direction of Benbow Street. Mildred was looking at their backs as they headed off down the road when she saw a figure appear on the path from where the noise had come from. She recognised him of course and could see his long curly hair hanging down and he had his leather jacket on as usual. He had his hands in his pockets and looked over towards her.

Mildred instantly looked at the floor a little embarrassed.

Upon looking up again she saw him take a hand out of one of his pockets and he held it up towards her as if giving a wave or some form of acknowledgment. She looked at the floor again as her face flushed and took a couple of steps backwards towards her gate. Still with tin in hand she lifted the spoon away from it getting ready to hit it when she noticed Missy was staring at her.

"Oh good Missy, go inside, it's time for dinner, I don't want to miss Bang Goes Your Money."

She looked over at the man again and he smiled; he returned his hand back into his pocket and turned around and went into his own driveway and then she lost sight of him.

She didn't know his name but had walked passed his house many times. All she knew was that he had a tank in his window with a lizard inside it and that she was very grateful for his help.

Chapter Ten:

THE PASSING OF LADY TEMPEST

TUESDAY

Jessica, not for the first time today, considered that she was not making the best of impressions and should probably keep her mouth closed from now on. Before following Nubia up the stairs she glanced across at the buttons on the lift panel. Strange that in such an old house it didn't go up any further.

At the top of the staircase Nubia said "There are five main floors in the house, hundreds of rooms and two attic areas. My office and my workers can be found further down here on the second floor."

There is clearly an area below as well Jessica thought to herself but considered it wise not to mention this right now, she had a feeling that the subject would be off limits.

Peeling away from the top of the stairs they preceded to the right into yet another corridor. Passing by more wooden panelling and still on red carpet Jessica could see they were approaching a large diamond shaped opening that had other corridors moving away from it at every point. Directly in front of them four figures similarly as the floor below sat at an enormous oak desk moving their hands keeping busy with something.

Even with the noise of Jessica and Nubia approaching they didn't look up and sat neatly in a line behind their desk and kept on working. All wearing white cloaks their faces were not visible.

Jessica could not help herself this time "Madam Nubia I must ask but who are they?" Jessica whispered as quietly as she could.
"Oh you don't need to whisper Jessica, you cannot offend them. You won't have seen them in recent times but these are some of my clerics." She stopped and turned to look at her "I have many" she said with a smile. Jessica averted her gaze from Nubia and looked at them all uniform in movement as well as in appearance. The closer they got the more there seemed to be a very cold and unnerving presence around them.

Resuming their pace as they passed by the desk Jessica was still looking at the ceilings and artwork as Nubia took both of them down the left fork from the diamond shaped lobby. Jessica casually turned her head around and she could see that the cleric furthest away from her had lifted its cloaked head and was staring straight at her; she instantly felt a chill and the hairs on the back of her neck stood up as she looked at the deathly pale face.

As they continued down the left fork she could see they were approaching a large doorway that was set into the left hand side wall. There were pillars running up the sides of the walls with a highly elaborate archway at the top, probably about 12 feet in height.

Jessica stood opposite the door conscious that when she had stopped before on this strangest of house excursions it had not yielded a very positive response.

The inside of the archway was probably about five feet deep and she could see a symbol lit up to the right although this symbol looked to be different from the others that she had seen so far.

The door itself looked like solid oak and had many old lines and cracks running throughout it. The door appeared to have old metal fortifications fixed to it that now looked surplus to requirements; speckles of rust could be seen around the old screws holding these ancient security measures, clearly the victim of outside weather exposure at some point. The door was heavily scarred from another date in time and there was a huge crest in the centre that had been chipped in places and a large crack ran throughout it.

She noticed this doorway and the cold vacant space inside the archway was unkempt, dusty, and generally unclean unlike everywhere else she had seen on this floor and what she had seen of the long walk.

"May I ask what this door is for?" Jessica asked Nubia who by now was in her familiar pose watching her.
"Why, that is the offices of the Reeve my dear." She smiled and tilted her head slightly to the right almost as if Jessica had asked an obvious question.
"The Reeve?" asked Jessica as a couple of questioning frown lines appeared across her forehead.
"Yes, the Reeve" Nubia nodded her head a couple of times and her smile still remained. "Come, this way, we are nearly there; don't worry about that the clerics keep watch."

She took a final glance at the battle scarred door before they moved to what appeared to be the final door at the end of the corridor.

Walking straight up to the door set inside its own archway, Nubia pushed the door open offering no resistance to her at all. On her approach Jessica looked and could see the symbol on the right hand side but clearly Nubia did not need to use it.

"Please take a seat." Nubia casually waved her right hand ushering Jessica towards a very old high backed chair that was around 8 feet in height.

"Thank you." Jessica gave a little smile as she took a quick look around the room. There was a couch under the main gothic looking window that she suspected Nubia may stand on to look outside. The curtains were heavy and old and tied back, shelving that held curious looking ornaments were quite low down presumably so she could reach them. There were various portraitures of very imposing looking women. From a quick glance and not being an expert the artworks looked to be very old.

Jessica gently put her bag down on the floor to the side of the seat and delicately perched herself on it; shuffling her bottom backwards to try and get more comfortable she put one hand on each of the grand wooden arm supports.

She was not comfortable in this very hard seat, wriggling herself around and fidgeting she tried crossing one leg over the other but she knew this was probably a formal meeting so she uncrossed her legs and resumed the former position looking like someone of importance who was sitting on a throne.

She could hear the ticking of an old clock coming from behind her; she hadn't noticed it as she came into the room and chose not to turn around to look at it considering it best to keep her focus on the lady in front of her.

Nubia was looking at notes on her desk before pulling her own chair in and then making use of it.

Sitting back she placed one leg over the other and pulled her hands together making a ball and rested them on her knee. A curt smile had appeared on her face.

"Your appointment to degree level 6 and your naming ceremony is imminent following the very sad passing of Lady Tempest; your appointment was not mine to make." Her words lingered in the air for a little while. "As you are aware the Council preside over such matters, especially in times of stress" she said quite bluntly. "Your being here today is due to that very sad occasion. Lady Tempest whom I understand you met once was an intellectual who undoubtedly would have proceeded to higher degree levels. Most unusually she was very popular with the Council for someone of such a lesser degree" Nubia said with clarity and conviction in her tone. "She most certainly shined. It's immensely sad that she has passed, even more so in the manner of how it happened." Her eyes dimmed and her lips rose slightly on the right hand side of her mouth.

"What did happen?" Jessica asked with a solemn face and softly spoken words. Nubia looked down at the floor before raising her head to look at Jessica with a very slight nod of the head. "She was the victim of a most tragic road accident." "My that is terrible" Jessica said quite upset on hearing this; she had been informed by Abrielle her own elder that Lady Tempest had passed over but not in the manner of how it happened.
She questioned without thinking largely due to her own experiences just an hour or two before. "Was she in a self drive car at the time?"

A huge frown came across the face of Nubia and her eyes widened, she resumed her composure and her eyes softened a little. "No she was hit by a large bus."

They both sat in silence. Nubia had placed one of her hands on her chin and was rubbing it and Jessica was looking at the floor.

"We are most disturbed by this" Nubia said gently bringing the paused silence to a close.

"She was at a place where she was not supposed to be, far from where she was supposed to be in fact." Her words were more of a mumbling than anything else as she was clearly deep in thought. "The very idea that she would walk out into a road and be so careless for such a precise intellect who we all had so many hopes for" she was shaking her head back and forth in complete disbelief.

"We are still looking into this" she said with some certainty.

Nubia broke from her thoughts.

"Tea?"

Jessica looked back up.

"Would you like a cup of tea Jessica?" Nubia enquired.

"Oh, yes, that would be wonderful thank you."

Nubia got to her feet and walked a short space over to a singular table where Jessica could see steam emerging from a large tea pot. Picking up the teapot Nubia started to poor black tea into small china cups.

"But here we find ourselves Jessica having been only nine years since you received your first visit from Abrielle your elder. I'm informed she does support your higher appointment as it so happens."

"And you do not?" shot straight out of Jessica's mouth before she had even realised what she had said. Nubia lowered the tea pot and stopped pouring at hearing this spontaneous remark.

Recomposing herself "There are others whom are more qualified than you but my views are not requested or taken into account; that is not the role of the curator. My role within the Order is clearly defined as are those of clerics the keeper and others."

She resumed pouring.

"Order and process has not changed for a long time, a very long time and we ensure balance and prosperity, recent events of this nature are most troubling, most troubling indeed" she said whilst shaking her head. She reached across for the silver tongs that were on its own china plate and dropped a slice of lemon into Jessica's teacup.

Nubia walked over to her desk and placed a cup in front of Jessica and put one on her side of the desk before resuming her seat.

"Presumably this is why I was brought here, to discuss my appointment? I have never seen this place before but things seem familiar for some reason."

Nubia, having already picked up her cup, lowered it in surprise at hearing this.

"Really?" She looked directly at Jessica with a concerned frown and did her best to make eye contact with her. "You have been here before Jessica but it was a very long time ago." She lowered her chin. "It would be most peculiar if your memory served you of such times past" she paused trying to assess Jessica's face, who made little eye contact. "Memories fade but history will always remain" she said with surety and she took a sip of tea. "With your enhanced degree and the celebration of your new name more trust will be placed with you and upon you, more responsibilities and more knowledge and that is why you are here today, preparation for what is to come in the future."
Placing the cup in the saucer Nubia crossed her legs again and her hands resumed the ball position that they had been in before.
"You will have your own office here; your navigator will always bring you of course if you so wish. How to use it properly will be explained to you in due course and you will be informed as to when you do need to be here. Your new degree level will allow you to enter whenever you feel it necessary; most do when a time of reflection is needed."

Jessica nodded and tried to hide a smile that was itching to get out upon hearing that she will have her own office in this grandest of places.

"Is that why it is so quiet here now?" she asked.
"There are many in the Order as you know but here, here in this special place, unless otherwise instructed, is our quiet home and has been for a long time, a

very long time. It is a very rare occurrence that the house is full and I do not like the noise if truth be told" she lifted an eyebrow at the very thought of the calm tranquillity of this place being disturbed.

"I remain here with the lady of the house and other essential members of the household and of course the clerics stay here, they never leave these grounds."

Lifting the cup again and taking a very delicate sip Nubia replaced the cup and dabbed slightly at her mouth. "Your new level will allow you access to certain parts of the house but there are many areas that you will not be able to see as yet; with knowledge, maturity, and a more enhanced degree level of course that may change; another decision that is out of my hands" she spoke curtly with a matter of fact tone.

"Your admittance here is for your thoughts and for you alone to spend time upon reflection. Your office will be ready once your certification has been awarded to you this coming Friday."

They both sat in silence drinking their tea.

"I must ask Madam Curator" Jessica shuffled in her seat with curiosity "my car, how on earth did it do that? It was almost by magic."

The curator slammed the cup down on the saucer sending some tea over its sides and with such an abrupt noise Jessica jumped in her seat spilling some of her own tea down her top.

"We do not speak of those things here!!" Nubia said with an enraged tone, her face had reddened with anger.

Jessica sat aghast from this outburst.

Wiping the spilt hot tea off her fingers "I'm sorry, I meant no…"

"Your car and its devices are nothing but technology from the world outside of here combined with our specialist teams and knowledge and they are nothing more. Whilst I do not embrace technology we have no choice but to accept it and thereby have to utilise it. The world outside craves new developments and new technologies, they have a thirst for it" Nubia scowled.

"Our principles and our goals are unchanged but regrettably we have had to evolve, if we do not others may."

Nubia looked down pensively at the spilt tea and picked up her spoon and was stirring the lemon in great haste.

The only sound in the room at this moment was being made by Jessica whose hands were shaking following this outburst. The noise of china on china could be heard as she struggled for composure holding her cup and saucer. Gulping and trying to break this silent deadlock Jessica thought an apology was in order.

"I'm sorry about my banging of the car horn; I thought I saw something in the garden."

Nubia looked up to hear more.

"Something moving in the garden towards a large statue, wearing a black cloak" Jessica added.

Nubia shaking her head with the most dismissive of smiles returned her gaze to the floor. "You tried to get the attention of a watcher by banging a car horn at it did you?"

She looked back up at Jessica "Most peculiar, I've never heard anything of the sort; it is actions like that that concern me about your appointment" she scowled.

Jessica could not bear the sound of china on china any further and placed the cup and saucer on the desk.

"What you saw was a watcher performing daily chores, although strange that it was alone close to the great statue of Salma."

Nubia's body language had an air of concern about it as she looked at the floor in consideration.

Jessica coughed slightly and shifted uncomfortably on the seat. "May I ask Madam Nubia, why is it here, watchers, I've heard of them but I don't fully understand?" She was confident that she had asked a sensible question this time.

Still looking at the floor Nubia spoke in a quiet tone.

"It's time you were informed of some of these things Jessica so I will say this on the matter."

Jessica looked on with interest watching Nubia's fingers tighten in their little ball. "The watchers are the last remnants of an old bloodline, a poisonous bloodline that sort damage to the Order a long time ago. They do not like us; they do not like our ways and what we stand for, if they had their way we would live in

darkness."
She looked back up "They are evil."

Jessica swallowed thankful that she was not holding the tea cup any further.
"There are more here of course, there always are and when here they have their appointed duties. Some maintain the house, some the gardens and the farming area as well as other chores that we assign to them. They wear black robes when here as outcasts as a reminder of days of old, our clerics wear white as they represent purity and passiveness. The watchers underneath their dark robes when they are in their natural state are quite unpleasant to look at up close I'm afraid."

There was a long pause before Nubia resumed.

"We try not to talk about them here; their bloodline was corrupted a long time ago. In time you will have access to information that will explain further but for now all you need to know is that they serve their place when they need to and on occasions they need to be reminded of their place but they are servants nevertheless."
"Watchers try to resist harmony and balance and that is why they are here to remind them of such." Their place here in the lower parts of Loxley goes deep, quite deep and that is where they belong in the dark places."

She looked at Jessica with tense eyes "They always become more active close to a gathering as they can sense it as we collectively meet. Many roam freely on the outside of here I'm afraid, we detain them when we can. A poisonous cast from a long time ago, they endure and that is why the Order is necessary to ensure they do not succeed in their overall goal."
"And what is that?" Jessica asked with some concern and curiosity.
She looked back to the floor and shook her head "I cannot say" and with that the room became silent again.

Nubia stretched her fingers and resumed her hands into a ball and placed them on her knees.

"There is one more thing before you leave. This is vitally important and requires your most utmost attention and care."
Jessica nodded her head with interest "I understand madam curator, what is it?"

"Although today's meeting is a matter of degree process something has arisen that is more unusual, very in fact, throughout my time as curator." Her head shook a couple of times before she looked up and gathered her thoughts. "It is an unusual occurrence but I spoke with a member of The Grand Council a few days ago. I do not want to go into the full details about it right now but she was very specific when she informed me of this."

Nubia placed both hands on the desk looking directly at Jessica.

"I know that she already has an elder who calls herself by the name of Daphne, and that you in turn are her elder."

"Daphne?" Jessica asked with a mixture of curiosity and concern.

"Yes, Daphne; you are to keep a personal watch over her and more so the one who calls herself Mildred; the reasons why and the balance of which has not yet come to pass. This is your duty Jessica; this is what you need to do for the good of the Order."

Jessica, whose eyes were now as wide open as they could be, nodded slowly taking all of this in.

"I have been informed and thus I am now informing you; you are trusted with this information and your progress to a higher degree status in the future will depend on your personal diligence in this matter. Mildred I understand is especially of some interest."

Jessica swallowed the saliva in her mouth and considered what was being said.

"It would be my honour madam curator" she humbly offered.

Nubia nodded "Despite my misgivings about your early appointment to this level, I'm assigning you to this task and I need for you to observe her; see that it is done."

The look in Nubia's face suggested the meeting was over.

Jessica straightened her skirt with both hands and stood up to leave; she gathered her bag and could see inside that the navigator cursor was flashing almost as if awaiting instruction.

"Your car waits for you outside but I will escort you out" said Nubia standing up.

They left the room and moved to the stairs and Jessica noticed on their way out that the doorway to the Reeve was very slightly open and the clerics had left their desk and were nowhere to be seen. In a role reversal this time Nubia was behind her and Jessica could feel her eyes bearing down on her back watching her every move.

As they descended the last step Jessica looked across the grand lobby and the main entrance at the front of the house and took a couple of steps towards them.

"Where are you going?" interjected Nubia.

Jessica paused motionless.

"You arrived by means of the back door and you leave in the very same manor of whence you came."

Jessica gave an awkward smile and a nod of embarrassment and headed down the long walk in the direction of the tapestry. When she reached it she turned right into the corridor of clocks noticing all of the doors were still closed. She could hear Nubia's footsteps a couple of paces behind hers as she headed towards the exit rooms.

She felt somewhat relieved to be leaving as she reached the final door noticing the flickering candles again, she turned to Nubia.

"Thank you for your time and invitation Madam Curator."

"The invitation was necessary Jessica" she laughed to herself before resuming her crazy smile "but the time was mine and you are welcome to that; on this occasion," she said nodding her head a few times almost approving of her own excellence.

Nubia stepped forward and the heavy doors moaned once more as they opened. Jessica could see her car was already outside waiting for her.

As they faced each other Nubia looked up at her. "Good luck with your endeavours Jessica and please keep watch over Mildred."

Jessica considered shaking hands but as Nubia's were now behind her back again she thought better of it.

"Thank you" she said walking out of the doors towards her car.

"Oh Jessica, one more thing."

Jessica turned around looking at the lady of short stature with the archway towering above her.

"Do inform us if you ever see a figure wearing peculiar glasses." The tight lipped horizontal smile had appeared across Nubia's lips again. She stepped back a few paces as the doors came to a close with a loud thud.

Jessica sat in her car, started the engine and took the navigator out of her bag and placed it inside the cradle. Feeling the peddles move under her feet she was moving away from this most amazing of places on the strangest of days but at the forefront of her mind all she could think about were two key things. 1 there hadn't been a cat in sight and 2 what an incredibly rude little woman Nubia is.

Chapter Eleven:

THE PALM OF DUAT

WEDNESDAY EVENING

Mildred looked over at Missy with some concern, her bowl was full with cat food yet she seemed largely disinterested in it.

"What's the matter Missy?" Nahla briefly looked up at her.

Mildred banged the empty tin of cat food down on the side a little harder than she meant to and grabbed her tea cup and saucer "we'll resume this conversation later" as she rushed towards the front room upon hearing the music starting for Bang Goes Your Money.

And there he was; on the screen in her own home. What a nice man Mildred was thinking, looking at De'Hoof Monterrey, the presenter of the show.

Running down the stairs showing off his sparkling gleaming teeth before kicking a leg to the side and throwing his cane behind the scenes for someone to catch 'The Hoof' as he liked to be known opened up both arms. "And let's meet today's contestants" and with that the cheesy smile appeared as he turned around lifting his left arm in the air as the contestants peeled in waving excitedly at the camera.

Mildred so engrossed with the programme had now taken a seat looking at these lucky people on the show; she was tempted to wave back at them were it not for the cup of tea in her hands.

"So tell us all, what is your name and where do you come from?" De'Hoof's smile was beaming even more than usual this evening.
"Hello De'Hoof I'm Julie and I'm from Wiltshire." Julie flashed an enormous smile running from ear to ear upon hearing rapturous applause coming from the audience to the announcement of her name. She was clapping herself, over-whelmed by the occasion.
The presenter pointed at her "And you can call me Hoof" he said and spun around and re-pointed at her. Julie was absolutely gushing at this personal invitation "Thank you Hoof!"
"No thank you Julie" as he took her hand and kissed it increasing Julie's blushes along with his own cheesy smile that could probably be seen the whole length of the country.

"Good luck Julie" Mildred said out loud and went to clap her hands forgetting she had a cup and saucer in them spilling tea all down her floral coloured skirt.

Suddenly three loud bangs came from her front door. Mildred jumped spilling her tea down her top now as well. She froze and gently rested her tea cup in its tea laden saucer and put them both on the table in front of her. She looked at Missy who was looking directly back at her and got up and turned the volume down on the television. Looking at the screen De'Hoof's voice started to fade away.

Getting to her feet very quickly and really quite bothered that her programme had been interrupted she walked briskly towards the front door. "I really hope it's not those boys again Missy." Her skin flushed with anxiety and she could feel increased warmth spreading throughout her body as her pulse elevated many beats very rapidly.
"Quite what I've done to them Missy I just don't know." She grabbed at the front door handle quickly and pulled on it very hard. The door sprang back past her; no one was there; her pulse was ever increasing as she felt some anger race through her. She went to slam the door shut when she saw an envelope on the floor.
Mildred often questioned whether her faculties were all in order as she had

gotten older but her vision save for close reading was impeccable and she could see in the most neatest of handwriting.

'Mildred
Number 1 Rocke Road
Shrewsbury
Shropshire
United Kingdom'

She took a step forward and leaned her head outside of her doorway, looking left and right. She couldn't see anyone and could just hear the light noise of the road starting to wind down for the evening. She bent down and picked up the envelope and stepped forward one last time continuing to look around. With no one there, she stepped back and closed the door.

Nahla was looking at her, not that Mildred had noticed, as her eyes were fixed on the envelope. She walked into her kitchen both hands firmly clutching it reading her own address over and over again. Curiosity frown lines were riddled all over her forehead and she looked up at her clock, it was 19.09. Looking casually to her right she was surprised to see on a very rare occasion that she seemed to have her cat's attention.

In a very soft voice she muttered "Strange time of the evening for post don't you think?"

Turning the white envelope over she could see it was sealed with wax and a crest was stamped into it. She recognised it instantly and with excitement and relief that the local boys had not played a prank on her, she sat down at the kitchen table and broke open the seal.

She took out the solitary piece of heavy card inside it.

Holding it out in front of her so that she could read it properly the card had a gold seal going all the way around it with the familiar crest of her club in the centre.

By permission of the Grand Council of The United
Kingdom Kat Chamber it is with great honour that you are
hereby invited to the yearly gathering.

To be held within the Dogpole Suite of
Dovercote Mansion, Wroxeter, Shropshire
Time 19.00 Date 13th August
You must present your invitation upon arrival,
failure to do so will not permit entry
Dress code optional
Please do not bring cameras

She had received two invitations like this before and never understood why they left it so late to send them out. Quite why they never used the postal service like everyone else she couldn't understand.

She had never been to the Dovercote Mansion before; it sounds very grand she thought to herself with a smile.
Looking at the invitation again *'The Grand Council'*, her smile continued as she shook her head. She had never met any form of Council from the club, let alone a *'Grand Council'*, they certainly were very strange as she giggled to herself.

Unfortunately she was not allowed to keep her two former invitations as they were always taken upon arrival. Shame really as they would be very nice mementos to keep and she could put them upon her wall next to her certificate. She stared at the card almost brooding and bit at her lips deep in thought. She had never asked to join this club, it was almost put upon her like she didn't have a choice, not that she minded of course but all the same.

'You were chosen Mildred' she recalled that very first time that she met Daphne. Shaking her head slightly she realised that she had never really questioned anything; they definitely had some strange ways about them in how they ran their cat club, including that they could not spell the word cat properly and used 'Kat' instead. But why exactly was she chosen?

She continued staring at the invitation as the card started to bend in her hands.

'You've always known you were different from others' she reflected on that meeting

nearly three years ago; how could Daphne have known that she was not allowed to keep pets as a child?

There were quite a few things that just did not add up and more questions were developing the further she considered it. Why was there so much secrecy and why do they meet in quiet places out of the view of others?

'All will be revealed in time' she looked up at her clock oblivious to what time it was actually telling. She looked down at the floor and could see that Missy had now curled herself up in a ball and was sound asleep; no doubt waiting for me to go to bed knowing full well that her cat liked to slip out at night.

She put the invitation down on the table and crossed her arms looking at Missy. Why were you brought to me? She continued to labour the point in her mind, it was quite clear that Daphne had not come from the local cat's shelter and there was a presumption on Daphne's part that Mildred would take the cat from her in the first place.

Daphne had stated that she had an affinity with animals but that was news to her; she would have liked to have had pets as a child and had considered one for company as she got older, even more so when she lost her job. The roof over her head needed to be paid for as well as her daily living so it was completely absurd when Daphne informed her that the club would pay her a monthly bursary therefore covering her living expenses; Daphne's visit to her was within a week of her being made redundant and for that reason she had never asked questions. Apparently she was the guardian of Missy and therefore would be rewarded as such. She had never heard of any club that paid members to be part of it so therefore her questions that were becoming ever more apparent she had kept to herself.

Daphne had informed her at that first meeting there *'were many others'* but her certificate did not have a membership number on it and her phone was quiet for the most part. The other members didn't call her save Daphne and Merewood Close Mildred.

She stood up and went to the wall in her front room where the certificate hung; it was pristine of course as she cleaned it more than anything else.

She very gently took it off the wall and stared into it. She could see her curious reflection in the glass and could see the cloche hat she was wearing and she turned her head to the side so she could see the woven flowers that were embroidered into it. She never used to dress like this she thought thinking back to her former life.

The crest of the club took pride of place on the certificate. Her name wasn't on it and the name of her cat wasn't on it either. Printed in simple and clean text it said.

MEMBER OF THE UNITED KINGDOM KAT CHAMBER

Much didn't add up; she cared for Daphne almost like the sister she never had. Jessica seemed to be a little odd but then the other members she would meet at the monthly meetings all somehow seemed *'different'* in their own ways and didn't speak regularly with her.

She placed the certificate back upon the wall and resumed her seat in the kitchen and looked down at the invitation on the table. She picked it up once more in both hands as it started to bend again in the centre as her thoughts were questioning her own actions or lack of.

She turned the card over for the first time and could see there were three handwritten words.

'Don't forget sandwiches'

Sandwiches, sandwiches, sandwiches kept turning in her mind so much so that she was completely oblivious to the pictures on her TV screen in the front room showing the closing credits to Bang Goes Your Money.

Julie had lost.

He had been brought below again as all the watchers were before there was even a hint of darkness. Duat was now sitting in his chamber undisturbed deep below ground. Since his incarceration here and when not being forced to carry out mundane tasks for the Order he would spend most of his time in a flow like state of thought intently focused upon events of the past and the days that are yet to come.

In this cold and silent place, tiny amounts of steam would emanate from the exposed holes in his skull that vaguely represented his nose. He lifted his head up and turned his head to the side, left first and then to the right stretching his neck muscles until there was a large cracking sound. He pulled down the hood of his robe and let out a huge but almost silent sigh; he watched the hot steam emit from his mouth before it dissipated in front of him. This simple action was enough to take him out of his state of concentration and he moved his focus to the old walls of the room he was sat in.

With controlled breathing he looked down at his hands knowing that he was now able to take off his gloves as the security restraint measures had been removed for the day. He flexed his fingers inside the gloves he was forced to wear for many hours on end performing tedious chores for those above.

He, like other watchers, took great care in protecting their hands, especially the right one. Some had abilities through the sense of touch that could allow them to read others, feel others and control others to some degree. All watchers had different abilities and never had there been one blessed with all. It is for this reason that those who imprisoned them above made them wear gloves and other implements covering their hands as they feared what they did not know.

Those who reside in the grand hallways directly above where he was sitting right now were incredibly nervous of these gifts, these abilities; these powers; these art forms within their own right. Duat knew they feared watchers and their fears were real; "as they should be," he muttered from the deep place watching the warm steam appear in front of him again.

Every day without fail the Escarrabin would take him along with other watchers that were incarcerated in the deep places of Loxley up to the above where the security officers of the Reeve would ensure that his hands and thin skin were not exposed to the light of the sun or to others.

Duat took off his gloves and placed them neatly at his side. Stretching his right arm out in front of him he thrust his fingers forward as far as they could go stretching them to the point that the fingers tips were now veering upwards and curved against its natural movement. Extending his fingers back and forth repetitively as if aiding much needed circulation, he looked at his nails; they were sharp, filthy and very long, it disgusted him. He turned his hand over and looked at the turquoise colouring of his palm and the life that moved throughout it; it is this colouration, this gift that made him unique. Not all watchers possessed the high level of abilities that he did in fact he knew none ever had.

Bringing his hand towards his face he could see active blood vessels moving through the mixture of dark green and blue colours that could only be found within the centre of the palm of his right hand. He knew that should he choose to look down at his left hand there would be no such indications of any flow of blood even when he had stretched that arm and fingers out as far as he could; he stretched the arm all the same but as he did so his focus still remained firmly upon his right palm. The gift that he bears never stopped his curiosity and he spent many hours watching, while imprisoned, the life move around inside it.

Putting both of his hands on his knees he was reasonably positive the Reeve was not aware of his chamber as well as the others. The lifts from the above do not go deep and only to the first floor and it is there that they assemble everyday for the Escarrabin to collect them and take them above. The Escarrabin didn't venture deeper and he knew that they feared the darkness; they dressed as soldiers but had hearts of cowards. But over hundreds of years the watchers had created tunnels and chambers that stretched as far wide as they did deep. They were quite ingenious really; he smiled slightly at the thought as saliva ran from his mouth.

The watchers imprisoned in the darkness of this place made a point of being easily found when it was time for them to be taken to the above.

The original walls of rock and iron of the below were created in another era when times were not so dark, not so suspicious, not so threatening, they were laid down here in times of relative peace. The manor house had detained watchers for a long time now and all they had left were the tools that had been left behind from the past. Progress had been made of a new tunnel system that would lead to the surface beyond the walls of the house above but there was still further to go and not enough time. Having a close proximity to the Order and observing its inner workings had been useful; watching them, studying them and despising them, they who call themselves the enlightened.

He stood up and walked over to his table and to the one solitary glass upon it, a wine glass that had been empty for only a short period of hours. He breathed in deeply as he picked it up at the base with his left hand and placed his right palm around the main body of the glass and gripped it tightly. He could feel the deep colours moving throughout his palm and held it there until he was satisfied. Replacing the glass on the table he brought his right palm up to his eye. He flexed his fingers and watched turquoise patterns move to the end of his fingers.

"Time" he muttered whilst staring at an old shelf cut into one of the walls in front of him. The clocks above in the manor house were a constant reminder to the Order that time is precious, time is short and time will always bring change, it was a leveller of balance and it had been foretold. He was very well aware of the prophecy; it had been explained along with their fears of it. The chimes strike to remind them of their inadequacies "We do not need such devices" he spoke whilst looking at a very old pair of weighing scales and an ancient unturned hourglass.

Chapter Twelve:

PALE HANDS OF CLERICS

THURSDAY MORNING (EARLY)

The Curator as ever was keeping a watchful eye upon her clock, it was almost time. Placing her teacup down she stood up and walked from her study into her office and went straight to her desk.

Looking at the old phone on her desk she pressed one of many extra buttons that had been built into it over the years. She remained with her finger on the button for around 15 seconds.

"Yes madam curator" emitted from the separate speaker next to her phone.
"Well, you took your time!"
"Sorry madam curator, we have been very busy..."
"My office please; thank you" she released the button instantly terminating the conversation.

Just tucked in the corner not far from the doorway into her office stood her hat and coat stand. Walking over to it she removed her jacket and gracefully put it on. Glancing down at the badge on her lapel she quickly took a handkerchief from one of the pockets in her skirt and polished it despite how shinny and clean her badge already was.

She knew that today would be a long day; it always was the day before the gatherings. She would be thankful once they had passed and peace and quiet returned to Loxley.

As curator her role was to ensure procedures were followed; her direct responsibility covered the whole of the United Kingdom and Ireland and all of its six regional areas as well as assisting all of the senior elders when called upon.

She stood in front of the only mirror in the whole of her office complex and living area. She looked old but then I guess I am she thought to herself. She ensured her presentation was precise as expected for the curator of the Order.

There was a knock at the door distracting her from assessing her 'laughter lines'.

"Come" she said and returned to her desk and sat down.
"You called madam curator." The cleric's head was bowed slightly towards the floor, her face unseen underneath the hood.
"Indeed I did. Have you seen any movements from the Reeve this morning?"
"No Ma'am - not a sound."
"Well go and give her a knock will you, I will be along shortly."
"Yes Ma'am." The cleric bowed her head a little further in acknowledgement of the instruction and left the office closing the door behind her.

She crossed her legs and put both of her hands into a ball resting them on one knee looking blankly at the door. Letting a deep breath out that sounded more like a sigh she did not approve of this new Reeve but her considerations in these matters were not taken into account. She sat waiting patiently in contemplation, today indeed would be a long day.

Mildred was clicking her teeth together with some concern; her hands were on her hips. Missy appeared to be sleeping but looked to be in some sort of discomfort; her paws were constantly twitching and on occasion a little snarl would be heard from the side of her mouth. Whether she was having bad dreams or she was in pain (or both) she could not be sure.

Mildred's concerns had started earlier that morning when for the first time in ages she didn't have to call the cat to come in to be fed. She was already asleep downstairs and hadn't moved since.

I wonder if I try and bang a tin gently whether it will help? And with that she went over to the larder and pulled out a tin of cockles and tomato flavoured cat food.

Taking a spoon out of a draw she gently hit the tin...
Nothing:
She hit it again...
Nothing:
She hit it again somewhat harder with a tapping motion...
Still nothing.

Placing the tin and spoon on the side she was now becoming increasingly concerned and reached out and stroked Missy up and down. She felt warm and could feel that her pulse was fast, maybe a little too fast at times, feeling like a double beat.

"What ever is the matter Missy, how can I help you?" her words falling hopelessly flat.
She knew from the past that Missy did not like the vet and usually even the mention of the 'VET' word would draw some form of reaction that was inevitably negative.
She stood over Missy with her hands on her hips again deciding that a purposeful and assertive voice would be an appropriate course of action.

"Missy I am going to wait for one more hour and if you do not get up or start to feel better I am calling the vet."

She waited for a response but none was forthcoming.

"Oh my, this really is not good" concern etched across her face.

She heard a door slam and saw Mr Jenkins running down his path having overslept. His usual early morning wakeup call never happened this morning.

There was a knock at her door again.

"Come," the curator glanced over her shoulder and could see out of the corner of her eye a white hooded figure step into her office.

"Ma'am, the Reeve is aware that you require her presence."
A frown had appeared across her forehead as she turned around to look directly at the cleric.
"The Reeve is always aware that my presence is required the morning before the day of the gatherings, especially when a member has passed on;" commonplace impatience lingered in her tone.
"Yes Ma'am" the cleric whose head was already slightly bowed nodded her head down further in acknowledgement.

The Curator was staring at the cleric as she extended her chin, tilting her head slightly to the right. "Well, is there anything else?"
"No Ma'am, not at this time."
"Well, very good then, off you go, off you go." Her right arm was making a swishing motion indicating that the cleric had no further place here.

"Damn useless creatures" she said under her breath as the door closed whilst she did up the top button of her formal white shirt. Checking her clothes one more time in the mirror and brushing them down she stopped to look at herself again. Turning her head slightly to the left and then to the right there was no avoiding it she thought, the frown lines on her face seemed to be multiplying of late.

She made sure that her doors were closed behind her and for the final time that the badge on her lapel was facing the right way round before moving off in a purposeful stride down the corridor with her arms behind her back.

The Curator always walked with purpose and dignity even on the very rare occasion when she had no idea what she was doing or where she was going. 'Standards must be kept and a respect of order must be shown at all times' she would often inform lesser degree elders as well as clerics who *(in her opinion)* needed constant reminding of their place.

She walked towards the end of the corridor approaching the diamond shaped lobby area as the archway for the offices for the Reeve came into view on the right hand side. Stopping outside she scowled at the state of the doorway and noticed that the door was slightly open. Shaking her head and still with hands behind her back she turned abruptly to her left and could see three clerics were sitting at their long desk but the one that should be on the right was missing. It required investigation as she walked towards them.

"Where is the other one?" nodding in the direction of the empty seat, "and why is the Reeve's door open?" head gesturing towards the battle scarred door of the Reeve.

All three heads were still bowed towards their desk, their hands moving working away at something.

"EXCUSE ME" she said loudly and with further impatience "AM I TALKING TO THE WALL?"

Three heads remained bowed.

"You there on the left; look at me!"

The cleric on the left side and the right side lifted their heads.

"Not you, my left not your left!"

The cleric on the right bowed her head back down resuming her former position.

"Where is the other one, cleric?"

"I'm sorry but I do not know Ma'am."

"There should always be four here at all times, no excuses, no exceptions."

"Yes Ma'am."

"Let me try another one and let's see if you do better this time. Do you know why the Reeve's door is open?"

The echo of the question bounced off the walls throughout the diamond shaped lobby with no answer forthcoming.

"Pull your hood down so I can see you."

The cleric looked up at her to meet her gaze.

"Pull that hood down from your face."

With pale hands the cleric lifted both hands towards her hood and pulled it backwards.

The curator paused momentarily looking directly at the deathly white face of the cleric and the whites of her eyes.

"There, I wanted to make sure that you understood" she said whilst bobbing her head up and down.

"I'm going to ask you one last time. Where is the fourth cleric and why is the Reeve's door open?"

"Probably because I left it open Nubia."

She spun around to see the Reeve leaning against her doorway with her legs crossed.

"And your missing cleric has been doing some cleaning for me."

The Reeve spoke very calmly looking in the direction of the cleric. "You can pull your hood back up."

The curator spun back around to see the pale hands pull the hood back over her face as the cleric looked back down towards her work.

Scowling profusely the curator abruptly headed towards the doorway of the Reeve.

"I really wish you would address me by my proper title in front of others."

"I'm very sorry." The Reeve bent down to her and whispered "curator" into her ear.

The Reeve had a mischievous smile across her face as she resumed the leaning position against her doorway.

"You know, you can be quite rude to them sometimes" maintaining eye contact with the curator, "you'll never get their trust or respect like that."

The curator maintained her eye contact with the Reeve.

"One day you may really upset them and they may not be there for you when you most need it."

"I know what I'm doing Reeve, order and process..."

"Yes, yes I know all of that, however, stress is not a good thing either and has no place here" she paused momentarily. "I do wonder if you could ever handle the responsibilities that I have" she smiled slightly her words more of a statement than a question.

The curator completely un-amused retorted "well I'd make sure the bloody security doors were closed for a start" and with that she pushed the Reeve's heavily fortified door fully open and walked through. 'I really miss the old Reeve' she thought to herself.

Mildred could not take her eyes off the cat phone as she considered what to do next.

She knew that Missy did not like seeing the vet and for that matter she found the vet quite a strange individual in her own right; both of them were happier away from her.

As she was not the owner of a car it would mean either having to take Missy with her on the bus in the carrier *(she hated putting her in the portable cage)* or ask for the vet to make a house call.

Rubbing her chin in thought, observing that Missy was clearly in some discomfort, she walked over to the phone and picked it up and brought it back into the kitchen with its long wire trailing behind. "Right Missy, you see this?" Missy's eyes remained closed.

"If you do not open your eyes right now I'm calling Miss Fennaway." She waved the cat shaped phone around at Missy as if making some sort of idle threat. "Mmm, what do you say to that then?"

With no form of response forthcoming she placed the phone down on the side and replaced her hands back on her hips.

"Oh come on Missy, do something please, you are worrying me." Her voice was wavering as she crouched down to stroke her cat. She could feel Missy's tummy rising up and then going back down and that the pulse rhythm felt very unnatural.

She walked to the sideboard to find the number for the vet. She had hoarded many bits of paper over the last few years. 'One could never be sure when someone may come in handy' was the usual justification for the reasonably organised mess.

Pushing the animal psychiatrist's flyer to one side she only had to sift about a third of the way through the stack before she found the number scribbled onto a piece of paper for Miss Fennaway.

Grabbing the cat phone "last chance Missy" and in a futile gesture she shook the phone for one last time.

Sighing at no reaction she dialled the number and whilst waiting for it to be answered she didn't relish the thought of the odd lady she was about to invite into her house for the first time.

'Fennaway Veterinary Practise – how may we direct your call?'
"Oh good morning, I'm most upset, it's my Missy, I would like to..."
'Please press 1 for appointments.'
"What?" Mildred was staring incredulously at the cat's bottom.
Returning the phone to her ear quickly...
'Press 2 to speak to Miss Fennaway.'
'Press 3 to have your pet put down.'
'Press 4 for anything else.'

She turned around having been distracted by seeing Missy twitch her legs and she hit any button on the phone.
Encouraged by seeing her cat move for the first time in a while. "Missy...Missy are you okay?"

'You have selected option 3; you wish to have your pet put down.'
"What, no wait, stupid phone!"
'First please tell us the name of your pet.'
"Miss Fennaway, I want to speak to Miss Fennaway" she was almost yelling down the phone now.
'Thank you, we understand you would like Miss Fennaway to be put down.'
"What! No, no, customer service, customer service!!" she was yelling down the phone and stomping both of her feet in frustration.
'Please tell us what type of pet you would like to have put down.'
"It's a cat and I don't want her putting down!!"
'You wish to have your cat put down; thank you, directing your call.'

Mildred walked into the kitchen now staring angrily out of her window drumming the fingers of her left hand on the counter. It's no wonder I like to stay alone she was thinking to herself and in that very moment her mind wondered away somewhere thinking about her former life.

Nubia helped herself to a chair in the main office of the Reeve and sat down as abruptly as she had entered; she hadn't sought any permission for her actions and bypassed all of the other rooms to get there.

"Oh please do take a seat, you are most happily my guest" the Reeve spoke over the back of the curator.

Nubia looked forward very unimpressed at the chair behind the Reeve's desk "I see you have a new chair."

"Yes, the old one was uncomfortable to sit on."

She shook her head disapproving of this new type of Reeve and her lack of following customs. But as ever Nubia was impatient and wanted to proceed with matters quickly.

"As you are aware Reeve the day before a gathering following the sad loss of an elder a new elder must be appointed in order to maintain balance."

The Reeve sat in the new chair looking directly at her; as yet she had not blinked once. "If I already know these things Nubia why are you reminding me of them?"

"I like to ensure that processes are followed as they always have been. It's important and I need to be sure that you have made the appropriate security related arrangements." She was nodding and talking at the same time before crossing her legs and wrapping her hands in a ball as they rested on one knee.

"What makes you think that I wouldn't have Nubia?" She finally blinked and tilted her head slightly to the right still maintaining eye contact. "I'm aware that you did not support my role here and that I am fairly new in post."

The curator looked towards the floor with a slight admission of guilt.

The Reeve leaned forward making sure that she had the curator's attention. "Let me assure you right now so this is not mentioned again; my Order have full belief in me and what I do here and that is why I was appointed." The Reeve leaned back and resettled in her seat.

"The fact remains that you are of a new breed..."

"New?" the Reeve loudly interjected and for the first time today was assertive of voice.

"New, you say?" the Reeve looked away shaking her head smiling all over her face "I'm hardly new and neither are you for that matter, let's not lose sight of that, her smile had gone.

The room filled with silence as the Reeve looked on at the curator who was still focused on the floor.

Letting out a small sigh and breaking the deadlock.

"Would you care for a cup of tea Nubia?"

"No thank you Reeve; I've just had one" was the succinct response as the curator continued to look at the floor.

"I see" smiled the Reeve with a hint of a patronising tone.

"Let me stop you worrying Nubia. My security officers of the Escarrabin have their orders regarding their duties for all of the gatherings. I will also inform you that the Keeper is on her way, she carries word and will be here very soon." The curator looked up from the floor quickly "the Keeper is coming here, already?"

The Reeve looked forward towards her, lifting her chin with confidence as she did so. "Yes she is and you should have more faith, everything is in order."

The curator smirked at this and spoke with a patronising tone "faith is for dreamers and for the weak, a word misused by those outside. A Reeve should not use such words; it has been foretold that the time may come where we will all be tested and therefore we must be ready!"

"The time will come I think you mean Nubia!"

The curator swallowed upon hearing this statement from the Reeve and looked back at the floor; she knew that the Reeve was in the right if the prophecy of old was to be believed.

The only sound that could be heard in the office was the ticking of a clock. She took a moment to think.

"Do you have any idea who they may be?" the curator mumbled still looking at the floor.

"Who are you referring to?" The Reeve had a tinge of curiosity in her voice.

"The ones whom will ascend up the order?" the curator had lifted her gaze from the floor to look directly at the Reeve.

"No, no I don't, I have no feelings on the matter. Elder ascension is not the business of the Order Of The Reeves" she replied in a calm and controlled manner.

There was a knock at the door.

The Reeve looked towards the door breaking her gaze from Nubia "Come in."
"Ma'am, the vehicle of the Keeper is at the main gate."
"Good thank you."
Nubia turned around to the cleric "she's here already? Well don't hang around then, go and let her in" the curator quickly interjected flapping her hand again.
"Nubia, in my office I assert instructions, not you!" the Reeve's unimpressed eyes were firmly fixed upon her.
Turning to look at the cleric and speaking softly. "Please do go down and assist Raysmau in opening the front doors; we will be there to meet her shortly." The Reeve offered a gentle smile almost as if an apology for the guest in her offices' behaviour.

"Yes Ma'am" the cleric bowed her head and left the room shutting the door behind her.
"There you go; that is how easy it is. Speak nicely and you will be treated the same way."
"They need to be reminded of their place" growled the curator under her breath.
"And it sounds like you need to be reminded of yours...Curator."

Chapter Thirteen:

THE ARRIVAL OF MISS FENNAWAY

THURSDAY APPROACHING 11AM

Having been infuriated earlier by *'phone technology'* Mildred was now sitting with a cup of tea in hand having regained her usual calm demeanour.

Composed but worried she looked down at Missy whilst biting her lip; she had no idea what could be wrong with her. She had fed her the same the night previously and she seemed fine when she went to bed, what could it possibly be? It was then that it also came into her mind that she had awoken briefly at some time in the middle of the night and couldn't remember if she had watched Bang Goes Your Money the night before; she recalled sitting up in bed thinking about it.
She was now scratching her head; most odd that something so recent she could not recall. She was struggling to remember the most part of the last hour before she went to bed, she must have mentally drifted off somewhere.

The clock was ticking in her kitchen, having replaced the batteries, as she sat there in silence waiting for Miss Fennaway. Somewhat anxious as she never had house visitors, she surveyed her kitchen and she could see through the kitchen doorway into the lounge and wondered if she needed to clean up a little. She was getting a little flustered at the thought of this peculiarly odd woman coming round.

She had met her twice before when she had read in her quarterly magazine that cats should have their health injections when they were very young. Having never cared for a cat or any pet in her life she had to read up on these things and also had to put her trust in whatever she read.

She had asked Daphne soon after she had delivered Missy to her what she would need to do. The only advice that Daphne had offered was that protecting a cat should come naturally to her, it was in her blood. They also hated injections and if there were any problems, to call Miss Fennaway and she gave her the phone number. '*Without exception Mildred always call Miss Fennaway if there are any problems; don't ever call anyone else*'.

So this was to be the third time that she would meet the vet and she was surprised that Miss Fennaway was available practically straight away *(when she had finally been able to speak with her)*. Why Daphne was insistent on her using the Fennaway practice she was not sure as she was at least an hour's ride away on the bus; there were other practices with good vets close by she had overheard in local gossip.

She stood up and wandered over to a small mirror that was in her front room. Why she was considering the appearance of her house and herself for that matter she did not know, presumably it would be her that would be paying Miss Fennaway after all. It had been quite odd that on the two previous occasions she had not charged her and when Missy had had her injections she had always taken her out of the room, something that she was not altogether comfortable with.

She heard the click of her front gate closing and she moved quickly over to the kitchen window and could see Miss Fennaway coming up the pathway.

Rushing to the front door she opened it in anticipation and could see the beaming face of the vet looking straight at her.

"Hello Miss Fennaway, thank you for coming at such short notice."
"It's Dr Fennaway actually but remember Mildred you can call me Kamilah."
Smiling Mildred pulled the front door fully open. "Please do come in, I'm sorry about the mess" apologising for any shortcomings before she even had the chance to think about it.
"Don't worry, I'm used to it" she was still grinning as Mildred noticed for the

first time that the vet's teeth were really quite discoloured.

"Oh, I see, well hopefully it's not too bad for you and you can cope" she smiled.

"Mmm, we'll see" and she gave a gentle shrug.

"Oh okay," Mildred was not enthralled at this response and she now watched as the stranger moved forward into her kitchen and seemed to be looking about and surveying her place almost in a judgemental way.

"Well, I should show you Missy."

"Oh yes, Missy...please do, they usually hide like Ninjas when I show up" she laughed to herself and kept laughing.

Mildred didn't join her in laughter as she had heard the 'joke' last time she saw her.

Mildred had moved Missy onto the couch in her front room in anticipation of the vet's arrival.

"Nice cushion." Kamilah turned around to look at Mildred, beaming her almost black teeth having seen her homemade cushion with the white cat on it.

"Er, thank you" Mildred paused momentarily and after seeing enough of the teeth "what about Missy" and she ushered her right arm forward in the direction of her cat.

"Oh yes of course, I'm quite sure it's nothing, people who look after cats can worry somewhat."

"You mean people who own cats presumably?"

"What now dear?"

"People who own cats Dr Fennaway." Mildred decided not to address her by her first name as informality didn't really seem to be getting her anywhere fast.

"Yes, of course, you are right," Kamilah swallowed and returned her gaze to Missy, "people who own cats."

Kamilah placed her workbag on the couch and then sat down next to Missy.

"Right then Missy, what is all this fuss about?" She took a stethoscope from her bag and placed the chest piece onto the cat and started moving it about the cat's body. Lifting her left arm she glanced at her watch whilst moving the diaphragm around and not keeping it in one place for very long. She turned around to look at Mildred with an absurd smile.

"Well everything appears to be in order here!"

"Do you not have to put the other end of the stethoscope into your ears?"
"What now dear?" the vet asked with a long smile still etched across her face.
"The other end with the ear things, do you not need to listen through those?"
Kamilah's eyes widened slightly upon hearing this "well, yes you can, er, of course...some do; but then I have done this job a long time. I work a lot on instinct" she was nodding her head as she spoke.

Mildred who was standing over the vet now had placed her hands on her hips watching every single move the vet made.
"But seeing as you have asked I will" beamed Kamilah and with that she placed the ear tips into her ears and started dabbing the chest piece over the cat again.

"As I say, everything seems in order."

Mildred having felt how fast Missy's heartbeat was pumping earlier on intervened. "Are you sure?"
Kamilah turned her head around and jumped slightly as Mildred was now practically on her shoulder.
"I sense your concern dear, let me check something else."
Kamilah rummaged in her bag and finding what she was looking for asked "would it be too much trouble for a cup of tea Mildred, would you mind?"
Mildred stood upright and gave a slight polite smile "well yes that would be fine" she paused briefly watching the vets every move "Earl Grey or Green Tea?"
"Whatever you are making Mildred I'm quite sure will be lovely." Her head was nodding slightly up and down as she said this still with her hand in her bag.

Mildred gave a quick and succinct smile and turned around to go into the kitchen.
Out of sight of Mildred, Kamilah took an oval shaped device out of her bag and pressed a power button on the side and a screen lit up on the top. There was a Velcro detachable part underneath that she pulled away to revel some sensors to the opposite side to the screen. She looked behind her to check that Mildred was still in the kitchen.

"Would you like fish paste sandwiches?" yelled Mildred from the kitchen having looked in the fridge and sensing that she could spare a couple.

"Oh yes please, that would be lovely Mildred, you are very kind, I love fish paste" she said deep in concentration with the fakest of smiles across her face, knowing full well that she couldn't stand fish paste.

Kamilah ran the sensors of the Signapher device across the body of Missy as different colours moved up and down as a graph appeared on the screen.

She froze upon seeing a red warning light appear with some text written next to it and swallowed heavily and switched it back off. Now with a tense face she looked forward in thought as she was suddenly distracted by Mildred coming back into the room and quickly scrambled to put the device back in her bag.

"What's that?" enquired Mildred looking at the vet moving things around in her bag hastily.

"Mmm, what's what dear?"

"The something that you just put into your bag."

"Oh it's nothing, Mildred, I just took a blood test, just to be sure" the words squeezed out between her smiling teeth knowing full well that it was the first and only thing she could think of.

"Oh, I don't think Missy likes needles."

"Oh come now Mildred, it's not like that anymore, new technology and all that, completely pain free these days." The vet was talking with her hands doing her best to reassure Mildred.

"I see" Mildred responded suspiciously and as she did so she passed the vet a cup and saucer with green tea in it. There were also four curly fish paste sandwiches placed on the side should she want those as well.

"Thank you very much Mildred" Kamilah said taking the tea cup and saucer from Mildred's outstretched hand.

Taking a sip of tea and spilling a little down her chin as she was smiling at the same time Mildred noticed her hands were shaking a little.

"Would you mind terribly if I made a quick phone call?"

Mildred paused to look at her.

"I have another client to see afterwards you see."

"No not at all, you can use mine if you like." and she pointed at the cat phone.

"That's a phone?" enquired Kamilah laughing away to herself.

"Oh yes and it meows as well if someone calls!"

Still emitting fake laughter as she looked at the phone "I see" she smiled "how extraordinary, what a crazy world we live in." She was shaking her head slightly as the certificate on the wall caught her attention.

With the laughter and smile having disappeared, Kamilah placed the cup and saucer as delicately as she could on the table trying her best not to bring attention to her shaky hands. She got to her feet and put a hand in her jacket pocket and pulled out a phone.

Pointing the phone in the direction of Mildred she smiled again "I won't be long" and turned around and started to make her way to the front door.

"You can call from here if you wish; you don't need to go outside." Mildred said with some curiosity.

"Client confidentiality you see, you wouldn't want me to be talking about your Missy in front of others would you?"

"Er, well I guess not." Confusion was etched all over Mildred's face as she sat down.

As the doctor walked out of the room she turned around to Mildred "Oh by the way, your cat is perfectly well, it's just a passing bug and I'm quite positive she will be fine in a few hours." Her smile was somewhat reassuring as she turned her back on Mildred and carried on towards the door.

With the exception of the ticking of the clock coming from the kitchen, Mildred sat in silence with her knees together and her feet turned inwards to each other looking down into her cup of tea. "You see Missy, Miss Fennaway said that you are going to be okay." She looked up and smiled at her cat but she was troubled, most troubled by the quick diagnosis; something did not feel quite right about all of this.

Curiosity brought her to her feet and she went to look out of the front room window and could see the vet further down her path talking to someone on the phone; she had a very concerned expression across her face.

Mildred shook her head and ran the fingers of one hand through her hair in worry.

As they left the Reeve's offices Nubia was very quick to notice that all four clerics were now sitting back at their desk, not that it changed her mood in any way. Slowing down her pace she could see that the former missing cleric on the right hand side was not busy with her work unlike the others, instead her head was raised up clearly looking at her.

"Nubia...Curator" the Reeve elevated her voice on the second occasion to make sure she was heard.
"Yes, coming" she responded and quickened her pace still looking over her left shoulder at the cleric. "Something not right with that one" she muttered under her breath.

At the top of the stairs the Reeve looked at the Curator. "I thought it was you that was always in a rush," she smiled "something bothering you?"
She shook her head. "No, I'm sure it's nothing."
"Very well then" the Reeve offered a brief smile looking down into the eyes of the curator.
They both descended the stairs to the bottom and veered to the left towards the main entrance doors.

The curator lifted her head to look up to the Reeve as they stood in the central lobby. Despite all of the grandeur that was on display she never once faltered or looked impressed or interested. The Reeve hadn't long been in post, whereas she had been based from the UK headquarters for some time, she never failed to be amazed with this part of the building. She was yet to figure out what this Reeve was all about, irrespective her Order had sanctioned her appointment and she had no choice but to accept it.

The clerics were in place as they should be. Six always sat at the main desk and when a special guest was due to arrive there would be three either side of the entrance doors and a further three would wait in the centre as aides should their assistance be needed.
Nubia could see that a handful of elders were loitering on the balconies above clearly having heard that the Keeper was due to arrive as it was a rare occasion that she was here.

Nubia finally noticed some reaction from the Reeve as she surveyed the security positions around the lobby and above.

Whilst the Reeve was one of the new breed that embraced technology there were never cameras allowed inside the grand mansion and that was absolute as headquarters is the most private of places. That was not true of the road outside of the grounds as security devices were in place to help protect and conceal the hidden entrance to Loxley.

The Reeve glanced up to the upper tiers of the house as well as surveying ground level ensuring that her own personal security team were in place, the team known as the Escarrabin. They were as discrete as they could be in their ceremonial wear but with the absence of cameras that could monitor they were clearly on show for all who cared to look. The curator glanced at the three clerics standing in line behind them and then looked up at the Reeve.

"Ahem..." She murmured trying to get the Reeve's attention.
"Shouldn't the head of the Escarrabin be..."

She was interrupted by the sound of an unseen gate moving and then the heavy door of the Security Order Of The Escarrabin started to open to the left of her. The Reeve turned her head to her left and looked down. "As I told you curator, everything is quite in order."

Nubia found herself looking at her feet again before she was distracted by the sound of heavy footsteps emerging from the doorway. A loud crash echoed around the lobby as the door was sealed again controlled out of sight to them by another member of the Escarrabin.

In full ceremonial clothing Raysmau the chief security officer of the Escarrabin stepped forward wearing the colours of the Keeper. With the lower half of her face and neck shielded in a black mask she walked towards the main entrance doors of the grand lobby with her cloak trailing behind her. She turned and nodded at the clerics on the front desk who were all now looking towards her. The very old and heavy oak doors slowly parted opening inwards. The sounds of creaking wood and mechanical moving parts could be heard as they moved the sheer weight of the doors creating a harrowing sound all around the lobby.

Two distinct thuds echoed as the huge doors found their resting place. Everyone on the ground level of the lobby could now see the Keeper's immaculate car directly in front of them.

Her driver remained in place as the huge frame of Raysmau stepped through the entrance doors and walked over to the car and opened the door for her. Still holding the door she took a couple of steps backwards before offering a hand towards the Keeper.

"Thank you Raysmau that will not be necessary." She stepped out of the car composing herself looking at the frontage of this grand old home. "I know that I'm getting on a bit but I can still get out of a car by myself, even if I do have to use this cane sometimes." She tapped the wooden cane that bore a cat's head at its tip upon the gravel a couple of times.

"Yes Madam Keeper" Raysmau said with her head bowed.
"You are well I trust?"
"Yes Ma'am well and here to serve."
"That's good to know" she smiled not being very discrete as she looked directly at the enormous size of the head of security that is only answerable to the Reeve. "I do not have any bags, flying visit today."
"So I am led to believe Ma'am."

She started to walk forward before turning around and looked at Raysmau with a big smile across her face "And how is our curator?"

Raysmau averted her gaze and looked at the floor. "The curator is very efficient at her job" she said with polite tact.
"Mmm" she smiled, "no change there then." She took a further step forward towards Raysmau and looked up at her, "At least you answer to the Reeve and not to the curator."
Raysmau looked down to her "Yes Ma'am" and offered the hint of a smile.
"I trust that she is settling in well?"
"Yes Ma'am, I have a very good bonding and understanding with the new Reeve."
"That's good to know."
The Keeper started to walk towards the grand doors of the headquarters, her cane dragging its way across the gravel along with her long gown. She heard the car door being closed behind her and could now hear the heavy boots of

Raysmau catching up to her reasonably slow pace.

As she got closer to the doors she could see a couple of the Reeve's security team watching her every move from the lower balcony and the clerics' heads directly in front and to her left and right were bowed. Ahead she could see the smiling face of the Reeve and the usual stare of seriousness from the curator.

"Madam Keeper, how lovely to see you again." The Reeve nodded her head slightly in reverence.
"I would say it was lovely to be here Reeve, but given the circumstances."
"I know, we are quite troubled by recent events."
They were both nodding in agreement as the Keeper looked down to her right.
"Hello Nubia, I trust you are keeping well?"
"I am also as concerned as the Reeve" the curator responded.
"I'm quite sure that you are" the Keeper was unmoved by this response.
"Please come this way Ma'am." The Reeve extended her arm indicating they were to make their way to the stairs. "Thank you Raysmau." She nodded towards her head of security who took three paces backwards and nodded back to her before turning to return to her doorway.

"I'm very sorry that Lady Safiya was not here to greet you today" the Reeve offered by way of apology to the Keeper. "She is away on business at the moment and not due here until tomorrow morning."
"Yes I am aware she is very busy but thank you all the same Reeve. I've known Safiya for years and it's not her that I've come to see."

The loud thud from the heavy doors closing behind them made the curator turn around. She looked at the three clerics behind them and nodded and extended her right arm and waved her hand to dismiss them. The other six that had been at either side of the main doors also now moved away to get back to their previous duties. She briefly looked up and noticed out of the corner of her eye that a singular cleric was stood back slightly watching them from above.

She turned back not giving this too much thought as security is the Reeve's concern. She was more focused upon why everyone was addressed by their proper title except for her. She really did not care for the name of Nubia sometimes.

Chapter Fourteen:

THE REEVE'S FIRST SCROLL

THURSDAY: AFTER 11AM

The Keeper was studying the Reeve's main door with a wry smile across her face and leant forward on her cane to run her right hand over it.
"This old door tells many stories" she said very quietly and calmly looking at the worn markings and running her fingers over the cracks through the main seal.
The Reeve directly to the right of her offered a smile in return "Shall we?"

Without asking, the curator stepped in front of them putting her hands either side of the door and pushed her weight against it. The door groaned upon opening as most did within this old house.
"Please Madam Keeper" the curator extended her arm ushering her to come inside.
The Reeve was without words as the curator invited the Keeper into what was supposed to be her private part of the house.

The three of them moved forward as the door behind them started to close. They continued passed other rooms that held historic records of the Reeves' and their Order.

The Keeper could see other clerics were sitting working in a room on their left hand side before they passed the grand security briefing room of the Escarrabin.

One of the Reeve's personal bodyguards, in ceremonial dress with her helmet under her arm, stood with her head bowed as the Keeper passed by.

The Reeve's main office door was already open (*much to the curator's displeasure*) as they walked in and took their seats.

"Would you care for a cup of tea Madam Keeper?" The Reeve asked as she watched the Keeper steady herself with her cane and sat letting out a little sigh. "Yes, thank you very much Reeve." She wrestled with her long gown before she was comfortable. "I'll summon a cleric to see to that" the curator said as she went to get back up.
"That really won't be necessary Nubia, I'm quite capable of making us some tea." The Reeve spoke with a smile and the curator sat back down directly to the right hand side of the Keeper.

"You both are probably aware that I have met with members of the Grand Council this week as terribly saddening as it is at this time."

The Reeve pouring tea was listening with intent interest.

"We are most concerned about events regarding Lady Tempest. Reeve I trust that you are still investigating this?"
"I am but factual matters are still a little vague at this time. I have assigned Kalara, one of our most skilled and loyal security team, to devote her time to this one subject alone."
She brought a cup of tea over to the Keeper and passed it directly to her.
"I'm sure that in time more facts will present themselves but for now it is classified in public records as an accident."
"What about outside involvement, are questions being asked?"
"There is some curiosity as she did not have a family but upon receiving notice my team entered Lady Tempest's home and removed her certificates and work files. We replaced her main computer with one of our sterile models that I keep here so there are no records or association."

There was an audible tut from the curator; both the Reeve and the Keeper looked at her with some displeasure.

"Nubia you have made your feelings very clear about the use of computing and how we have changed our processes, but this is the way it is and will continue to be" the Keeper said looking directly at her.

The Reeve, with a slight frown, passed the curator a cup of tea before pouring one for herself and taking a seat behind her desk.

"I have been able to access the civilian policing records and their systems and there is no suspected third party or any inference of foul play at this time. However we are monitoring this."

"I see; I do not need to tell you that we do not need outside Police looking around into our affairs so I guess that is something to be thankful for."

The Reeve nodded "I suspect in public records it will remain listed as an accident; we, however, will keep an open mind until I am fully satisfied."

"Good, thank you Reeve."

"And what of her cats?"

The Keeper looked directly at the curator in some astonishment whilst the Reeve was shaking her head looking at the floor.

"You know the cats were presented back to me Nubia as is process. Why do you ask of such matters that do not concern you?"

The curator met her eyes briefly before looking downwards at the cup of tea that was balanced on her knee.

The role of the Keeper was a very important one but like the Reeve she conducted her affairs in secrecy. Secrecy was incredibly important, as long as Nubia knew about it.

There was momentary silence in the room as all three of them took sips of their tea.

"Most troubling" the Keeper muttered whilst staring into her tea stirring the occasional tea leaf.

The Reeve, anxious to ask, looked up towards the Keeper. "Have the Council advised you and have you been able to bring word?"

Looking up upon hearing the question the Keeper looked directly at the Reeve "Yes I bring word."

Replacing her tea cup back in its saucer and leaning over to rest it on the Reeve's desk she took her right hand and placed it into her left inside pocket of her ceremonial robe and brought out a very small gold leafed scroll that was secured with a wax seal.

"You can open it now Reeve" she said and passed it to her.

It was to be her first time being entrusted with the opening and security of one of the scrolls. Before her appointment at Loxley her elder had prepared her for such delicate and important matters.

Taking the scroll she pulled at the seal that cracked and opened quite easily. A few fragments of wax fell onto her desk as she brushed them aside.
Inside contained a singular name and an address.
The Reeve looked up at the Keeper and met her gaze.
"She's reasonably local to here."
"Yes, she is, not at the other end of the district."

Nubia was bobbing her head in interest trying to read what was printed on the scroll when there was a loud knock at the door.

"Come" said the Reeve averting her gaze from the scroll to the doorway.
A cleric appeared at the door with head bowed and all three turned to look with interest at the interruption.

"I'm sorry to disturb Ma'am but there is a phone call for the curator."

"What...now, right now! Well can it wait, can't you see we are having an important meeting?" the curator blasted at the cleric.
"I'm sorry madam curator but I'm told that it is most urgent."
"Well...Well, it had better be!" she said spilling some of her tea on the Reeve's desk as she put the cup and saucer down with some anger.

"Please excuse me ladies" she offered by way of apology as she turned around towards the door. "Well, show me the way then!" she fluttered an arm at the cleric berating her for interrupting their meeting. The cleric turned around and moved back into the corridor and the Reeve and the Keeper both watched the curator slam the door closed.

Both of them looked at each other not sure what to add before the Keeper leaned forward. "This is why she should never have been put into the Order Of The Reeves!"

The Reeve gave the faintest of smiles and resumed reading the few words perfectly written on the scroll.

Mildred was talking into the cat's bottom for the second time today.

"I've made an amazing luxury chocolate truffle cake, honestly, it's to die for!"
"Well, let's not go crazy!" Mildred said to Mildred of Merewood Close as they were both in fits of laughter.
"And I've made some lovely cupcakes and some cat treats that all of the members can take away with them."

Suddenly Mildred's laughter stopped. Oh, that's much better than giving everyone a card she thought to herself and she started biting her nails again.

"You okay Mildred?" she asked into the sudden silence.
"Yes, I'm fine well, no not really, my Missy is unwell."

"Oh really, what on ever is the matter with her, did you call Fennaway's?"
"Oh, do you know Miss Fennaway as well then?" Mildred asked with some curiosity as Merewood Close was in Coningsby in Lincolnshire. Although in the same district as her in the Kat club, it was quite some miles away from Shrewsbury in Shropshire.
"Oh yes, my elder recommended her."
Highly odd, Mildred thought to herself, as well as thinking about cat treats and fish paste sandwiches all at the same time.
"Well she came over and prodded her with a stethoscope and told me that she would be fine. She then rang someone, said she had to leave, that it was just a passing bug and that I shouldn't worry.

"Well I'm sure that she is right, I trust my elder's recommendation on these things."
"Yes, me too I suppose, I hope that she is right. Miss Fennaway can be a little peculiar can't she?" Mildred said laughing to herself albeit fake laughter.

"I wouldn't know, I've never met her, she was just recommended. My Misty has never needed a vet."

"You didn't take Misty for injections?"

"You had your Missy injected, heavens on earth whatever with?"

"Well, I don't know. I read it in a magazine and overheard a couple of ladies talking about it in The Tudor House Café...apparently you are supposed to." She was waving her arms in the air clearly clueless about these things. "Stops them getting bugs or something..."

There was silence between them both before Mildred queen of cakes decided to speak up.

"My elder said that my cat was mine to keep and protect and only call the vet if you need to. Apparently Miss Fennaway understands these things and she also told me that cats do not like injections, so I never did."

"Oh" Mildred sat in worried silence looking over at Missy. "Well I guess that I had better go and see to Missy."

"Okay Mildred, I do hope that Missy feels better again soon."

"Thank you Mildred, that's very kind of you."

"I'll tell you what; I'll make extra special cat treats for you. That will perk Missy right up." She could almost sense Mildred down the phone beaming away happy with her marvellous creations.

"Thank you Mildred, I'll see you tomorrow evening."

"Looking forward to it Mildred, goodbye for now."

Mildred put the cat's bottom down staring helplessly at Missy; what was I thinking by getting everyone a card! She was now lost in her thoughts. Her homemade cardigan and cards will be out shone by cupcakes and cat treats, she was sure of that.

"Daphne
Number 27
Crosshouses Road
Much Wenlock
Shropshire"

The Reeve read out aloud.

Gently putting the scroll down on her desk she returned her eyes to the Keeper.

"She will fall into the Shropshire and North Wales local region and of course the middle section of England and Wales for larger events and gatherings." The Keeper spoke in her usual calming way.
The Reeve was nodding.

"She will be in good hands. The local region is well supported and of course has Jessica who is about to be elevated to degree level 6.
"Indeed" said the Reeve still nodding in agreement with everything she was hearing.
"The Grand Council have sanctioned this new member; Daphne apparently came of age within the last couple of months so her time is now."
Leaning forward on her cane taking a more serious stance The Keeper looked assertively at the Reeve.
"Reeve, always around the time of the gatherings the watchers are more active, always trying to find out if there are new lines of ascension. You know of quite a few occurrences recently where reports have been made of them being seen on the outside. To our knowledge they are not aware of the new Daphne but it's safe to presume they may know of Lady Tempest's passing and the suspicious manner in how she passed. If that is the case we need to be extra vigilant, they will roam more than usual, especially in the hours of darkness."

"I understand Madam Keeper."

"Her new elder will be disclosed tomorrow night and until such time that she is presented with her cat, we need to keep this close to our chests and contain these facts only within this room."
"Of course Madam Keeper, I will see that it is done."
"Well thank you for the tea. I need to depart as I have others to see and have to travel down to the lower section now. Much to do with so little time."
The Reeve smiled. "There never is."
"Time?" The Keeper smiled back and steadied herself to her feet "I know."
The Reeve stood at the same time "Do you need a hand Ma'am?"
"No, no, thank you. My envoy will be here to see you on Saturday morning with four new cats, one for Jessica along with Daphne's first cat. She will of course

have two others for the other two elders that will be promoted."
"Do you know who is being elevated from degree level 8 to 7 and from 9 to 8?"
"No, I'm not aware as yet. With the course of events the Grand Council are leaving their decisions until very late. All will be announced tomorrow evening at the local gathering I am assured."
"I see" the Reeve nodded.

The noise of the door behind them bursting open startled both of them and they turned around to see the curator puffing out of breath and red in the face.

"What on earth is it Nubia?" The Reeve said almost at the top of her voice.
"I have just been informed of something most troubling."
"Well, what is it?" said the Keeper.

Pulling her jacket together and straightening her back, she took a brief moment in the knowledge that she knew something that both of them did not.

"I have just had a phone call from Fennaway; a cat in this district is showing the signs."

The Keeper retook her seat; all three of them were now looking at each other worridly.

Chapter Fifteen:

LADY EBONEE

THURSDAY AFTERNOON

Having gone through her wardrobe yet again and still arriving at the same conclusions Mildred made her way down stairs to the front room.

Looking across to her couch she could see that Missy was still unmoved. It upset her looking in the kitchen at the untouched food and the full water bowl. Glancing up at her clock she could see that it was approaching 2. The cards should have been at Mr Franks shop some hours ago but with Missy being unwell and Miss Fennaway coming round, time had been lost and it had slipped her mind.

She sat down next to her cat, placing a hand on her tummy and could still feel that her heart was beating much too fast. Sitting there she felt helpless and alone and distrusting of the vet's opinion.

She had been staring at the wall for far too long with her knees together and her arms draped over them. With a blink she snapped out of it and looked down at Missy. "I do hope you are better soon, I can't go to the gathering with you like this" she was stroking her cat gently. "I have to go and see Mr Franks now but I won't be long." She bent over and gave her cat a gentle kiss on the head. "See you in a bit."

She walked into the kitchen and grabbed her oversized purse bulging with receipts and dropped it into her equally oversized bag. Straining to get her shoes on as the buckle was too tight she was fidgeting with her feet and ankles until they were forced on. She felt guilty about leaving Missy while she was unwell but she had also made a promise to Mr Franks by placing the large card order. So as much as she disliked it she would have to go.

As the door slammed behind her, she set off down her pathway completely oblivious to everything; leaving her garden gate open she slowly walked down Rocke Road towards the shop. She hadn't even noticed that as she was approaching the bus stop a couple of the youths from the day before were sitting there.

"Here she comes, here she comes!" one said laughing.
"Helloooo Mildred" the other one cackled as they both laughed away at her expense.
"Leave me alone please" Mildred said very quietly looking at the ground as she continued to shuffle forwards.
"Oh why Mildred, you not banging your cat tin this afternoon then?"
"Nah, it's not feeding time yet" said the other "feeding time is always at 7; you can set your watch by her!"

Mildred looked immediately to her left, the man with the long hair was not there this time and all she could see was his lizard starring at her from inside his tank in the front window.

"Say, where is that stupid cat of yours anyway?" one of them said.

Mildred stopped walking and lifted her head and looked at them. "It's my Missy and she's not stupid."
Upon hearing this they were practically rolling around in laughter. "Oh my days" one of them said whilst playfully punching the other one before doing something that may have resembled some sort of 'high five'.
Mildred looked on at them as a couple of tears rolled from her eyes down past her cheeks.
The one who had said about her 'stupid cat' suddenly stopped laughing and nudged his mate. Both of the boys were looking at her as the laughter and their smiles faded away.

Mildred looked forward and continued on her way. She could still hear 'crazy cat lady' being mumbled from behind her, clearly the boys having regained their confidence now that she was not looking directly at them.

With her right hand she brushed a couple of tears away hoping that her cat would be okay, she also wondered why people could be so mean.

"Are you okay Mildred?" Mr Franks enquired having noticed that Mildred did not say her usual good morning upon entry to his shop. Looking at his watch he could now see that it was afternoon in any event but something did not seem right with her.

"Yes, I'm fine thank you" she said putting a brave face on the events of so far today.
Mr Franks could see that she looked upset.
"What on earth is it Mildred?" he asked now truly being distracted from his newspaper.
She shrugged whilst looking towards the floor. "It's just the boys at the bus stop, they make fun of me."
"Well boys will be boys Mildred" he rasped shaking his head in this not all together welcome observation or show of empathy.
"That doesn't make it right Mr Franks!" Mildred's snappy response upset her further.
"Indeed it does not Mildred and one day they will learn to better themselves."

Mildred listened to the words wondering if the boys would ever better themselves.

"Is that everything Mildred, unlike you to get so upset about stupid boys?"
"My Missy is very unwell, had to have the vet round earlier."
"Oh I'm sorry to hear this Mildred, did you call vets at Castle Hollow?"
"No Fennaway's Veterinary."

Both of Mr Frank's eyes lifted up to the left trying to access his brain functions "mmm, not heard of them" he shuffled with his newspaper suddenly feeling a bit awkward. "Anyway, I hope that he was able to help."

"It was a she."

"I'm sorry, what Mildred?"

"The Vet...the vet was a she, Miss Fennaway."

"I stand corrected Mildred; in any event I hope that she was able to help."

"Not especially...anyway, did my cards arrive?"

"Indeed they have, all 44 of them!"

"Well that's some welcome news on a terrible day so far."

"I'm pleased to say that they have exactly the same cat on the front as the one you saw yesterday."

A big smile stretched across Mildred's face for the first time that day and she put her bag down and dried her eyes. "That really is pleasing news, thank you."

"Not a problem, I've got them back here for you, just bear with me a jiffy."

He pulled across a very old and dusty looking curtain and she watched him disappear out to the back of his shop.

Looking around she noticed how dirty the shop was in its corners - she had never really noticed before. The labels with the prices on were all hand written with a black marker pen. The lino on the floor was turning up in random places and pictures hung on the walls that were quite discoloured. Why there was a faded 'Monet' picture in a frame in this shop was anyone's guess.

"Here we are Mildred" and he placed the stack of cards that were wrapped individually in cellophane onto the counter "the envelops are already inside them."

Mildred looked at them and sure enough they were exactly the same. "Oh that is amazing Mr Franks, I'm so happy" she said whilst picking up the card from the top of the pile.

She lifted it towards her face and then turned it around and immediately the smile disappeared as she read *Printed words inside say HAPPY BIRTHDAY*. Her eyes flared in a mixture of shock and panic and she threw it on the side before grabbing another off of the pile.

"No, no it can't be."

"Whatever is the matter Mildred?"

"These are birthday cards!"

"Yes that is correct, exactly as you ordered" as he reached under the counter and held up the one from the previous day.

She snatched it from his hand and turned it over and it read exactly the same as the others.

She closed her eyes in utter disbelief.

"Well did you not know it was a birthday card Mildred, did you not check?" The Franks man rasped with stuttered laughter as he put his hands on his hips. "I thought it highly odd to order 44 birthday cards at once, but who am I to ask and each to his own."

"Her own" she snapped and closed her eyes in annoyance.

"What now Mildred?"

"Each to her own."

Mr Franks looked down at his counter.

Mildred let out a considerable sigh and looked down at the floor again. "I'll take them, would you happen to have a black felt tipped pen as well please?"

Having paid, she made her way to the door and didn't offer a goodbye.

She started slowly walking down the road with her thoughts berating her. 'You are going to a gathering and want to make a good impression and instead you give everyone a birthday card, you stupid woman!' She was stomping her feet now heading in the direction of home.

'Seriously could this day get any worse?' Her stomping came to a halt as she looked up and could see the boys were still at the bus stop. Looking down at the floor she about turned and took the long way home.

All three had now sat back down somewhat concerned with the news that Nubia had just delivered.

"What exactly did Fennaway say Nubia?" the Reeve enquired.

"She spoke very quickly as she knew that she was being watched; she informed me that the cat Nahla is suffering" she puffed still out of breath from running.

"Was she scanned?" The Reeve questioned.

"Yes and the results were exacting. The sensors detected her pain centre was

coming from the region of her heart; it is as foretold."
"Okay, okay, let's not get ahead of ourselves." The Keeper gently interjected "It may just be bad timing, that's all and nothing more."
"Fennaway insisted the readings on the signapher device were quite clear Madam Keeper," The curator asserted.

They sat motionless.

"Which elder is Nahla with? I struggle to remember sometimes where every cat has been placed and with whom." The Keeper asked looking at the curator.

"She is with Mildred, from Rocke Road in Shrewsbury, 9th degree elder, one of the new intakes." Nubia said letting out a sigh whilst looking down at the floor biting her lip and fidgeting in her seat.
"This is indeed perturbing for any cat but for such a young one to be displaying these signs" said the Keeper with a shake of the head.
"Yes and her elder will not even know her real name as yet" the Reeve was nodding in agreement.
"Oh honestly Nubia what is it" the Reeve was bearing her eyes down on her having noticed her uncomfortable demeanour and fidgeting behaviour "is there something else that you know or need to share with us?"

She looked up with a guilt ridden face glancing between the Keeper and the Reeve.

"Curator, speak up now please!" The Keeper spoke for the first time today with the authority that is becoming of her rank.
Letting out a large sigh the curator knew that she was entirely useless at keeping secrets sometimes.

"I had been advised to keep an eye upon the Mildred of whom we speak."
The Reeve looked incredulous as her eyes lifted to the ceiling and shook her head to the left and right before resuming her composure. "Are you serious Nubia, security is my department."
"That it is Reeve" The Keeper said joining her in support of this statement as they both now looked directly at the curator.

Nubia clearly quite anguished looked at both of them "I was told to keep it secret."

The Reeve practically slamming her hands on her desk, "this is outrageous and from you of all, the one who sticks to rules and conformity throughout everything. You need to start talking to both of us right now!"

"Yes, I know, okay, okay." She was scratching her head and gathering her thoughts. "I wasn't entirely sure of the facts and I just didn't want to bother you with it (she lied). The source can be unreliable at times...and so...I just wanted to check it, that's all and nothing more." She was trying to speak with her hands raised in a feeble attempt to create a calming effect but with her fingers shaking at their ends she was failing miserably.

"I was unaware that you had sources curator, in fact I was unaware that we even had 'sources' within the Order." The Keeper's eyes were fixed firmly upon Nubia and her voice was filled with concern.

Nubia was struggling to maintain eye contact with either of them, the Keeper due to her importance and rank and with the Reeve, well, just because she just didn't like her and she knew that she was very much in the wrong.
The Reeve leaned forward on her desk "curator, you will talk to us."
She closed her eyes and gathered her composure.

"I was recently contacted by a very senior elder who informed me that she had been told a great event of imbalance was about to happen. She was very concerned that the prophecy of old and the foretelling of the stopping of our time and dominium were imminent."

The Reeve and the Keeper both looked at each other in amazement.

"Dominium?" The Reeve smiled and lowered her chin towards the Keeper with mouth aghast "dominium you say...of which dominium you speak of?"

Nubia clearly upset by her own words was struggling to maintain her composure and could only offer a softly spoken reply. "Us Reeve, our dominium, our place here, the end of our time."

Upon hearing this the Reeve slumped back into her seat eyes wide looking at the Keeper.

"Okay, Nubia...Nubia." The Keeper had raised her right hand as an offering of peace and calm.

Nubia looked up towards the Keeper. "These are truly dreadful words that you speak Nubia and in any event should never leave this room but you must tell us more about what you were told."

"I promised that I would look into it and equally I promised not to tell anyone."

"Well, why was I not told about this?" questioned the Reeve in some astonishment.

"Because you are new, a new breed that does not follow tradition as it should be." Nubia snapped "Look at the way you dress, like you are wearing a suit for business. You are not a banker and you are not trusted by all you know."

The Reeve slapped her hands on her desk again. "Ridiculous! This is outrageous." She was now looking at the Keeper for some support.

"Now then both of you stop and calm yourselves!" The Keeper was now pointing towards both of them with her cane.

The Keeper was deep in thought and leaned over to the curator. "Who told you about this Nubia?"

"Oh Madam Keeper, please do not ask, I promised that I would not repeat her name."

"I'm quite sure that is the case but irrespective you have gone behind the back of the Reeve who for that matter has the support of the Grand Council as well as myself and these are very serious statements that you are making. So I ask you again who told you this?"

Nubia's hands were now in a ball resting on one knee as she twitched excessively torn between what to do.

Letting out a huge sigh. "It was Lady Ebonee" she said giving in and looked at the floor feeling full of betrayal.

"Lady Ebonee from Dundee; Lady Ebonee who is a member of the Grand Council?"

Nubia having not lifted her head was still looking at the floor before she nodded a couple of times.

"Oh well that explains it then," the Keeper said while shaking her head, "she may well be a very respected member of the Grand Council but she's as nutty as a fruitcake. Her unique take on the 'prophecies' has to be heard to be believed Reeve," she said with some amusement. "Don't get me wrong, I love her and admire her deeply but the older she gets the more wayward she becomes."

The Keeper was still shaking her head but her face was quizzical. "Most unnatural for a Member of the Grand Council to behave in this fashion and bypass others and the ranks of order."

"Maybe the others would not have believed her Madam Keeper" the Reeve said whilst looking at Nubia as she leaned forward on her desk. "Maybe she knew that someone else would, someone who lives in deep paranoia of the prophecies and the passing of time, maybe someone that would do her bidding."
Nubia looked up quite angered by this statement "I did what I believed to be right" she snarled.
"I'm sure you did Nubia but this sheds a whole new light on things!" the Reeve said now looking directly at the Keeper. "So tell both of us, how exactly were you going to do this, how exactly were you going to look into this?"

The curator swallowed and looked at them both with a shameful expression etched across her face.
"I made contact with Jessica who is the elder of Daphne..."
The Reeve practically threw herself back in her chair rolling her eyes and let out a couple of small unintentional laughs "Oh, this is all starting to make sense now."

"What, what is it?" the Keeper asked looking confused.
"Shall I say or shall you?" the Reeve bluntly threw the comment at the curator.
"Well...?" The question hung in silence for a couple of seconds.

"Don't worry Nubia; I'll fill in the blanks for you!"

The Reeve explained whilst still looking directly at Nubia. "What our curator did, Madam Keeper, was a week or so ago asked me for navigational enhancements to be made to Jessica's car and for her to have her own personal navigator. I didn't think the request was that unusual as she is to be promoted to a level 6 elder at the gathering tomorrow night and as such she will have a higher level of security access. So I asked for my security team to do just that and make the adjustments that she requested.

What is unusual however is that I know that she summoned Jessica for a meeting here privately with our curator only two days ago. Invitations to headquarters for an elder holding only a degree level 7 status is out of the ordinary; so now this all makes sense. Is that what happened here Nubia, am I somewhat close?"

"She is about to be made a degree level 6" she snapped..."But yes that is what happened, it is as you say" Nubia nodded her head slightly a couple of times and sighed.

"So you've either told Jessica about the prophecy of which she is not of the appropriate rank to hear or you've asked her to spy on Daphne and Mildred; am I right?"

The Curator was shifting in her seat whilst gathering her thoughts, "No, I've asked for Jessica to keep an eye on Mildred and to report to me anything unusual, Daphne is none the wiser." She was looking directly at the Reeve.

"And we were none the wiser as well it would appear" the Keeper said looking at Nubia.

"As I say, Madam Keeper, I thought that I was doing the right thing!"

The Reeve and Keeper were looking at each other slightly unsure of what to do next.

The Keeper lifted her right arm up again and motioned it up and down for them both to see. "Let's keep some calm as the event has already happened now, there is nothing we can do to change this. It however may well be worthy of an internal investigation another time." The curator looked up upon hearing this before the shameful expression on her face turned down towards the floor again.

The Reeve looked towards the Keeper "I know that I do not know Lady Ebonee but I have heard rumours about her 'thoughts' away from the Council all the same; but do we think there is any validity in what she is saying?"

"Well yes indeed..." the curator spoke out before being cut off by the waving arm of the Keeper.

"It is highly unlikely..." She was then cut off by the curator.

"But the prophecy states there will be three events and this bears the mark of the first."

The Keeper looked furiously at Nubia for cutting her off.

"Indeed it does; the prophecy foretells that one of our kind will bear hallmarks of pain from the heart 24 hours before the collective union of the Grand Council of the Enlightened."
"Such as a gathering?" The Reeve put forward "but the Grand Council are not meeting tomorrow."
"Whilst that may be technically true Reeve, they will be present at other gatherings all over the world and therefore it could be considered as a collective union."
"Could it be entirely possible that here, within this region, that Nahla is the one showing the pains of the heart?"
"Nahla is a special cat…."Nubia mumbled before being cut off again.
"All of the cats I present are very special Nubia; there has been no indications thus far that Nahla is any more special than the others; if this is to be, time will tell." Her words lingered in the air as she was looking directly at the curator.

"What would you wish me to do Madam Keeper?" the Reeve said.
"We must not get ahead of ourselves. This may be a coincidence of time and nothing more, and until such time we will remain calm. It is true that there must be some concern that we have lost one of our own with the passing of Lady Tempest and that one of our cats is displaying great pain; not to mention that a senior elder is making the sort of claims that she is to you Nubia. But for now they are claims and nothing more and nothing less." The Keeper spoke with her hands suggesting calm from everyone.

The Keeper was deep in thought. She knew that events sounded very suspicious, but she also knew that the curator had a tendency to panic unnecessarily, so she needed to be careful with her words from now on.

"If there is any truth in these claims there will be a secondary event this evening; that is what was foretold. Until such time we remain calm and conduct our affairs as we always do – Yes?"
"Yes Madam Keeper" said the Reeve who had been focused on every word she spoke. Nubia nodded a couple of times whilst biting at a finger nail.

"Good; Reeve will you store the scroll in the archive please?"
"Yes Madam Keeper, I would be very happy to."

"Good" the Keeper responded and put her bodyweight on her cane as she stood up.
The Reeve stood up as well whilst the curator sat still chewing her finger nails.

"We have been a presence for good for thousands of years through many times of adversity even at its most stubborn; there is nothing to say that anything is going to change to that effect." She looked at both of them. "And on that note I bid you both farewell, Reeve...Curator" and she nodded to both of them.

"I'll see that Raysmau guides you out Madam Keeper."
"So be it" she gave a half smile towards the Reeve accepting her offer.

On the way out of the door she glanced over at Nubia who hadn't moved from her seat, her face was filled with fear.

Her words had clearly not reassured her.

Chapter Sixteen:

BEHIND THE GATE OF RAYSMAU

HEADQUARTERS THURSDAY LATE AFTERNOON

Duat offered little resistance as he knelt down and put his hands behind his back. He listened to the familiar sound of cuffs being put across both of his wrists.

"Make sure those gloves are still secured Gamila." Alian one of the Reeve's elite security team, known as the Escarrabin, instructed her fellow security officer.
He was lifted back to his feet by way of his cuffs, his palms covered by the leather gloves.
"What are you doing over here one who calls himself Duat?" the tone of questioning was reasonably hostile.
His head was bowed down and could not be seen under the hood of the full length cloak that identified him as an outcast.
Alian moved around to face him. "I will ask you again and for the last time, what are you doing here?"
Duat remained motionless.

Alian bowed down slightly in an attempt to look Duat directly in the face, partially seeing his chin and jaw was enough to make her grimace. His saliva ran freely without him having the ability to wipe it away.

"Last chance watcher."

"I am more than a watcher" Duat muttered under his breath.
"Oh really?" Alian nodded at Gamila "pull his hood down."

Duat contorted in pain instantly as the bright sunlight of the August afternoon bore down upon him. Unable to protect his eye his head was flaying left and right and both of his arms were wrestling against the cuffs.

"Hold him" Alian yelled as Gamila stood on the back of his knees forcing him to kneel down again.
"There, as you should be watcher."
Alian crouched down to look directly at Duat and could see that the vessels in his huge solitary eye were swollen and multiplying at an incredible rate as he hissed in pain.

"Not so easy without goggles is it? My, you are ugly watcher." Alian stood back before glancing at Gamila and nodding so the hood could be put back over his skeletal like head. The hood was pulled back over shielding his eye from the sunlight.
The noise of the hissing started to change to the more familiar high pitched cry that watchers made when under threat. His breathing was gaining momentum again as his convulsions started to ease.

"There you see, we can be reasonable but so much for your statement, you are clearly the same as the other watchers."

Alian nodded at Gamila again to bring him back to his feet.

Dipping her head slightly to look under the hood she could see saliva running between the gaps in his teeth and the two misshaped dark crevasses separated by the thinnest line of bone that represented something of a nose. He was breathing heavily and noisily sounding like an animal in distress.

"I will ask you again and for the very final time, what are you doing over here Duat?"
He remained motionless and had gathered his composure reasonably quickly.
"Madam Raysmau informed me that the curator had reported that you were seen in this area only two days ago, why is that?"
Angered that no response was forthcoming from the watcher "I see..."

Frustrated with his lack of compliance she leaned forward towards him. "In fact I see very well with both of my eyes Duat." A smirk had appeared across her face only to be met by a deep hiss by way of response.

"Then before you go back into the below to your rightful place you have an appointment with Madam Raysmau," she stepped back from the watcher.

"Take him away."

Gamila grabbed the handcuffs with her left arm and pushed at his shoulder with the right and started walking him back to the manor house.

Alian watched Gamila lead him away. He offered no resistance throughout despite his strength. She looked up behind her at the great statue of Salma. Why Duat had been here again for the second time in as many days she had no idea.

Duat was escorted unceremoniously through the private doorway into the manor house used by the Escarrabin. He knew that Alian had now caught up behind them, hearing the unmistakable footsteps of her heavy footwear on the stone tiled flooring below.

As they entered the grand lobby Duat looked up from under his hood and could see six clerics were sitting at their desk and there was a scattering of what his captors referred to as 'the elders'. Movements within the lobby had stopped, as everyone looked on at the events taking place in front of them, as Duat was ushered towards the archway that led to the quarters of the head of security.

As they drew close to the outside of the archway, Alian moved up in front of them and leaned forward to the door and pressed the intercom.
"Control, go ahead" was the quick response through the intercom.
"Control this is Escarrabin Alian, with a prisoner, requesting to see Madam Raysmau."
There was a short pause as the request was considered followed by the sound of heavy locks moving from the door. Unseen by them, the sound of a gate being dragged across stone echoed within the archway until a crunch of metal was heard as the gate came to a standstill.

Under his hood, unseen to the others, a twitch of a smile had appeared on Duat's face at the simplicity of their *'security measures.'*
The heavy door opened automatically as another member of the Escarrabin appeared looking very unimpressed at the sight of the restrained watcher.

Alian stepped forward to her fellow Escarrabin. "We need to speak with Madam Raysmau; this watcher has been roaming again."

A frown appeared across the face of the security guard and gatekeeper upon hearing this.
"I see, please wait here Alian, I will see if she is available." She pressed at a button on the wall to the right of her as the door started to reclose.

The two Escarrabin spun Duat around so he was facing the lobby again for all to see. The six clerics were reasonably unmoved but the elders were looking on and talking amongst themselves.

Duat surveyed as much as he could see from under his hood, looking at the pillars and architecture of the lobby and the supposed *'art'* that graced their walls. He could see that other guards had appeared having obviously heard of his presence in the grand lobby. He looked upwards to the first floor balcony to see two other security guards and one solitary cleric were watching over him. The saliva ran down his chin to the floor and his breathing was heavy; the noise of it must have bothered them as his head was forced back down again from one of the guards behind him.

The sound of the door reopening echoed throughout the lobby and he was spun back around and led into the security chamber of Raysmau. He looked up to meet the gaze of the security guard who had let them through and a very uncomfortable expression had appeared across her face as she looked directly at him. His head was pushed back down again to see the very worn sandals he was made to wear and his filthy, long and chipped toe nails. Being pushed and dragged at the same time, he could see the very neat and clean floor tiling he was being escorted over; his head was brought upright upon hearing the doorway to Raysmau's office being opened as the heavy gate swung back across the floor behind him.

It wasn't to be the first time he had looked on at Raysmau sitting behind her desk. She had very pale skin and was still dressed in her formal robes. He had been told that the Keeper had been here at the manor house earlier today.

He was led towards her desk and his hood was pulled down again so she could look directly at him.

Because she had seen him before, his appearance didn't surprise or shock her. He knew that the way he looked made others uncomfortable; that is the ones who are not used to seeing him and other watchers in their natural state. The head of security had knowledge and experience of such matters and some intellect too, much to his amusement.

He looked at her jet black hair that was tied up neatly and secured by a leather band giving the appearance of a long tail emerging from the back of her head. The lower half of her face and neck was covered with a dark mask that had been moulded to her face as was the custom for the head of security for the Order, no doubt in a futile effort to display the colours of the light and of the dark against the paleness of her skin.

He acknowledged her by turning up the left side of his mouth slightly, awaiting the words of wisdom that she no doubt was going to offer him this time.
She raised her hands behind her neck and unclipped the moulding that freed the skin around the lower part of her face.
Raysmau broke her stare from him to look at the security guards as the mask fell onto the desk.
"Well?"
"This watcher Ma'am was found to be wandering in the gardens again, nowhere near where he was supposed to be, towards the front of the house around the great statue of Salma."

"I see." She was expressionless and returned her gaze to the watcher.
The sound of a snort from the nasal passages of Duat disrupted the silence provoking her into speech as she watched beads of dribble fall to her clean floor. "Watcher, you've been in my chambers before and yet you are brought to me again. How are you to learn if you are not punished?" She leaned back in her huge heavily carved wooden chair resting her right elbow on an arm rest and moving her thumb and fingers around each other as she spoke. "Your duties here are maintaining the garden around the lake, not towards the front of the

house! Why is it I'm told that for the second time you have been found in this area, an area that is out of bounds to you?"

The watcher stared and said nothing by way of response.
"I'm addressing you, the one who calls himself Duat."
Maintaining eye contact he sneered in his deep voice "You cannot order me around like a dog or like these imbeciles that try to chain me." He nodded to his left and right ensuring that the security guards knew what he thought of them.

Alian smiled whilst Gamila scoffed upon hearing this.

"No? You think differently of yourselves?" he said taking it in turns to look at both of them. His deep voice was only broken up by the sound of saliva moving in the gaps of his teeth. "You are valueless, worthless and of no purpose, you just serve her" he was now nodding in the direction of Raysmau "and that Reeve upstairs!" He returned his gaze to the centre to study Raysmau's reaction.

Raysmau was unmoved having been on the end of Duat vocalising his thoughts once before; she was still rolling the thumb and index fingers of her right hand back and forth listening but not really paying attention.

"I am all too aware of the vileness of your mouth watcher. What concerns me is that many watchers have stood here in this room over the years but you are the most disruptive and lack the most discipline. Today's excursion in the gardens will require punishment and the punishment you receive will teach you discipline and order. You have not been here very long and for your sake I hope that you are a fast learner and you will fall into line. Do I make myself clear?"

Duat was unmoved expecting such a reaction and it didn't really make any difference anyway.

She leant forward from her chair maintaining her stare directly at him and there was calmness in her tone. "Let me be clear with you watcher, if it were my decision you would all be banished for eternity. You talk of purpose and yet you have none yourself. You are the remnants of a bloodline that was crossed with vileness and evil a very long time ago; I'm amazed you still survive, let alone why."

"Our numbers are much more than you realise slave of the Reeve, the Order will learn this in time and very much to your personal cost." The gaps appeared in his teeth again in what resembled something of a smile as the familiar hiss of the watchers emitted from his mouth.

Raysmau looked at both of her security team and started sniggering with laughter. Duat glanced to both sides of him and could see Raysmau's security guards were also sniggering along with her.

"You of course refer to the so called prophecy; about the end of our time and the onset of the darkness of yours, so that you and your 'kind' will rise from the dark places and your ugliness can walk across the dying plains of the world and call it your dominium."

"That is not the name we call it."

Their laughs were silenced as the heavy and broken noise of the watcher breathing could be heard again.
Raysmau slumped back into her seat and resumed the circular motion of her thumb and index fingers.
"It disgusts me to even set my eyes upon you, the paleness and thinness of your skin, that oversized vein that runs to your eye is full of nothing but poison."

Gathering her thoughts her tone had become much calmer. "Fortunately there are always cures for poisons and you are no different from the others and it is **you** that will learn in time."

There was anger in her eyes now. "Take him below!" She gave the instruction at a volume that probably would have echoed around the grand lobby outside of her doors.

Alian and Gamila immediately grabbed him by his cloak and handcuffs. "Not all poisons have cures slave, the futileness of your ticking clocks is nothing compared to when the last grain of sand falls." He spat towards Raysmau as he was spun around and they led him towards the door.

"Oh watcher" she said and immediately the security guards stopped moving and turned him back around again to face her.

"You know it does occur to me that we have not been in the below for quite some time, maybe it is time that I ordered my team to search those caverns that you dwell in."

She stood up and walked around to the front of the desk and stood just in front of Duat her huge frame bearing down on him, "I personally have not taken the lift down for quite some time."

Duat considered re-taunting her further but thought better of it, the last thing that he needed was her below ground right now.

"Nothing further to add?" She brought her face toward his; saliva was running down his chin as he snarled at her.

"You are a relic of the past and relics remain buried and consigned to history. If you are brought before me again your punishment will be severe and life below will become difficult for you as well as the others!" She stepped back from him and sat on the edge of her desk.

She nodded at Alian and Gamila to take him away and they escorted him out of her office. Duat turned his head to look at her one more time as she sat motionless on the edge of desk before his hood was pulled back up and he was dragged back into the main lobby ready to go to the lift that only goes down.

Staring at her friend for any positive signs of change, she ran her hand down Missy's belly for probably the hundredth time today. "I don't know what to do to fix you Missy?" She looked helpless as the twitches and spasms of her cat continued.

She looked at the cushion she had made of the innocent cat minding its own business that Missy was sprawled out upon. In two minds or even three as to what to do she remembered that she had 44 cards to prepare. Slumping back into the sofa remembering her failure to even get a simple thing like choosing an appropriate card right, she had visions of the other Mildred's ham and cheese sandwiches and even worse the other Mildred's cat treats and cup cakes. Letting out a sigh her hands were on her knees and she leant forward and looked down to see her wrinkled stockings and scuffed brown shoes. With the exception of the clock ticking from the kitchen nothing else could be heard as she looked around her front room and all of its old furniture and the bits of paper everywhere that she hoarded. I used to wear makeup she thought and briefly pondered on her life before this...this...she shook her head slightly and flexed her toes and shook her shoes off and got to her feet to go to the kitchen.

She went to the fridge and looked inside at the three plates of stacked fish paste sandwiches and tugged at the cellophane of one of them. Taking out a solitary white bread sandwich that was curling at the sides she brought it to her mouth and took a small bite. Looking towards the ceiling she closed her eyes and then looked back down at the sandwich with a bite in it. "It tastes like fish paste" and threw the remainder on the side. Looking into the fridge again and taking out a brown sandwich this time, she hoped this one would taste better. She had a couple of chews of it and came to the same conclusion as the previous sandwich and threw the remainder of that one on the side as well. Kicking the fridge door closed she had forgotten she had taken her shoes off and feeling instant pain she hopped around the kitchen holding her foot "Ouch!!" she yelled in anguish and frustration. Wincing in pain she threw herself down on one of only two chairs next to the kitchen table.

Red faced and biting her lips deep in thought as her toes throbbed, she could see the cards on the side and the solitary black marker pen next to them.

Closing her eyes and letting out a deep sigh her plan initially was to write a personal message inside a card for each of the other members of the club, that plan was now on hiatus. Now she would be crossing a line through the words 'happy birthday' and just printing 'from Mildred with best wishes'. She shook her head knowing they were going to look terrible, really terrible. She didn't even know the names of the other members, it was meant to be a way of introducing herself. She knew that she would have to write 'from Rocke Road' after her name as there were so many other Mildreds.

She looked back to the ceiling again pondering....Why are there so many Mildreds, Jessicas and Daphnes? There weren't any Emmas, Joannes or Sharons anywhere in sight, that's highly odd isn't it? She lowered her head with a frown as she questioned herself on this simple thing that until now she had never really considered.

Outstretching her right leg to flex the toes of her throbbing foot she winced and she had had enough, it will just have to be fish paste sandwiches and that's that! She got up and went over to the side and grabbed the cards and placed her less painful foot on the pedal of the bin and held them over it. As the lid opened she saw the picture on the front of the card. The pedal was still pushed to the floor as she glanced over at Missy and could see the side of her body rising up and down her heart beating ten to the dozen. Looking back at the card she felt a wave of guilt that she could throw away such a beautiful thing. She took her foot off of the pedal and the lid reclosed and picked up the black felt marker pen and sat back down. It was an unceremonious opening of the first card as she threw the cellophane over her shoulder onto the kitchen floor. Opening the card up and seeing 'Happy Birthday' as clear as day she crossed it out with the pen and started to write in it. She would do that another 43 times before bed time and it would be quite a pile of discarded cellophane before she finished.

Chapter Seventeen:

THE STONE STAIRS OF THE BELOW

THURSDAY EARLY EVENING

The old lift juddered to a halt and the steel grill was pulled across as he felt an encouraging push into the familiar surroundings of the first floor of the below.

"Kneel down Duat." He could hear the two Escarrabin stepping out of the lift behind him. He obliged hearing the sound of uniform moving behind him and feeling the presence of one of them directly over him removing his handcuffs.

He heard them both step away from him feeling that his arms were now free. With his left hand he pulled his hood back down; still kneeling on the floor he turned to face both of them.

Bringing himself upright he brought his right hand up to his face and wiped the saliva from his mouth and chin and staring directly at them, shook it off to the floor.

He watched Gamila pull the grill back into place and the lift automatically went back up to the grand walkway of Loxley.

"Look at you both" he spat "would you not rather take the lift back up?"
"The lifts only go down watcher" Gamila said walking back towards him "you

know that."

"Clearly they do not." Duat spoke as he rotated his shoulders and flexed his fingers.

"The stone stairs are there as a reminder to you, your kind and the others that dwell down here, that you need to walk to the above, you have to earn your right to walk on the outside."

"And now it is you that will need to walk to get back to what you refer as 'the outside'."

He laughed at their ridiculous practises and spat some saliva to the floor.

Both of the Escarrabin looked at each other almost with some concession to this observation.

"Everyone below, whether it is us or your kind, have to ascend by way of the worn stairs, it is the way things are done." Alian flipped a succinct smile as she informed the disinterested watcher.

"Pathetic" Duat spat whilst breaking out a little smile of amusement as his breathing became more audible.

"I'm so glad that we are of some form of entertainment for you watcher and as Madam Raysmau has stated, punishment will be coming to you!"

"We will see" he smiled.

Alian walked forward to him. "You do not unnerve us Duat."

"Are you sure of that?" Duat gave a broad smile uncaring of the saliva running down his chin and the echoing hiss of his deep voice.

Alian stepped back a couple of paces upon hearing noises coming from the darkness behind him.

The sounds of groans and the call of the watchers that was familiar to them, echoed around the chamber. The random candles that had been lit earlier in the day offered little vision. Alian could see silhouettes in the dark moving towards them as the candles flames started to flicker.

The noise became more intense as the shadows moved closer. Alian and Gamila both looked at each other as the shadows multiplied sensing volatility in the atmosphere.

The echoing high pitched calls from the darkness grew louder and they were certain they were outnumbered by some margin.

"Alian!"

"I know, I know!"

They both reached behind them. It had been many years since a Scatterblade had been drawn within the grounds; they were carried mainly for ceremonial purposes now.

"Go back to where you came." Alian shouted as a warning as she swallowed and raised her Scatterblade seeing that three hooded figures had now appeared behind Duat. There were certainly more behind them, potentially many more as the volume of noise increased.

As the three came closer now clearly seen to the Escarrabin within the dim light they pulled their hoods down one by one. Alian could see the gaping holes of their noses and the warm mist emitting from them as their breath met the cold of the below. Her eyes were flitting between the three of them staring directly at the pulsing vein that led to their singular eye. It was then that the other figures in the shadows came forward with their volume amplified. There was a sudden loud roar from deep in the below followed by multiple bangs, the sound of which made two of the watchers turn around to look and the hairs stood up on the backs of the neck of both of the security officers of the Escarrabin. Duat however never moved or flinched, only his breathing could be heard.

He stood up and looked at both of them. "You are unnerved slaves, I can see it." Taking a step towards them his pulsing eye looked directly upon them as the loud roar came up again from the depths and echoed all around them.

Alian pointed the Scatterblade at him, her hand starting to shake uncontrollably as the adrenalin raced through her.

"That will not help you, you cannot win, we are many." He removed his gloves and let them fall to the floor and held up the turquoise pulsing palm of his right hand and took a step forward.

Alian jumped feeling the hand of Gamila on her shoulder.

"We should go" and dragged at Alian's uniform pulling her towards the worn stone staircase.

Duat lowered his palm with a menacing smile as he watched them move quickly up the stairs in retreat to the upper doors.

Gamila reached the top of the stone steps first and ripped her glove off and pushed her palm as hard as she could onto the scanner. Watching the scanner move up and down her palm she glanced behind and was relieved to see that they hadn't been followed. "Come on, come on" she yelled at the security scanner.

The locks of the door gave way and it started to open and they practically fell through the doorway into the grand walkway the other side. Moving around to the other side of the door as quickly as they could they pushed back on the door trying to speed up the automatic mechanism that would seal it shut again.

Gamila looked down the grand walkway and could see an elder staring at them both quizzically as they were forcing the door closed. Two clerics who were sat at a desk just off the walkway also looked on.
"Well don't just sit there, help us!" Alian screamed.
Both of the clerics got to their feet and ran to the door and started pushing with them.

Upon hearing the door seal and the symbol to the right of the door turn green all four of them let go.

Gamila nodded towards the clerics as they made their way back to their seats before she fell to the ground breathing heavily. "You okay?" she said looking at Alian who was equally out of breath and was now crouched down drawing heavy breaths, alarm written across her face.
"I'm not sure; what just happened down there was horrible?"
Gamila was nodding, "I've never experienced anything like that, never seen them be confrontational. Something is going on, they are usually so quiet."

They both looked over at the elder that had been watching them, her eyes still fixed firmly upon them with some alarm.

"We had better report this to Raysmau" Alian said.
"You drew your blade, which will be seen as a weakness and that you showed fear."
"Maybe we shouldn't mention that but I'll be honest Gamila I was scared."

They both sat there gathering their breath realising they were creating a lot of attention.

Gamila spoke as quietly as she could. "What do you think made that noise from below; I've never heard that before or anything like it?"

"I really have no idea, I hope that is the last we hear of it. It came from somewhere very deep; somewhere none of us have been in a very long time, if ever."

"BERNARD.........BERNARD!!" the tone of voice was short as usual as Mr Meacher stood at his gate in Darwin Road. Hands on hips he looked around in embarrassment seeing if anyone was watching this nightly display he was told to do.

There was no sign of his cat; in fact there were little signs of anything going on. He hadn't recalled the road being this quiet in some time. Looking up inhaling the clean air it was a beautiful evening with a completely clear blue sky. It would mean there would be a little bit of a chill later he considered knowing that he needed to keep the house warm as his wife was so unwell.

The only distraction was coming from somewhere near the top of the huge horse chestnut tree further down the road. He could see branches moving and the leaves on the end of them pinging up and down. No doubt it was the cat that belonged to the woman who lived on Rocke Road yet again, the one who always dressed way older than her years. Only a matter of time before Mr Watkins would be showing up again on cat rescue; he shook his head and put his hands in his pockets and returned back into his house...cat-less.

"Ignoring him again are you?" Sikari asked looking directly at Said.
"I am" Said replied in his usual deeply spoken tone.
Sikari smiled.
"I'll go when I am ready and I'm never ready when I am addressed as Bernard."

They were perched on one of the fences of the school. It was summer holidays and, with no children around, they were taking advantage of the peace and quiet as even at this hour there were usually staff and groundskeepers still milling about during term time.

They noticed on the other side of the road that Sam the squirrel had popped up having just descended from one of the other trees at a great rate of knots and leapt on top of a garden wall eyeing up the bird table with nuts on it.

"Look at him Said, he's quite the hunter."
"He's a damn lunatic" he grunted as they watched on.

They both sat in silence watching the squirrel twitching its fluffy tail weighing up everything around him. He quickly jumped down into the garden out of sight of Sikari and Said before they saw him reappearing clawing his way up the bird table before jumping on top of the cluster of nuts sending them everywhere. He sat there holding one between his paws gnawing away before grabbing another couple and then hurtling himself down the post of the bird table and then back up to the top of the wall before he disappeared up the tree again.

"He really is quite the little thief" Sikari continued.
Said, as usual with little to say, just nodded in acknowledgement.

"You two!!" "Oi, you two" the voice had come from above and both of them peered up along the road in front of them. "Look at me!"
"Well I never" Sikari spoke with some surprise.
"So it would appear that scruff of a cat can climb after all." Said spoke whilst looking up in some amazement seeing Scamper at the top of Stan.

She was waving at them and had an uncontrollable grin of stupidity across her face.
Sikari lifted a paw to wave back. "What are you doing?" Said said, "Don't encourage her."
Sikari dropped his paw back down.

"Nahla won't be happy, she always wanted to climb to the top of Stan first" Said mumbled, still looking up with some amazement that the great Stan had been conquered by the daftest cat he had ever met.
"Have you seen Nahla today Said?"
"No" he spoke watching the antics up above.
"That's very odd, usually would have seen her by now."
Said broke his gaze from the tree upon hearing this. "I'm sure it's nothing, the woman she stays with makes a fuss of her."

"Hey guys, hey guys." They both looked up above again. "Er guys, I think I'm stuck, yep, I really think I am."

Said shook his head and jumped down off the fence and wandered off, with Sikari not far behind him.

"Guys……….guys." The branches were twitching and the leaves were shaking excessively as she gulped. Scamper with no owner to call the fire brigade for her would have to figure this one out for herself; it would probably be a very long night.

Looking at her television screen Bang Goes Your Money had long since passed as the cards had taken her so long to write.

Mildred glanced over her shoulder from her couch and could see 44 neatly stacked birthday cards and breathed out a sigh. The 44 bits of screwed up cellophane all over the kitchen floor was just a minor detail and could wait.

Stretching out her right hand like she had some form of writer's cramp she looked at Missy to her side. There had been no change and she was clearly still in some discomfort. Glancing over to her sideboard she was staring at the rear end of her telephone considering if she should call Fennaway's again or maybe even the other vet that Mr. Franks had mentioned earlier on.

Placing her hand on Missy's tummy she felt something was seriously wrong and she sat there worrying. Fennaway's assertion that it was probably just a bug was doing very little to reassure her.

Hearing the clock ticking she leaned forward from her sofa to look over to the kitchen and could see that it was approaching 9 o'clock and getting on for her bed time. But how on ever could I possibly sleep with my friend in pain she thought and watched her hand rising up and down on her cat's belly.

"It's no good, I've got to call her Missy, something needs to be done!" She got to her feet, walked to her sideboard and snatched at the phone. Finding the number again she redialled having no idea if the phone would be answered at this time of the evening. She only had a landline office telephone number for her and not her personal mobile that she had seen her carrying earlier on in the day.

She could hear Fennaway's phone ringing at the other end and after only two rings it was hastily answered without the annoying answering service this time.

"Hello Mildred" came the instant response to the phone being picked up at the other end.
"Dr Fennaway, it's Mildred from...how did you know it was me?"

Kamilah banged the phone against her temple in disgust of her error. "Well Mildred, it's only because we spoke earlier, so I guessed it may be you dear." She smiled to herself pleased with her response.
"But didn't you say that you had another client to see after me?"
There was a muted pause.
"Well, er, yes I did but that turned out to be a false alarm, it can happen around these sorts of times if you understand me?"
"No, not really, what sort of times are those?"
Kamilah screwed up her face again "I mean the time of the year...that sort of thing dear."
"Oh right, well okay."
"Anyway, how can I help you?"
"Well thank you for taking my call at this hour, I didn't think you would still be in the office right now."
"Well, as I say, at these times I need to be on-hand to help my very special clients."
"Thank you Kamilah" although Mildred had no idea why she would be referred to as a 'special client'.
"You are most welcome dear. Now how can I be of assistance, is Missy still unwell?"
"Yes, she really is and does not seem to be improving, what can you suggest please?"
"Well the most important thing is to keep her warm and give her lots of love."

There was another period of silence as Mildred shook her head and rolled her eyes.

"Is that it, is that all you can suggest? I don't think Missy hugs are going to fix

her Doctor Fennaway!"
"You say that Mildred but hugs are good, it's been medically proven."
"Really...by whom may I ask?"
"Look I sense your concern but these bugs do pass their way through in time, they always do, you will see."
"Well I am truly sorry to say this but I'm upset and concerned, I think I need another opinion."
"Well whatever do you mean dear?"
"I heard of another vet in this area, I think I will call them."

"NO, no, no, do not do that Mildred I implore you!" Kamilah's voice had become stern and sounded full of concern, so much so that Mildred pulled the phone away from her ear in some shock at the outburst.
"Well why on ever not, it's my cat, I can do as I choose."
"It's not..." Kamilah regained her thoughts "It's just that vets, us vets, have a code and we do not exchange clients. It's an unwritten rule that's all I mean nothing further. Would you like for me to speak with her?"

"The other vet, I do not know if it's a her; I've not called them before?"
"No your cat dear, would you like for me to speak to your cat?"
Mildred's eyes widened to the point of popping and her mouth fell open upon hearing this. She pulled the phone away from her ear again, staring at the cat like shaped object that she was speaking to the certifiable vet on.

She could hear muffled words coming from the cat's head of her phone "Mildred...Mildred are you still there?"
Placing the receiver back to her ear still in stark amazement. "Yes, incredibly Miss Fennaway I am still here." She had removed the Dr. tag from addressing her as clearly the vet needed a different type of doctor all together.
"Let's just try?"
"Just try what Miss Fennaway?"
"Please put the phone to the cat's ear please."

Mildred, on what was a very unfunny day thus far, found herself giggling slightly in some amusement. "Really?"
"Yes really Mildred."
"Okay, you know what, I think I will" and with that she placed the phone over the right ear of Missy. She sat there thinking 'if anyone could see me now'

shaking her head at the absurdity of the situation.

"Have you started yet I can't hear anything?" her words were broken with laughter.

With eyes focused on Missy she could hear faint noises coming from the phone that were spoken words of some kind. Her laughter and smile quickly drained from her face along with any colour as she watched Missy's legs stretching out together at the same time. She could see her right eye open slightly before quickly reclosing. Missy's legs remained outstretched and Mildred could still hear sounds emitting from the phone before they abruptly stopped and Missy's legs relaxed and she brought them back into her body.

"Mildred...Mildred are you there?" The muffled sounds of the vet could be heard from the other end of the phone.
"Yes Dr. I am still here, what on earth was that?"
"She will be fine very soon, I'm sure of that."
"But what exactly just happened, I saw Missy open an eye?"
"I just shine a little when it comes to cats dear."
"Shine, what on earth…"
"Have you ever read about people who can talk to horses Mildred. Did you ever see the programme of a lady who said she could speak with dogs? Well, it's no different here, I have a way with cats, that's all."
"But they're bloody lunatics!"
"Not so Mildred, not so at all."
Mildred's mouth remained agape, positive that the vet on the other end of the phone was smiling as she had made this absurd announcement.
"Anyway, I must go dear, please do not worry. The cat will be fine come morning I'm quite sure of that, it's as I said, just a bug."
"Well, I…"
"Must go, goodbye for now dear."

Mildred heard the phone go down at the other end but she still clutched at it her end hoping for further words from the doctor but nothing was forthcoming. The phone fell between her legs as she looked at Missy; her cat's heart was still racing and she was clearly still in some discomfort.
As she stared at her old furniture again confused, with the exception of the ticking from the clock in the kitchen the house was silent. You could have heard

a pin drop.

The cat doctor who shined was most unnerving.

The curator sat at her desk looking at the swinging pendulum of her clock. It was just gone 9pm and she looked like she had the weight of the world on her shoulders. She had been locked deep in worry ever since the Keeper had left earlier on.

Facing a probable investigation about her conversations with Lady Ebonee and her actions thereafter she had wrestled with whether to contact the member of the Grand Council or not. Now that the Reeve knew about these things she daren't risk trying anything unless she had to. This new Reeve and her embracing of technical *'things'* probably meant that she would listen in on her phone calls from now on. She would have to be careful.

Collectively Lady Tempest's passing, Nahla's pain and Lady Ebonee's predictions were becoming quite unsettling. In fact she would describe it as much worse than that and she could feel stress pains in her tummy as she moved with some discomfort.

Locked deep in thought whilst biting at her nails, she was shaken out of it with a start by her phone ringing. Shaking her head and glancing back at the clock she wondered who on earth it could be at this hour.

"Yes what is it?" she answered the phone with some ill-patience and rudeness. "Nubia it's Kamilah."
She leant on her desk pressing her phone as tightly to her ear as she could, hanging on every word. "Nahla has got worse, much worse. I've communicated with her and it may well be the sign, the sign of the predicted Nubia."

The phone fell to her desk from Nubia's clammy palms. The time of the gathering was approaching. She looked nervously at her clock again and it told her what she already knew; it was three hours before midnight and counting.

Chapter Eighteen:

INDEBTED TO RATS

LATE THURSDAY NIGHT

A watched clock never tells the time or it was something like that Nubia mused of the old saying she had heard somewhere a long time ago.

Nevertheless she was watching, watching intently as the minute hand of the ancient clock in her office was now resting at two minutes to midnight.

Her shoes were off and her legs tucked in firmly under her chair as she sat and waited. She was gnawing at her fingers again when she noticed how worn down her fingernails were and how sore they looked at their ends. Snatching them away from her face she was recalling in her own mind some of her interpretations of the prophecy.

The words spoke of three signs and only three that bore the hallmarks of the beginning of change and a change of order. The gates of those who thrived in darkness would take their place at the seats of power eradicating the world of men. In doing so they, from the dark places, would consume the light, plunging the world into a place of chaotic ruin and evil and a new level of dark rule.

The first sign would signify illness and great pain of one of their own and it would show itself 24-48 hours before the meeting of the Grand Council, the

Council that had been bound by secrecy for thousands of years to ensure the prophecy never came to pass.

She scratched her head and her teeth were chomping together.

She recalled that throughout history over the last 700 years or so only on two occasions had all three prophesied events materialised. Those events were witnessed not just by the Order but by those on the outside, those who were without knowledge. On both occasions they had even recounted events in their historic literature, albeit not knowing the significance of what it really meant. She struggled to raise the briefest of smiles in recollection, knowing full well that those who led their life on the outside of this place, this house and this great Order, had been protected from darkness for as long as time had been recorded.

Her face was a picture of anguish recalling that on one occasion they of the dark places were very nearly successful in achieving their goal. The cats of the Order were key in maintaining not just the survival of the Order itself but the equilibrium that exists throughout human existence right up to the present day. Those outside of the council and the Order the world over were still (in the main) oblivious to how close they nearly came to perishing. They owe us an enormous debt of gratitude and the cats had prevailed.

She was not sure that what was happening to Nahla was potentially the first sign. The Keeper claiming that it may just be timing did little to ease her as the words had been spoken with concern. Nerves were always tested at the times of the gatherings not just at the national headquarters of the United Kingdom but other headquarters the world over.

The showing of the second sign would cause much concern although the second requires the third if the prophecy were to be complete. Midnight is the time of the showing of the second sign. The timing is not a coincidence as on this day gatherings would be joining in unison all over the world in a celebration of tradition and their upholding of order and balance. The prophecy foretells of a second sign or event showing within the same time zone as the first so therefore midnight had to be the time here if Nahla was carrying the prophesised pain. She gripped her desk with both hands watching the clock hands with every passing second. She never blinked as she saw the minute hand reaching the 12 o'clock position. She started to wince and listened.

Tick...

She froze as the clock hit the midnight hour and turned her head to the right slightly pushing her ear forward to listen below. Clocks all over the house and especially from the corridors below could be heard chiming the midnight hour.

She was breathing much harder than she realised and slowly let her hands fall away from the desk. Minus shoes she got to her feet hearing the chimes below and walked over to her window to look outside. The night sky was perfectly clear and the flickering of stars could easily be seen wherever she looked. Standing on her couch and craning her neck to the left and right there was nothing out of the ordinary to be seen. She walked quickly back to the clock and studied it. The hands were moving as it approached a couple of minutes past 12 o'clock and the clocks below were now silent but for the ticking with movement.

Relaxing her body and taking a deep breath she put a hand against the wall and bowed her head in relief. She went back to her desk and practically collapsed in her seat and fell forward to lean on both elbows clawing at her hair with both hands.

Letting out the hugest sigh of relief and glancing once more at the moving clock she remembered the bottle of Scotch that she had tucked in her desk. Reserved for special occasions this was almost certainly one of those. A toast was probably not in order but a good measure was.

Taking out a tumbler from her desk along with the half empty bottle she poured herself a large measure and let go of the cap that rolled its way off the desk onto the floor.

Looking at the glass fondly she sat back and shook her head; she was mightily relieved but also tired from worry. Nahla was not the first sign then after all thankfully. She sat back in her chair and looked up at the old ceiling; she fell asleep with calm almost instantly.

A few hours had passed as Duat sat alone with his thoughts. Events of earlier were still on his mind contemplating the fear he had witnessed in the

Escarrabins faces. Their reaction to withdraw and reliance on their Scatterblade weapons amused him greatly. Their actions were not unexpected; they had not been tested in a very long time.

The 'mighty security of the Escarrabin' he mused shaking his head at their uselessness. They were of little threat to him and his strength was ever evolving. For the watchers it was time they took a stand. Their incarceration here in this place was out of fear, he knew and they knew that others roamed on the outside waiting for the one to unite them. Their roaming was often without purpose, their ambitions quelled by the Order, they needed unison.

Movements in what they call *'the below'* were silent now. In the dark hours of early morning the sounds would be active again, the tunnelling, the anger of being held against their will and their lack of freedom to roam. The one that lay further down was becoming more unstable, it was angry and needed passage.

He could hear the slight sound of scurrying on the dirty stone floor outside the entrance to his chamber and beckoned the rat over to him.

Picking it up Duat looked closely into its dark eyes. "So strong you are survivors of old, ruthless as well as cunning, we are indebted to you." He pulled his hood down and lifted the rat to his face. Watching its nose twitch he could see its front teeth were dirty and worn, its tail had wrapped around his left hand.

"I have something for you my friend." He clenched his right hand and then reopened it and he stared at his turquoise palm alive with movement. He brought the rat towards his palm and held the rat directly beneath it. A drop of his blood started to roll down his hand; he placed it millimetres from the rat's head and watched it drop into the rat's eye. "You may have your time again my friend as we will have ours; I know you will never be far from us." He put the rat down gently on the floor. "Now go."

He watched the rat go out of his chamber and looked upwards towards the stone ceiling.

"It must be near." He walked towards the wall of his cell and placed his right hand flat against the stone. Closing his eye he listened to the above, he could hear light pacing movements coming down the walls into his palm, he concentrated further.

"Any time now...any time now." He waited patiently knowing that the time was imminent. His mouth opened in anticipation as the saliva fell between his misshaped and broken teeth.

The sound of dozens of chimes travelled down the wall all at once as the clocks above talked to each other from all over the house. His eye was now open wide and he took a couple of steps back from the wall knowing that overhead the clocks were chiming the hour of midnight. He walked over to his ancient set of weighing scales that a long time ago may have passed judgement rather than the weighing of precious stones. He looked at the large hourglass to the side of it and picked it up.

Smiling as he looked at the bottom vial full of sand he walked over to the only table that was in his room.

Crouching down so he was now level with the table he inhaled deeply and turned it over and watched.

The first grain of sand had fallen.

Nubia woke with a start, the sound of ringing having abruptly woken her. Putting a hand up to her face as she let her head come back down, her neck was incredibly stiff. She opened and closed her mouth a couple of times and grimaced of the dryness of her mouth.

Blinking a couple of times she looked at the undrunk glass of whisky on her desk realising that she must have fallen asleep. Adjusting her vision to look at the clock face she could see that it was 1.09 am and wondered who on earth could be ringing at this hour.

In a tired and croaky voice she said "yes" as she answered the phone still opening and closing her mouth.
"Nubia, is that you?" She recognised the broad Scottish accent instantly.
She coughed a couple of times to clear her throat. "Lady Ebonee?"

"Yes, tell me are your clocks ticking, have there been any signs?"
Still blinking her eyes half asleep Nubia looked at the clock again. "Yes," she coughed, "yes the clocks are fine."
"I bet our beloved Nahla is still unwell though isn't she?"
"Er, well yes, the last I heard but that was..."
"It is as I thought! Many have struggled to interpret the great foretelling..."
"Lady Ebonee, I really do not think we should have this call right now. The Keeper knows that I have been talking to you" she interrupted.
"Yes I know, these things get back to me and it's high time they started to listen to me. I get mocked you know."

Nubia let out a deep sigh. "Lady Ebonee I may be subject to an investigation and this phone call may not be private if you know what I mean?"
"How so? Don't worry about that, anyway, it is as I foretold, your clocks are fine."
"If you knew the clocks would be okay and there is no second sign why did you ask for me to keep a watch over Mildred?"
"Well your clocks are not fine deary far from it; they haven't reached their destination yet."
Nubia had a vacant expression on her face with the phone pressed to her ear whilst looking at her clock.

"Respectfully Lady Ebonee, whatever do you mean?"
"Well it's not the last minute of the last hour yet is it?"
She shook her head "I'm sorry, what was that?"
"The last hour, THAT is the foretelling, not the first"
"Lady Ebonee, I..."
"Please ensure that new Reeve of yours is prepared, this will be a big test for her. Must go, bye deary."

Nubia heard the phone click at the other end and she let her phone fall out of her hand onto the desk.

With a pained expression across her face and her tummy jangling their nervous pains she was locked deep in worry again.

Nubia looked across her desk; the tumbler of Scotch was just where she needed it.

Chapter Nineteen:

THE DRAWING OF
THE SCATTERBLADE

FRIDAY 7AM

Despite the warm air of the August morning filtering its way through the open window Mildred was lying in bed with her sheets pulled up all the way to her neck.

She hadn't slept well with so much on her mind, trying to sleep was almost pointless. She was worried about Missy and very concerned that her symptoms had not improved. Deciding to give up on trying for any more sleep she sat up and looked at the end of her bed. Missy was still there unmoved from where she laid her down last night. Pulling her knees up to her chest in contemplation she always loved it when Missy slept at the end of the bed as rare as it was. But this morning was not one of those occasions and Mildred felt great discomfort as her cat lay in pain. Blankets were all around her and her little head was propped upon the cat cushion that she had made.

Feeling waves of guilt that she was even considering going to the gathering she was torn as to what to do for the best as she could not leave Missy like this all alone. If she started feeling better then of course that would be fine but looking at her now that didn't look to be any time soon.

She was still perplexed and somewhat perturbed by the very odd *'I just shine a bit'* vet who tried to have a conversation with her cat and much to her bemusement on the face of it, may well have done just exactly that.

Rocking the bed a little "Missy…………..Missy!" but her cat just lay there, her tummy rising up and down. She flapped her arms at a loss. "Well I guess that I do not shine at all then eh Missy!"

Rubbing her chin she realised that she had a bad taste in her throat and opened her mouth and reclosed it a couple of times and got up to go to the bathroom to clean her teeth. Looking in the mirror she blinked a few times and could see the bags under her eyes and the dark discolouration of her skin that surrounded them from her tiredness. She started to wash water over her face looking at the fresh lines that seem to have appeared and stared at how unkempt her hair was these days.

Her face was pale and looked a picture of sadness as she tried to break a smile and all that offered were fresh wrinkles around her mouth. A sad face made her look younger she contemplated, as the water drops ran off her into the sink below.

She hadn't worn makeup in a very long time and she looked to the left and right of her face assessing the battle damage of her age and could see a few grey hairs appearing around her hair line.

She opened the door of the tallboy directly to her right that revealed nothing but sparseness inside. All that remained from days past was an unused flannel, medication that she had not taken in some time, one old pink lipstick and a near empty and very out of date pot of foundation.

She ran a hand through her hair that got caught in some of the knots and let out a sigh. Middle aged, old furniture, no makeup and a sick cat, that's my life, how on earth did it get to this?

She walked back into her bedroom with hands on hips and stared at Missy. She had a duty to her only friend in the world.

That talking cat woman had better have some answers.

Outside of her chambers Raysmau could hear her gate being moved across the stone floor as she got to her feet and left her office.

"Good morning Ma'am."
She nodded at her security guard as the main door opened to let her out.

There was a lot more activity in the grand lobby area this morning, more so for quite some time. Gathering days were always testing for her security team and she would need to spend some time with the Reeve later talking through any last minute security updates.

Lady Safiya's arrival back at the manor house did not dictate for pomp and ceremony as she was here more often than not but Raysmau always made a point of greeting her. Dressed today in her usual uniform that bore the mark of the head of the Escarrabin, she stopped and bent down on one knee to brush over a very slight marking on one of her boots. She nodded at the clerics on the main reception desk to open the front doors.

The huge doors started to open and she could see Lady Safiya was nearly at the main entrance doors already. Behind her the chauffeur driven car was already moving away.

"Good morning my Lady" Raysmau nodded. She noticed that she had no bags with her.
"Hello Raysmau" she responded quite curtly out of respect for Raysmau but was clearly not in the mood for talking.
"Are you okay my Lady, you look troubled?"
"One of my level and age is always troubled Raysmau." She stopped walking and looked up at the head of security. "In fact, I do not recall a day when I was not troubled with something." She resumed walking and Raysmau stepped with her. "Tradition, everything is always about tradition, these gatherings sometimes are more trouble than they are worth. We should bring elders that are to be elevated here, give them their cats and be done with it. Watchers are out there Raysmau, these gatherings create attention." She stopped walking again. "Far too many chatterboxes Raysmau, you understand what I mean?"

Raysmau was unsure whether to smile or not so just offered a blank expression. "I'm not altogether sure what you are referring to Ma'am."
"No, of course you're not" she responded not unsurprised by Raysmau's usual diplomatic response.

"Rumours, rumours, rumours of prophesied events that have not come to pass, that is what I'm referring to, too much chatter!"
It did of course occur to Raysmau that Lady Safiya, a degree level 1 elder and head of Loxley Manor, was now doing a bit of gossiping herself.

"I see" Raysmau added with a hint of a smile for reassurance. "Well I can assure you that I'm not hearing these things Ma'am."
Lady Safiya looked up at her directly into her eyes. "Mmm, well I guess that's something then; could you ask a cleric to send some tea up for me please? Apparently my bags are being dropped around the back."

"I will see to it personally" Raysmau nodded and watched one of the most senior elders in the country head off to the stairs that would take her to her offices and living quarters.

Raysmau was just about to walk off when Lady Safiya turned to her. "I trust my cats are okay?"

"I'm sure they are quite fine my Lady, I've heard nothing to the contrary."
She grunted and turned around and kept walking.

It was always a pleasure greeting Lady Safiya, Raysmau thought with a twinge of amusement, as she nodded towards a cleric for attention.

The curator heard a knock at her outer door.

Stepping out of her private quarters into her office she could see that her door had already been opened and recognised the Reeve in her familiar pose leaning against her doorframe, stood with one leg crossed over the other.

"I suppose you are here to gloat?"

"Why would I do that Nubia? We should be happy that there has been no second sign." She took a few paces forward inviting herself in.

Nubia looked her up and down. She was wearing one of those ghastly business type suits again and with the exception of the badge on her lapel, there was no other indication of her rank and title. Nubia grunted with disapproval.

"So I trust that your clock is fine, the ones downstairs seem to be in order?" Nubia sat at her desk deciding not to look up at her. "My clock is fine Reeve."

"Good, good."

Nubia could feel that the Reeve was looking around her office and probably looking at her as well.

"I'm assigning two of my Escarrabin earlier than scheduled to the local gathering, just as a precaution."

"I see but I have no idea why are you telling me this Reeve, you've made it clear that security is your domain?"

"I'm just informing you that I'm keeping a good eye on things, today of all days."

Nubia looked up upon hearing this, sensing that she knew something.

"Good, very glad to hear" was all that she could think of saying whilst looking at her wondering if she knew that Lady Ebonee had been in touch again.

"Anyway, I was just passing by; I'll carry on my rounds." She turned to go out of the door as she glanced back over her shoulder. "Glad that your clock is fine" she added and then disappeared out of view.

Nubia was staring at the now vacant but still very much open door. She got to her feet and walked over to it and gently pressed it closed. In the short time that she had been here never had the Reeve just been 'passing by' as her quarters were at the end of the corridor in any event; she was up to something, she was certain of it.

Alian had arisen from her bunk over two hours ago; it was still a few hours before her shift was due to start. There were three other bunks in her room and one was currently being used. She quietly slipped into civilian clothing so as not to disturb the sleeping member of the Escarrabin and made her way out of her room.

Stood in one of the corridors of the Escarrabin security block, she ran a hand through her hair and removed some old debris from her eyes with the other. Her night had been one of interrupted sleep.

Based towards the rear of the manor house, the security block could contain anything up to sixty members of the Escarrabin, although it was very rare that it would be full. They would travel regularly protecting various headquarters and members of the Order the world over.

Currently there were twenty-six Escarrabin based at Loxley Manor although Raysmau had informed that more were arriving later today; usual protocol on gathering days. She walked bare foot down the corridor stretching her arms above her head and yawned and turned into a corridor on the right. The door where Gamila stayed was already open.

Leaning her head through she was not surprised to see that Gamila was sitting on the end of her bunk. She nodded towards her to come outside as she could see that two others were sleeping in the room.

"So you didn't sleep either?" Gamila said looking at the reasonably tired appearance of Alian.
She shook her head.
"I think we need to report what we saw."
Alian nodded in agreement.

"That should include that you drew your Scatterblade Alian, you did threaten a watcher with it."
"I know. I've been trying to weigh it all up but irrespective Duat would probably blab it out with pride to Raysmau anyway when he is given his punishment. It would just be a matter of whether she believed him or not."
"Other watchers saw it though who could support his words, although their words are often full of lies."
They both raised their eyebrows with that statement and stood in

momentary silence.

"Okay, get dressed then and I'll meet you back here in 20 minutes and we'll go and see her" Alian said receiving a nod from Gamila.

Gamila had pondered all night on the previous day's events. "Alian, what was that?"
She turned to her. "What?"
"The noise, the noise and the banging from the below. What do you think it could possibly be?"

Alian shook her head and was biting at her lip. "I have no idea, but it can't be good, something very dark from an older time. I've heard rumours before but never really paid them any attention."
She turned around to walk off. "See you back here in 20."

Gamila leant against the doorframe and could feel her pulse had risen. Explaining what had happened to Raysmau was one thing; her ordering them back below to conduct a search and to establish what lay below, was another.

The watchers were bowed on both sides as Duat walked into the holding area on the first floor of the below.

He walked past all of them looking towards the stone stairs and the empty lift shaft.

Turning around to face them he pulled his hood down and held his right hand out directly in front of them. "Rise my friends." One by one they all looked up at him and the moving complexity of his right palm; he was not like them.

"This has been planned for a very long time." He walked forward to them. "For far too long you have been bound by chains. Our numbers are growing and when those on the outside of this place hear of me and my presence here we will unite." He looked to his left addressing them one by one. "The time of change has already started, the time and realm of the watchers is now." He looked to the right. "Those of the above are unaware of the powers I possess that have grown considerably since my voluntary incarceration here. I feed off this place and these walls and I know what lies below."

The watchers looked at each other taking in everything they were hearing. They had not been led in a very long time.

"What lies below has awakened from a very long sleep. It feels my presence here, my strength and my powers grow and I offer it hope."

He lashed out at a watcher with his left hand grabbed his cloak and brought him down to his knees.

Pulling down his hood he placed his right palm on the top of his temple and pressed. "Do you see?" The watcher was reeling in pain. "DO YOU SEE!" he yelled. The watcher's torso went into spasm, his head shaking looking upwards, as his eye streamed in pain that he was powerless to break away from.

The other watchers looked at each other with concern and took a step backwards witnessing one of their own in great pain. His arms were flailing at his sides but the strength of Duat held him down before he let go and removed his palm from the watchers head. The watcher fell to the floor shaking.
Duat brought his palm up to his eye as the patterns of turquoise began to fade. "Rise my friend."
The watcher on all fours, came back upon his knees and looked up at Duat, his eye was bloodshot and he was breathing heavily.

"Well?"
"I see Master." The watcher lifted his hand removing the saliva from the gaps of his mouth.
"Tell us."
"Master?"
"Tell us of what you saw."
"Fire, fire on water, us walking among those outside."
"You see outcome my friend."
"The Escarrabin, their master and the Order have little knowledge of our numbers. Our numbers multiply; they do not even know how many of us are here below."

Duat looked down at the kneeling and scared watcher. "You have seen greatness my friend; from now on I will call you Bellator."

The watchers heads all moved together upon hearing the familiar sound of the lift moving from above. Duat looked at Bellator. "Get up."

"Know this, for those who are about to come out from that gate, their time is precious and withering by the minute."

Raysmau, for the second time this morning, could hear the gates moving outside of her office. Frowning she looked up at her clock as she was not expecting any visitors or arrivals at this time.

There was a knock at her door.

"Come."
Raysmau was looking at one of her security team. "What is it?"
"Ma'am, Escarrabin Alian and Gamila request to speak with you."
"Now? I have a lot to do today as have you for that matter." She got up from her chair and walked around to the front of her desk. Perching on the end of it making herself comfortable she looked at her guard. "Very well, send them in, it had better be important" and swished a hand out in front of her.

The security guard stepped back a few paces and Raysmau could see her lean around the corner to speak with them. "She'll see you now; doesn't look too happy about being disturbed though."

"Doubt we will make her day much better" said Gamila and she stepped forward with Alian into Raysmau's office.
"Thank you" Raysmau said with a curt tone towards her guard. She was now looking directly at the two Escarrabin in her office in what was clearly an unplanned visit. The door was closed behind them.

"So?"

"Ma'am an event happened yesterday that we thought you should be made aware of." Gamila spoke with concern etched across her face.

This was met with a deep frown from Raysmau. "An event?"

Both Gamila and Alian looked at each other.

Not always known for her patience, she stared at both of them. "Well?"

Alian swallowed. "Well Ma'am yesterday afternoon."

"Late afternoon" Gamila interjected.

"Yes about late afternoon you may recall that we found a watcher in the gardens at the front of the house, not where he was scheduled to be."

Raysmau had a blank expression on her face. "Of course I recall. What of it? Punishment will be assigned in due course."

"There was a little more to it...afterwards." Alian was looking uncomfortable as she spoke.

Raysmau was lightly shaking her head. "Well proceed Escarrabin; there is a lot to do today."

Gamila took it upon herself to continue. "We took him below as usual but he was not alone."

Raysmau had a confused look upon her face. "Well who was he with, what are you talking about Gamila?"

"He was not alone in the below."

"There were more watchers down there; we couldn't say how many as it was too dark and we didn't have our vision goggles with us. We think maybe more than is accounted for." Alian spoke as a couple of beads of sweat developed on her temple.

Raysmau opened her mouth to speak.

"That's not it Ma'am; they amassed together."

Gamila was nodding in support of her colleague's statement.

"What on ever do you mean, amassed together?" Raysmau's lack of understanding was testing the tone of her words.

"We felt very threatened, it's the first time both of us has ever seen anything like it."

"The watcher that calls himself Duat is having some form of effect on them, some form of influence Ma'am" Gamila added.

Raysmau crossed her arms and blinked with a vacant expression.

"And that's not all Ma'am."
Raysmau shook her head a couple more times listening to every word she was hearing, ushering them to continue.
"There is something else down there, something very deep, we both heard it" Alian said trying to maintain composure.

She leaned back from her sitting position upon hearing this and had a small smile on her face although she was not hearing anything that was even vaguely amusing.
"You heard what exactly Escarrabin...speak up?"
They both looked at each other when Gamila decided to speak on their behalf.
"We could not possibly guess Ma'am."

Raysmau put a hand up. "You are going to have to do a damn sight better than that. I'm not going to make decisions or go to the Reeve with 'you heard a noise'. What exactly do you think you heard?"

"Something large, something from the deep, a depth that neither of us has ever gone to and maybe no one has for quite a long time.......it was moving" Gamila said and looked at the floor.

Raysmau's face was full of disbelief. "Are you sure of this. Alian do you support this ridiculousness that I'm hearing?"
"Yes Ma'am I do and we had to retreat. I am also duty bound to tell you that I drew my Scatterblade." Alian lifted her chin up as she spoke and looked past her superior with her eyes focused on the wall behind.

"And did you?" she was looking directly at Gamila.
"Yes Ma'am I did."
"Did you threaten any of them?"
There was silence in the room.
Alian took a step forward "Yes Ma'am I did."

Raysmau stared directly at Alian speechless with what she was hearing. Gathering her thoughts she quickly stood up. "The drawing of a weapon on the headquarters grounds is strictly prohibited unless there is an undeniable risk to

life, something that has not occurred on these grounds for a great many years, a great many..." She now looked at Gamila. "Was there an undeniable risk to life?"
"I believe that events had the potential to escalate. The drawing of a weapon allowed us to escape safely Ma'am."
"Escape, escape you say! The Escarrabin do not retreat, even more so on our own grounds!" She stood up and they both looked upon the towering figure of Raysmau.
"Then you had better add that into your report" she snapped at them.
"Yes Ma'am" they both spoke in unison.

"You are both not due on shift for a few more hours yet. I suggest you go back to your quarters and I want both of you to submit your reports to me immediately. The Reeve will have to be informed of this as you drew your weapons – do I make myself clear?"
"Yes Ma'am."
"If what you are reporting is accurate this is a worrying development. However, I want your reports and we will take an appropriate level of action. Did you see anything to explain what the noise was?"
Gamila spoke for them. "No Ma'am but the noise or noises sounded like it was somehow contained below."

All three of them were stood in silence as Raysmau rubbed her temple.
"Well! What are you waiting for, off you go, there is work to be done."
"Yes Ma'am" they both said at exactly the same time as if it had been rehearsed a hundred times before.

Both of them took three steps back, nodded their heads and turned around and left the office very gently closing the door behind them.

Raysmau went back to her heavy chair and sat gently into it, resting her right elbow on one of the supports and twiddled her fingers round themselves in contemplation. Watchers considering attacking, a moving unexplained noise below and weapons being drawn in defence; there was much to consider about this unprecedented event. She would defend the Escarrabin's actions if and only if what they had said were an accurate reflection of events, but that would be difficult to determine.

She had heard stories of the below from her predecessor and for that reason she didn't discount what they were saying completely. The stories had been passed down through generations of the elite Escarrabin at senior level and each time there was a vow of silence that these stories, albeit of probable fiction, did not escalate to the point that they filter down the ranks.

Raysmau had some decisions to make and action would need to be taken.

How she was going to explain this to the Reeve as yet she did not know.

Chapter Twenty:

TALKING TO CATS

FRIDAY MID MORNING

"Oh good morning Mildred and how are you today?"
Mildred pulled the receiver away from her ear staring at the phone again in frustration, quite clearly if she were calling she would not be alright.

"Missy is still unwell I'm very sad to say Miss Fennaway."
"Well I'm most surprised dear, these bugs usually would have passed through by now. Has she eaten anything?"
"No, she hasn't eaten a thing!" Mildred's patience was becoming quite tested which was most unbecoming of her. The dismissive attitude of the vet was not helping one bit. "She hasn't moved all night!"
"Well now, how very peculiar. Let's see then, have you tried spoon feeding her some fish, cats love fish you see?"
"I know very well they like fish! If she hasn't moved all night, she doesn't require dinner right now. I'm very worried Kamilah and your words of reassurance are not helping."

"She may have overdone it and is just getting some rest dear, would you like for me to talk to her again?"
Sat on the end of her bed, her right hand that was holding the phone let go and it fell between her legs and she shook her head a few times.

"Mildred...Mildred?" she could hear the vet calling out her name.
She placed the phone back to her ear. "Yes I'm still here and no, trying to talk to Missy is not going to help and she's not even three years old, she does not need Missy nap time!"

"Well dear I really think that it would not hurt to try."
"I'm getting a second opinion, I'm getting a second opinion I tell you and I'm going to ring the other vet! This...this...what is happening is not natural."
"Now look Mildred that really isn't necessary, I can always come over..."
"No thank you very much; I'm going to call someone else, goodbye Miss Fennaway!"

Mildred hung up the phone. She was breathing hard and could feel her chest rising up and down and knew she was clenching her teeth. Her legs were now outstretched from the edge of the bed as she flexed her toes (including the sore ones from the previous night). Upset and also exhilarated that it was the first time in a very long time that she had stood up to someone, she almost didn't think that she had it in her. She shook her head a little, stopped grinding her teeth and got up to find an old phone book she knew that she had somewhere downstairs in one of the paper mountains.

"Missy, I will be back in a moment." She leant over to her cat and stroked her down one side. She could feel that her heart beat was still very irregular; she shook her head "we are going to fix this!"

Going downstairs into her front room she looked at her cat shaped phone on the sideboard and the masses of scraps of paper of phone numbers, receipts and information flyers that she kept on there 'just in case'.

She picked up a pile of papers and pushed them to the side revealing an old discoloured phone book that had been underneath them.

"Okay, let's see what we can find." She started flicking through the book looking for veterinarians. What was the name of the one that Mr Franks had said, she thought to herself, but could not remember before coming to the V section in the book. Veterinarians, found it! Surprisingly there were a few in her area before she saw an advert for Castle Hollow Veterinary practice and instantly remembered that was the name that Mr Franks had mentioned.

Grabbing at the cat phone she picked it up and dialled the number. Whilst the call was going through, she looked back up the stairs worried about Missy. The phone was answered at the other end after four rings.

"Castle Hollow Veterinary Practice, how may I help you?"

"Oh good morning. My name is Mildred and my Missy is very unwell and has been for over 24 hours. Can a vet come and see her please?"

"I see; may I call you Mildred?"

"You may. Can you help at all, I'm very worried?"

"I'm quite sure that we can. Let me take some details and I'll see if Dr Sarah Belloch can pop around to see you. It will not be for a couple of hours though, is that okay?"

"Yes that is fine but as soon as you can please, I need a second opinion."

"A second, has another vet been to see you Mildred?"

Mildred brought the phone away from her head and closed her eyes and frowned. She recalled that Dr. Fennaway said that vets did not like to take on each other's work.

"Yes, briefly but she hasn't been very helpful I'm afraid."

"Oh, I'm sorry to hear this, may I enquire what vet came to see you?"

"Yes it was Kamilah from Fennaway's Veterinary Practise."

"Mmm, that's odd, I've never heard of her and I've been the receptionist here for over four years" the stranger on the phone advised her.

Mildred's concern grew as she heard this.

"Well never mind Mildred, I may be mistaken. Let me take your number and the details of what is wrong and I'll arrange for our vet to come and see you. Missy is a cat I presume?"

Mildred gave the particulars to the friendly voice on the other end of the phone, happy that she was advised that Dr Belloch would be calling somewhere after 11am.She walked back up the stairs and sat next to Missy and put a hand on her head. "Please don't worry my lovely friend; someone is on the way for you."

She stroked Missy repeatedly on autopilot as she stared at the wall directly in front of her. How could one vet not have heard of another within the same area? It was true that Fennaway's was some miles away, but how could they not have even heard of her?

There was something very odd going on here.

Nubia's phone was ringing again as she reached over to answer it.

"Nubia I think we may have a problem, in fact I'm certain of it."
"What's the matter Kamilah, have there been some developments with Nahla?"
"Well of a sort in that there has been no change in her condition from yesterday."

Nubia was silent gnawing at the stumps of her nails.

"Are you not surprised by this Nubia?"
"No, not fully; I can't, I can't really talk about it over the phone."
"I see.........but has there been a second sign Nubia, the clock in my office is fine?"
"No there hasn't but it may be that the time of passage is not over yet."
"What! Are you sure, this is news to me? I thought the prophecy stated that a second sign would have shown by now and if that hasn't happened Nahla's condition is most odd and defies any possible explanation."

"It's just...I can't really say." She looked around her office checking no-one was spying and she started whispering into the phone. "I'm just saying that we may not have reached the final hours when a sign may show that's all."
She had the phone pressed as closely to her face as was possible. "Is there another problem other than Nahla still being very ill?"

"I just spoke with Mildred on the phone and she practically hung up on me. Whatever I say to her does not reassure her. She thinks Nahla has some form of bug and a serious one at that." Kamilah, not being aware of this, was now whispering into her end of the phone as well.
"So, so what, why is this a problem?"
"She has proposed calling another vet in for a second opinion."
Nubia's eyes flared upon hearing this and coughed almost choking on her words.
"You can't be serious, that can never happen Kamilah. It would be a massive security risk, who knows where all of this would end up?"
"I know, I know but she won't talk to me. I did offer to go over and see her but

she wants no part of it, or me I feel."
Kamilah was now looking around in her own office to ensure no one was listening "I did speak with her cat last night."

There was silence at the other end.

"Hello, hello?" Kamilah's voice reached out into the silence.
With a hand on her head. "You did what?" Nubia said in utter disbelief.
"I did speak very briefly to Nahla."
"What! Are you demented for crying out loud?" Nubia's voice had increased dramatically before realising what she had done and spun around on her chair making sure no one had suddenly appeared. Nubia immediately returned back to whispering although there was concern in her voice. "You can't be serious, why on ever would you do that?"
"She mentioned last night about getting a second opinion, I had to do something."
"Well you certainly did that!"

Nubia rested on her elbows. "Okay, so tell me exactly what happened?"
"Well naturally I was on the phone so I couldn't see Mildred but my best guess is that she thinks I'm a lunatic."

Nubia shook her head a few times as her face fell into her hands. "You know that Mildred is a 9th degree elder and doesn't understand these things. She doesn't as yet even know the name of her cat Kamilah. What were you thinking?"

Nubia sat back in her chair checking the nails on her left hand to see if there was anything left to bite.

"What an absolute mess this is Kamilah. If that cat is seen by another vet and those heart beats are detected they will take Nahla away, you can bet your life on it. If Nahla's condition is what we suspect, the vet may call in others to make further assessments."
A pained expression suddenly appeared across Nubia's face. "Oh no Kamilah, a discovery like this could even get into the press." Nubia was horrified; delicate matters such as these reaching the press could lead to questions being raised.

She put a hand to her mouth in shock. "She'll be seen as some form of extraordinary cat even if she were to then get better. They would question Mildred and she may mention that she is a member of the club. She's not aware of our Order as yet but nevertheless questions, and awkward ones, could be asked!"

Nubia knew that anything that could be associated with the Order, no matter how tenuous, leading to questions being raised in the press, needed to be handled by the security arm of the Order. They are exceptionally careful with these things.

"This needs to be contained Kamilah; no chances can be taken that could expose our kind." Nubia spoke with forcefulness in her tone.

"Shall I inform the Reeve as security is her area?"
Nubia's face scowled upon hearing this and she thought for a couple of seconds. "No, it's okay, I have someone close to Mildred on my side and we can look into this. In any event we need to ensure that another vet does not take Nahla away. If that happens there could be severe consequences and it could spark a chain of events."

Nubia shifted in her seat deciding very quickly to take the initiative. "I'll take care of this. Please keep me posted if you hear anything else and Kamilah, this is very important, whatever you do don't tell anyone about this."
"I understand Nubia, you have my assurance as ever but my Signapher was quite clear you know. It is as prophesised, the heart beats were unmistakable; Nahla doesn't bear the mark though..."

"No, the one who comes bears the mark. The one who bears the pain will have a part to play in the future - how much and what part they take is unclear. What is clear however is that the prophesised cat will carry the mark as well as the beats of two hearts. Whether those hearts are to be a force for good or evil only time will tell."

"But only if there is a second and third sign Nubia?"

"Indeed but for now until the second sign, if there is to be one, Nahla is carrying that pain - the prophesised pain of two hearts imbalanced, fighting against each other."

"The poor dear must be in terrible pain."

"No doubt."

"Leave this with me; I know just who to call."

"I'll leave it with you then Nubia and if I hear anything else I will let you know; goodbye."

Nubia heard the phone go down at the other end as she gently placed her phone back upon its cradle.

The pain of two hearts where only one exists, Nahla must be in extraordinary pain. The curator sat back in her chair, crossed her legs and put her hands into a ball on her right knee. In any event Nahla's suffering could be a prediction. Nubia looked at her clock watching the pendulum swinging back and forth listening to the gentle ticking noise. If the prophecy is to be believed the only way Nahla's pain will stop is when that clock does. If Nahla's pain is eased, then the pain of others was only just about to start.

The curator leaned over to her phone and picked it up again.

She couldn't be fully sure if the phone call was private but it was a risk she was willing to take.

Nubia could hear the phone ringing at the other end "come on, come on."

"Yes hello."

Nubia breathed a sigh of relief. "Jessica its Lady Nubia from headquarters."

"Oh...hello Lady Nubia and how are you today? It's nice to hear from you." Jessica's voice was one of surprise by the unexpected call, even more so on the day of a gathering; you would think she probably had other things to be attending to.

"Jessica I'm not so good to be honest and I need to talk to you about a most private development that could have repercussions. I'm going to entrust you with this most special of assignments."

"Erm okay...I understand." She didn't, as a wave of uncertainty moved through her. She thought it best that she sit down.

Nubia looked around her office again paranoid about privacy or possibly a lack there of. "Do you have anything further to report on Mildred?" she whispered. "No, nothing further my Lady. I spoke to Mildred on the phone recently and I'm picking her up to take her to the gathering later today."

"How recently did you speak with her Jessica, it's quite important?"

Jessica leaned forward on her chair; something was clearly up. "A couple of days ago. Why do you ask, is everything okay Madam Nubia?" she was developing the nervous shakes in her hands again.

Nubia leaned into her phone and crouched down ducking beneath her desk "Did she mention her cat to you at all?" she continued to whisper.

"Missy? No she never mentioned her."
"Nahla, I think you mean, but anyway, Nahla has become very ill and we are greatly concerned."
"You are concerned about Nahla being ill? It is always heartbreaking to hear of any cat being unwell especially one of our own but is this a problem of significance or something?"
"It may be...it may be." Nubia popped up from behind her desk to check the coast was clear.
She continued to whisper and ducked back down again. "I'll get straight to the point; we have reason to believe that she may be calling in another vet instead of Fennaway."

"I'm sorry Lady Nubia but I'm struggling to hear you could you speak up a little please?"
Nubia closed her eyes and bit her lips trying to gather patience. "Mildred maybe calling in a different vet instead of Fennaway."
"Well why on ever would she do that?"
"It's complicated, but in any event it is vital if another vet goes to her home that she does not take Nahla away. Do you understand Jessica, vitally important?"
"Yes, I understand." *(She still didn't)*
"Jessica I need you to get over to Mildred's house and put her under surveillance."

"Surveillance!" Jessica was horrified not knowing the first thing to do. "Yes that is right, surveillance."

Jessica gulped and sat upright. What could she possibly know about surveillance, as if this week had not been strange enough already.
"Go over straight away and report back anything you see but only speak to me. Do you understand Jessica? Only speak with me."
"Erm, well okay, I'll do that" Jessica spoke in a very soft tone and stood up with purpose albeit a clueless gesture.

"Oh and one more thing. Your cat Khepri; take her with you as she looks like Nahla to the untrained eye, just in case you have to swap them!"
Jessica's eyes opened widely in shock "Excuse me...swap them? em, well."
"No ifs, no buts Jessica, this is a matter of priority for the Order. You are entrusted with this task."
"Yes Madam Nubia, I will do my best."
"Yes, you do your best, oh and one very last thing. Make sure you take your mobile phone with you; Fennaway may need to speak to Khepri."

Jessica's eyes opened even wider "Excuse me?"
"Your cat Khepri, Fennaway may need to talk to her to explain everything." The silence was not lost on Nubia. "Well your cat is not a mind reader is she now, see sense Jessica. I'll send you my direct number now."

The phone was hung up at the other end.

Jessica stared at her now silent phone and dropped it onto the table. Looking at the blank wall in front of her with a confused look over her face, she gave a few shakes of her head. *'What on Earth was going on?'*

She sat back down dumbfounded by what she had just heard; running a hand through her hair the small and rude lady had elevated her pulse again.

Surveillance on Mildred…Nahla sick…Fennaway talking to Khepri?

She sat with her legs crossed and let her right arm flop over them as she looked at the floor beneath her feet and took a deep breath shaking her head slightly. Looking to her right she saw her three cat bowls and froze instantly as she saw them. She bolted upright and started shuffling her backside back and forth on her chair, her eyes scouring everywhere in the kitchen. Standing up, she spun around a few times with an anxious look on her face.

Well where the hell was Khepri?

Chapter Twenty One:

DR BELLOCH FROM
CASTLE HOLLOW

FRIDAY MORNING APPROACHING 11AM

Jessica tore out into her front garden with an oversized spoon in her hand wearing her equally oversized high heels and thrust her left hand into the recycling bin. Grabbing at one of the tins among the sound of clanging and the noise of empty cat food tins falling out onto her pathway, the disruption could be heard the length of the street, as she held the chosen one a hoist.

"MUGSY" she screamed "MUGSY"...........there was no sign of her.
She panicked and looked up and down her road. "MUGSYYYYYYY" she yelled as loudly as she could bashing the tin can with the spoon. She took in a deep breath and at the top of her voice she bellowed "MUGSYYYYYYYYYYYYYYYY." She hadn't realised she was kicking her legs out to the sides trying to encourage her diaphragm for more volume. She looked up and could see that some of the neighbours were staring at her. She froze, as, even a few doors down, the man cutting his lawn had switched his lawnmower off and he was now looking at her with mouth agape.

She coughed under her breath a couple of times unsure what to do next as their stares continued as she was behaving like she had just escaped from some sort of institution.

One of the neighbours whose conversation had been interrupted decided to comment on unfolding events. "Why do you think she needs her cat so urgently?" The other neighbour shook her head. "No idea, she's not right that one" as they both continued to watch the lady of cats.

"Aww, come on Mugsy where are you?" Her voice was now at a much reduced tone as she stomped her heels a couple of times.

She was at the front of her driveway with hands on hips trying to ignore the neighbours as she looked up and down the road. "Come on Mugsy, where could you be?"

It was no good and time was of the essence. She put the tin and spoon down on her garden wall and called out gently "Khepri" and she glanced across the road knowing for certain that she was now the subject of gossip. She turned around to face her house looking up and down and she rotated back and forth a couple of times and called out again, "Khepri" and suddenly her cat appeared coming through the neighbour's garden to her right before hopping over the wall and stopping at her feet.

She looked down at her cat shaking her head. "You know for the sake of appearances it would be really helpful if you responded to the Mugsy name sometimes!"

She walked to her car that was parked on her driveway and opened the passenger door. "Well come on we are going for a drive." Khepri glided casually over to the car and hopped up onto the passenger seat. Jessica fixed the seat belt and closed the door behind her and walked around the front of the car muttering to herself, "apparently Fennaway wants to have a conversation with you as well." She was shaking her head to herself before putting the navigator into its cradle as the car moved off.

Jessica looked down to her passenger seat and could see that Khepri was looking up at her. Out of her windows she could tell the neighbours were clearly talking about her. In the rear view mirror she studied her own reflection wondering at the craziness of everything that was going on. "What the hell do I know about Surveillance?"

The car disappeared from view and the man who had been cutting his lawn looked at the other neighbours across the road and shrugged his shoulders before starting his lawnmower again.

Mildred was peering out of her front room window in the hope that the vet was on her way.

She had brought Missy downstairs in anticipation of the vet's arrival and her cat was now lying on the couch with her head propped gently upon the cat cushion.

She walked into the kitchen and looked up at her clock and could see the minute hand was approaching 11 o'clock. She went to her fridge for some milk and took the half empty 1 litre bottle out and placed it on the side next to her kettle.

Noticing that she had left the fridge door open, she walked back over to it and crouched down taking the opportunity to peer inside at her plates of fish paste sandwiches. She noticed they were curling at their ends more so than yesterday. She opened her mouth and blew out a sigh before closing the door and returning to her kettle to turn the gas on. Opening her tea canister and taking out a single bag of English breakfast tea she dropped it into her cat mug and stood there waiting for the kettle to boil. It wasn't breakfast time but hey ho.

She was still mentally wrestling whether to go to the gathering or not. It had been on her mind throughout her troubled night's sleep and still remained with her since getting up this morning.

As the kettle started to whistle she turned off the gas and lifted it up pouring the boiling water over the tea bag and moved the cup to her kitchen table. Taking a teaspoon from out of her cutlery drawer and picking up the plastic milk bottle she sat down with them and stirred at her tea bag.

It's not right, it's not right at all; I can't go out when my Missy is feeling like this. I'll need to cancel, I'm sure the other members will understand. She sat back in the silence of her kitchen and looked over at the bundle of happy birthday cat cards and a sad expression appeared on her face. I meant well and wanted to feel like someone again. She shook her head slightly and picked up the milk and poured some in to her cup. Some say you should remove the teabag first but she didn't care for that today and stirred the milk into the tea.

She got up and went over to her pedal bin and stood hard on the bottom of the pedal so the top remained open. Sitting back down, she took the teabag out of the cup and balanced it on the end of her teaspoon and aimed at the bin. As if the spoon were a catapult she flicked it at the bin and watched the tea bag hurtle past the bin hitting the wall behind with a splat. She watched in dismay as the stained brown water ran out of the bag, down the wall to the skirting board, before the teabag gave up clinging to the wall and fell to the ground. Closing her eyes and letting out a large sigh she looked back down at her tea mug with the smiling cat on it. She spun the mug around so the cat disappeared from view as on the strength of it there would appear to be little to smile about today.

Sarah Belloch ended the route on her satellite navigation system having now reached number 1 Rocke Road. Turning her engine off, having just parked outside, from the passenger seat of her car, she picked up her notes passed to her by the receptionist on her way out.

She had had a quick glance at them earlier but decided to read through them again. Written on the new client form she could see that the cat's name was Missy and the owner was Mildred who was not registered with the practice. Symptoms included: breathing difficulties, unresponsive to stimulation, not eating and looks to be in pain.

She could see that the cat was a British Shorthair and was approaching three years old. No medication had so far been prescribed but there was a scribbled note that another vet had already seen her. She looked up upon reading this as it was rare in her experience that the same pet irrespective of breed or type of animal would see a second vet.

She looked to the right of where she parked and could see the bush outside seemed to have been cut quite recently and she could read the sign for Rocke Road quite clearly on the wall underneath it. The rest of the garden however looked very unkempt and overgrown.

Holding on to her notes she grabbed her bag from the passenger seat and stepped out from the car. It was a reasonably quiet road, there were a couple of kids at the bus stop further down but all in all it was fairly unremarkable. Houses on either side were of a similar age and architecture as many in this area were, probably around the 1930's. Closing the car door and pressing the remote to lock it she opened the small gate that allowed her to walk onto the small overgrown pathway to the house. Walking down the path she couldn't help but notice that the house next door had a beautiful well maintained front garden until she stopped upon seeing a couple of holes in the grass. Badgers she thought to herself with a little smile.

She continued to the faded blue door and not seeing a bell she knocked three times with her knuckles. Taking two steps back she looked around and could see paint flaking from the windowsills and there were cobwebs hanging in just about every crevice the house had to offer.

Movements could be heard from behind the door as she prepared her face for smiling. The door opened and a woman dressed way beyond her years appeared at the doorway.

"Hello, are you Mildred?"
"Yes I am."
"I'm Dr Belloch from Castle Hollow Vets" and she took an identification card from out of her pocket and held it forward towards the lady so she could see it. "Oh thank you so much for coming, my Missy is in a terrible state. Please do come in" Mildred said and stepped back holding the door open for her.

"Thank you, yes I believe she is having some problems." She stepped forward and was immediately hit by the oddest smell that made her nose twitch and her eyes squint. She put her hand to her mouth *'what on earth was that?'*

"Please do come forward, Missy is right in here."

It was not the first time that she had been in a house that carried a unique smell but this was a combination of mustiness mixed with fish and it was very overpowering.

She moved into what looked like the front room and saw an old TV set, a sparse amount of old furniture and the most incredible mess of receipts, carrier bags with the name of a shop on it and bits of paper with phone numbers on. Over on a very old couch there was her cat, wrapped up with her head on a pillow.

"Well hello Missy" Sarah said with a smile.
"Oh she can't hear you I'm sorry."
Sarah turned around to see that Mildred was very serious with her statement.
"Yes I see, I'm sorry. I always like to say hello when I meet a new animal, a new client if you will." She nodded and offered a smile that fell reasonably flat.

Now a little red faced she crouched down beside Missy and placed a hand on her. "Well, let's see what is wrong with you then."
"Would you care for a cup of tea, the kettle is hot?" Mildred asked her.
Sarah turned her head around to look at Mildred and smiled. "No, I'm fine thank you. I have just come from another call and I had one there, but thank you all the same."

"Are you sure, it's no trouble, I know that you are here to help?"
Sarah smiled back at her again "Well I'm certainly going to try."
"Would you care for some fish paste sandwiches, I have plenty?"
Sarah turned back around to look at Missy and closed her eyes...'So that's what the smell was'.

Raysmau was studying Gamila's and Alian's security reports of events that happened in the below the day before.

Although they should have been written independently they were both fairly near word perfect of each other. She frowned as she compared the two but it was not the first time in the history of the Escarrabin that security guards had colluded with each other to reach the same conclusion of their actions.

A Scatterblade being drawn within the grounds of headquarters had not happened for a very long time and to that end it needed to be reported up. Raysmau would always do her best to defend her team if she believed their actions were correct but the fact that they both felt threatened would need to be investigated further; there would be no avoidance of that.

Although not here long, Duat was unlike any other watcher she had ever met and she'd met her fair share over the years. There was something different about him; arrogant and ill disciplined – yes but she had seen some of those traits in other watchers in the past, he was different. They did not like being kept here, that was a fact, so sooner or later one would be disruptive.

She placed the reports back on her desk and sat back in her chair. If she were truthful she did not know how many of them were below, she doubted anyone did. The Reeve hadn't been here long and it would depend on whether her predecessor had provided any clarity on these matters to her. The Reeves throughout history were very private and Raysmau knew that the Order Of The Reeves knew a lot more about this old building and its secrets than she ever would. If this new Reeve were like others from the past they would only ever consult among their own kind.

Raysmau had met other Reeves before at her former placement as well as when they had travelled from other countries to visit the UK headquarters. When they did come here their meetings were under lock and key and to her knowledge the agendas or details of what was discussed were never recorded.

The possible noise from the below did concern her greatly though.

There was a part of her that wanted her two members of the Escarrabin to be wrong but she doubted it. Mistakes can be made but not for something like this and given the *'cloudy'* history of the below. She knew they were both good soldiers and their reports would be somewhere near accurate.

Mandisa her predecessor had recounted to her during a very private moment, that secrets of old had been left behind in the depths of the below as a resting ground of the past and from very dark times. It is in those depths where they should remain. She had informed her that to her knowledge much from the past had never been recorded anywhere. 'Sometimes dark events want to be forgotten, they need not be dwelled upon.'

It was her predecessor's duty to inform her, as her predecessor had before her, that only the Reeves knew of more exacting details of past events and that information was only passed to the next in line. When a Reeve passed, their secrets and any knowledge that had been passed to them was taken to the grave.

She recalled on one occasion Mandisa taking her hand. "I have never been to the very bottom of the below, it makes me shudder to think of it." Mandisa's hand had shaken slightly as she looked at Raysmau directly into her eyes. 'Only ever go if you really need to Raysmau, those grounds have not been walked upon for a very long time and those grounds do not need to be disturbed if they lie in silence. Matters that have never been recorded do not need to be reopened, do you understand?'

Her right elbow was balanced on her desk and she was moving her thumb around her forefingers of her right hand considering the words of her predecessor and what would she do.

There was no avoiding this, she would need to see the Reeve straight away and could only but hope that she did not send them all to the below.

She knew roughly the way to Mildred's house and although she had never been there Jessica was quite familiar with the area as Mildred only lived a few miles from her. The navigator sat in its cradle with a road map on it all the same. She felt quite relieved to be in control of her own car again as no instruction had been put into it.

She looked down at Khepri who was now asleep on the passenger seat of her car. "Guess you have no idea what's going on do you?" She could hear that her cat was purring slightly. "Surprised to hear that you are so at peace, thought you didn't like the car Khepri." With that she could see her cat open one eye. "Oh good, you are still with us then, don't suppose you can advise me on surveillance skills can you, you can just about get into anywhere when it suits you?"

Khepri's eye had already reclosed.
She shook her head. "Thanks for all your help!"
It wasn't long before she saw the sign for Benbow Street. Turning in she passed the Futility Pub and could see a shop up ahead and indicated to pull over.

"We'll continue this chat later then shall we?" Stopping the car outside a shop called 'Franks Convenience Store' she looked down at Khepri fast asleep on the passenger seat and opened the window slightly for some air. "Don't go anywhere now will you" she muttered before locking the car and turning to look at the peculiar looking shop.

Stepping inside she could hear a tinkle of a bell above her and could see a man directly in front of her reading a newspaper. He looked up at her and she offered him a slight smile and she closed the door behind her.

My word, Jessica thought to herself, looking at the most bizarre layout of any shop she had ever seen. Her nose twitching slightly, it smelt quite musty of dusty old floorboards or similar. She looked down and could see old lino and possibly broken bits of old carpet but she couldn't be too sure. One thing she was positive of, it was unlike the shops that she would usually frequent of late.

Glancing around she needed to equip herself for this afternoon's surveillance. She stopped to look at her watch, it had just gone past 11.15 so it wasn't quite afternoon yet but she had better get a hurry on.

What on earth do people need for surveillance? She was chewing at her teeth thinking about the last detective programme she had seen on TV. Cover the eyes, yes that's right I need some glasses to disguise myself! She stopped walking and closed her eyes in annoyance realising that she had left her sunglasses at home and stomped one of her heels on the floor. She looked over at the man who was now watching her having heard the noise.

"May I help you with something?" he rasped.
"Erm yes maybe, do you sell glasses?" Jessica watched as she saw the man let go of his newspaper and walk over to her.
"You'll need an optician for that and I'm no optician" he said with a combination of a laugh and a rasp as his body rocked backwards and forwards with his own amusement. Jessica did her best to offer a little smile in response to his 'humour'.

"I'm all out of sunglasses after the weather we've had but I do have these." She watched him walk to the other side of the chest height aisle and he lifted up a clear plastic bag for her to see. "These any use for you?"
Jessica's face fell looking at the huge framed black glasses with a red nose attached to them.
"What do you need them for may I ask?"

"Er...a children's party?" she offered more as a question than a statement. "Oh in which case these will be perfect for you" and he thrust the very noisy plastic bag straight towards her.
Jessica took the bag from him, her face a mixture of expressions as she held the bag aloft staring at the big red nose fixed to the glasses.

"You'll look a right clown in those!" he rasped as she lowered the bag down to waist height. He walked back towards his counter and briefly turned back to her. "Never cared for clowns much" he said and she watched him shuffle back behind his counter. "Do let me know if you need anything else?"
Jessica gave him a curt smile hoping that she would not.

She walked around to the other side from where the odd man found her new 'surveillance glasses' and could see a box that said *children's binoculars with up to x3 range!* She grabbed the box and glanced up to see sledges hanging from the ceiling. Her eyebrows rose at sledges being out at this time of year and the peculiarity of this place she was in - no wonder she was the only customer.

*What else, what else...*Newspaper! She would definitely need a newspaper to hide behind. She walked past the counter and dumped the binoculars and glasses with red nose on top of the man's newspaper seeing that the newspaper section was to the other side of him. "I can recommend today's Shrewsbury Gazette and Herald" he said wiping her items to the side off his newspaper.
"Hmm, what I'm sorry?"
"Today's Gazette and Herald."
She looked at him puzzled.
"For your newspaper."
"Oh I see, okay, thank you, how big is it?"
"How big?.....I've never thought to look how many pages" he shrugged.
"No I mean how long, is it a long paper, I need a long one?"
He looked at her with some confusion. "You mean a broadsheet? Well there is the Midlands Farmer?"
"That's fine then, thank you, I'll have one of those."
Looking at the expensive clothing she was wearing he could not help but ask "you like farming do you?"
She smiled casually back.
He lifted his arm and pointed behind her. "You'll find it over there, next to the cards."

Jessica noticed that he looked quite confused but she didn't have the time to think about his issues.

She went over to the corner where he had pointed and looked down and saw the newspaper and bent over to pick it up. As she looked up she saw a card of a beautiful cat and froze, it looks just like Khepri! She smiled and took it off of the rack, the likeness was uncanny. Clutching the newspaper and the card she went over to the counter and dropped them in front of the man.

"How much do I owe please?" as she put her hand into her jacket pocket.

"Well let me see here. He started totting up her purchases in his head and noticed the card. "Well I never, it's like two buses coming along at once."

Jessica looked up "excuse me?"

"Your card, with the cat on it, I sold 44 of them to someone only yesterday."

"44, that's a lot!"

"I've never sold so many birthday cards!"

"I'm sorry, it's a birthday card?"

"Yes, it's a birthday card."

"Oh, I didn't realise, leave it then" and Jessica pushed the card to one side.

"Well, without the card that will be £11.50 please."

Jessica pulled her purse from her pocket and took £15 in notes out and pushed them forward to him. "Keep the change, thank you, must dash." She grabbed her glasses, binoculars and farming newspaper and headed towards the door.

Mr Franks watched her struggle in her heels as she moved quickly on the uneven floor toward the door and practically threw herself through it. As the door closed he looked down to his newspaper and the unwanted birthday card with a cat on it and shook his head "out of towners!"

Chapter Twenty Two:

CLOWN NOSE AND THE SHEEP DIVING CONTEST

FRIDAY MORNING APPROACHING 11.30

Sarah Belloch could see firsthand that Missy was in some discomfort as she gently stroked her head. She tried to conceal it from Mildred as best as she could but a frown had appeared across her forehead all the same. She had never witnessed a cat clearly in this much discomfort that remained asleep.

She continued to run her hand down her. "She's a very beautiful cat Mildred."
"She's my world doctor, please do help her."
Sarah smiled at Mildred trying to offer some reassurance. "I'm sorry to ask some routine questions but has there been anything different about Missy's routine that you are aware of? Has she been outside a lot or eaten anything unusual that you can think of?"
"I'm not aware of anything different. She often goes out at night; she thinks that I do not know, but I do." Mildred offered the doctor a little smile.
Sarah returned the smile back. "So you can't think of anything that could have led to Missy being unwell?"
"No, nothing at all."
"I see." The vet placed her hand over the area of Missy's heart and immediately froze and her eyes widened. "I must ask you Mildred, I was told that you had seen another vet. May I enquire what they said?"
"Well nothing really. She ran some form of device over her and said it was a bug

and that she would be okay soon."

Sarah turned in an instant to Mildred. "A device, what sort of a device?"

"I really could not tell you, I'm not a vet. It was a handheld scanner of some sort."

Sarah frowned again but chose not to conceal it this time. "A handheld scanner?" She took her hand away from Missy's torso with some surprise. She shook her head slightly. "I've never heard of something like that, something that could lead to a determination of what is wrong so quickly. May I ask what veterinary practise did you use?"

"Fennaway's, it's about 15 miles from here, they were recommended."

"Fennaway's?" Sarah looked to the floor in thought. "I've never heard of them Mildred, that's odd, how did you say you heard about them?"

Mildred clammed up a little upon hearing this question. "A friend's recommendation."

"I see" Sarah nodded noticing that Mildred did not look her in the eye as she spoke.

The vet looked back down at Missy and placed her hand again over the area of her heart and looked at Mildred and smiled. "I'm sure everything will be fine."

She reached for her bag and took out a stethoscope and checking that the diaphragm was clean, she placed it over the area of Missy's heart and pushed the ear tips into her ears.

"Well that's somewhat reassuring" Mildred said leaning over the vet.

Sarah removed the tips from her ears. "I'm sorry Mildred, what did you say?"

"You are using your ear buds...to listen."

Sarah had a look of confusion all over her face. "Well yes Mildred, I have to listen, why would you say that?"

"Oh it's just Kamilah Fennaway had one of those but didn't listen to it until I asked her to."

Sarah, who was crouched down over Missy, leaned forward to Mildred as she heard this. "Excuse me?"

"I know, that's strange don't you think?"

Sarah nodded slowly. "Yes I find that most peculiar;" she turned to face Missy and replaced the buds back into her ears and listened.

She moved the chest piece around the heart area as she closed her eyes in concentration.

She stopped moving and her eyes opened in shock and looked down at Missy, whilst removing the diaphragm. 'It can't be', she thought to herself and replaced the chest piece for the second time keeping a watch on Missy's face. She swallowed and performed the same movements three times to be sure. Pulling the buds from her ears and letting the stethoscope sit around her neck she didn't want to look Mildred in the face for the moment.

"Is everything okay doctor?" Mildred spoke to her just over her shoulder. Without an instant response she asked for the second time "Doctor?"

She turned to Mildred and looked up at her "It's very early to tell but I must be honest with you Mildred, there is an irregular heart beat that concerns me." She turned her head back to Missy and placed a hand on her head and stroked her. She knew that in her career she had never seen anything like this before.

Standing up she looked at Mildred. "Would you mind if I just make a phone call please?"
"No, I don't mind, my phone is over there" pointing at her cat phone on the side.
"Well actually I'm just going to step outside. I just want to speak to one of the partners of the practise, just a second opinion you see."
"Should I be worried? Kamilah the other vet checked Missy and went straight outside to make a phone call as well."

Sarah stepped towards Mildred and placed a hand on her shoulder. "I'm sure its fine Mildred; it's always good to get a second opinion, quite common really."

Mildred looked at her not convinced that she was telling the truth. "Well okay, if you need to, my front door is over there" and she pointed exactly at the door that Sarah had already came in from.
"Thank you Mildred, I'll just be a moment."

Mildred watched as the vet headed to her front door pulling her phone from her pocket as she went. She heard the door close and ran straight to the window to watch and could see very quickly that she was speaking to someone on the other end of the phone. Mildred could see concern in the vet's face as she spoke and looked back around at Missy. "Missy what on ever is going on?" She turned back around to look at the vet but could not hear a word that was being said.

"David I'm telling you, it's unmistakeable. I can clearly hear the distinct sound of two heartbeats, both beating at different paces. The cat is in pain and almost comatosed from it, have you ever heard of such a thing?"

"No, I certainly have not, that's a first on me" the voice replied from the other end of the phone.
"And that's not all. She had another vet call by that I have never heard of and by all accounts she had run some sort of scanning device over the cat and said that Missy would be fine soon. How strange is that? She gave an instant prediction and didn't take her away."
"Scanning device, what sort of scanning device?"
"I have no idea and Mildred clearly doesn't know either. She's very concerned about the whole thing."
"Well, I'm not surprised." There was silence at the other end of the phone. "You'll need to bring the cat in for further checks. If what you are saying is true we will need to investigate this urgently."
"Yes I agree, I'll tell her and I'll bring her in."

Sarah looked up briefly hearing a car pulling up on the other side of the road before turning around to face the house. She could see the shadow of Mildred watching her from behind the old and stained net curtains.

"There was also something else about this other vet that concerns me..."

Mildred continued to watch and put a hand over her chest watching the body language of the vet outside of her house. She looked back over to Missy with sadness. "I think she is going to take you away from me Missy."

Mildred was lost and suddenly felt completely alone.

Jessica parked up her car on the opposite side of the road from Mildred's house. Although she had never been here before she knew that she lived at number 1 so how difficult could it be?

"I'm a natural at this" she exclaimed with some pride looking down at Khepri who was still sound asleep.

She could see a lady that she didn't recognise on the pathway outside of Mildred's house talking on the phone. I'm guessing that's her she thought to herself, the unwanted vet.

She leant down to the floor well on the passenger side of the car and grabbed her surveillance equipment. Tearing open the box for the 3 x zoom binoculars she noticed a printed label on the side that said 'for ages 4 and upwards.' Ripping them out of the cellophane bag she brought them up to her eyes and started twiddling at the plastic centre dial. Pulling them away from her face she realised she had them the wrong way around and tried again. "Khepri these are useless" as she looked at the grainy image in front of her eyes. They did work a little bit and she could see a stethoscope around the neck of the lady on the phone.

Putting the binoculars down on her lap she grabbed at the oversized glasses with their plastic lenses and pulled them out of their bag. Looking with some embarrassment at the big red nose that was fixed onto them she pulled at it trying to remove the nose whilst still watching the lady on the phone. She pulled and pulled. "God it won't come off!" The car was beginning to rock now such was her enthusiasm but it remained firmly fixed to the plastic of the glasses. She noticed the vet on the phone had looked over. 'They'll have to do!' and put them on and grabbed at the newspaper, pulling it up to her eyes so the nose was covered.

"Who you speaking to then I wonder?" Jessica glanced down at her sleeping cat who was clearly quite disinterested. "Bet she's speaking with someone about Nahla." She continued to watch when she noticed the lady looked over again. Jessica quickly pulled the newspaper up to hide herself and then pushed her fingers through the paper to make a hole so she could look out "that was close!" She noticed the lady on the phone had turned around facing Mildred's house. "Okay, no harm done, Khepri I'd better call Nubia and let her know I'm here." Reaching over for her phone and reading the text message that Nubia had sent her with a link to her number, she hit the dial option.

She could hear the phone ringing at the other end. "Exciting all of this isn't it Khep…"
"Hello who is this?"
"Lady Nubia it's Jessica. Just to let you know that I'm in position" *(I think that's what you are supposed to say she thought to herself)* as she looked at Khepri quite pleased

with herself.

"Who were you talking to?"

"I'm sorry My Lady, what was that?"

"Who were you talking to as I answered the phone?"

"Oh, I'm sorry" Jessica's face flushed a bit "I was talking to Khepri."

"Really, I'm not aware that you have the gift – do you?"

"Er...gift Lady Nubia, I'm not so sure what you mean?"

"Well...can you talk to cats?" her tone was impatient.

"Well, to be honest I always talk to my cats." She shrugged her shoulders a little as the newspaper slipped down.

"That's not what I mean" she rolled her eyes "can they understand you?"

"Well, sometimes, I think..."

Nubia shook her head "You obviously can't never mind, it would have saved us some time. So what did you want?"

"I was just reporting in to let you know that I'm here and there looks to be another vet here, she's speaking to someone on the phone."

"I bet, look, call me when you've been able to exchange the cats, Fennaway will call you in a minute."

"Lady Nubia, Khepri is my cat and I'm not comfortable about this."

"Nonsense, it's for the good of the Order and very important. You must get Nahla at all costs; Nahla must not be taken away. All costs Jessica, see that it's done!"

The phone went dead at the other end.

Jessica pulled the phone away from her ear. "My word she is so rude." Jessica hadn't realised that the newspaper had slipped as she was on the phone and looked over and could see the other vet was looking directly at her. She dived beneath the paper again and peered through the hole and continued to watch her.

"David I'll explain to Mildred about bringing Missy in for observation overnight. Look I've got to go, there is a lady wearing a clown nose in a car watching me. Something very odd is happening over here."

"A clown nose?"

"Yep, I'm not kidding, I'll see you in a bit."

Sarah glanced over at the car again and could see that whoever was in the car was now hiding behind a newspaper. She stepped forward to look more closely. *'I'm sure that newspaper is upside down'* she thought to herself before going back into Mildred's home.

Jessica watched as she saw the vet go inside Mildred's house and she lowered the newspaper.

"Well I guess I'd better do my research." She grabbed at her phone and went on to Google. She read the inscription on the vet's car *'Castle Hollow Veterinary Practise'* and typed it in and waited for results. Quite a few entries came up including their own website and Jessica noticed that the vet's practise was not very far away. She went onto the 'about us' page and there she was, the woman on the phone, the woman she guessed she was going to 'meet' *(somehow)*. "Dr Sarah Belloch BVSC graduated blah blah blah. Well that's her Khepri that's our girl, bit of a problem that they are not far away; we won't have a lot of time."

She put the phone back down and looked at Khepri. "Right, I guess it's just a waiting game now?" although how she was going to get to Nahla she had absolutely no idea.

She lifted the newspaper back up realising it was upside down and spun it around the right way.
I hope Fennaway has some ideas when she calls, she was thinking to herself and she started to scan the newspaper.

'Foul Play Suspected At Sheep Diving Success.' Shropshire farmer Royston Dingle is being accused of foul play and the use of performance enhancing drugs is not being ruled out, following his continued success at the annual sheep diving contest. "I refute any suggestion that I have been cheating" he said to the Shropshire Farmer. "I live and work next to the River Severn and my sheep often like to dive in, it's natural for them." Mr Dingle went on to state "Spend an afternoon at my farm and you'll see them dive off the river banks for a swim. They love it! I'll sue anyone who claims otherwise."

Things have certainly been hotting up...

Jessica was abruptly interrupted by her phone ringing.

"Hello."
"Jessica it's Kamilah Fennaway."
"Hello Kamilah, nice to hear from you; Lady Nubia said that you would be calling. May I ask, have you ever been on Surveillance, it's just that I have a question…?"
"Surveillance, what on earth would I know about surveillance Jessica?" she said interrupting her, "listen, put Khepri on the phone would you?"
Jessica pulled the phone away from her ear. She can't be serious.
"Jessica…Jessica."
Jessica could hear her name coming from the phone and she replaced it back to her ear.
"Jessica, I understand that time is of the essence so if you will please."

Jessica pulled the phone away from her ear again staring incredulously at it and looked across to Khepri who was still asleep. She put the phone back to her ear "Er, yes, hang on a moment." She leant out her left hand to Khepri and rocked her slightly. "Khepri, wake up" she watched as she saw her cat open both of her eyes and sit up.

Taking a deep breath whilst looking at Khepri she shook her head. "It's for you" and put the phone to the right ear of her cat.

Jessica could hear muffled noises coming from her phone and watched as Khepri's eyes widened and blinked as if she understood everything that was being said. She looked away shaking her head when she realised someone walking past was staring right into her car. She froze momentarily realising that she had forgotten to take the glasses with the clown nose off and that it would appear that her cat was taking a phone call. She whipped off the glasses and threw them on the dashboard and gave a little smile and watched the man walk off. I'm really not very good at this she was thinking to herself noticing the man turn around to look back at her car again.

Looking back down at Khepri, her cat looked up at her and nodded her head upwards. "Well, what does that mean, are you done?"

She brought the phone back to her ear. "Kamilah is everything okay?"

"Yes fine, she knows what to do, now make sure you get Nahla, goodbye."
"Kamilah..."

The phone was dead at the other end. Jessica threw the phone on top of the glasses on the dashboard and looked over at Khepri. "So, we sorted now?" Her cat stared back at her and blinked. "Well I'm glad you know what you are doing because I'm absolutely clueless!"

"Sorry about that Mildred, I hope you do not mind my making a phone call to the office."
"No that is fine Doctor; may I ask your thoughts please?"

"I know that this will upset you a little but I've detected an unusual heart rhythm with Missy and to be safe I want to take her to our clinic where we can assess her further. It's very important that we establish what is wrong and we have more specialist equipment at the surgery."
"Surgery! you are not going to operate on her are you?"
"For now Mildred I'm not fully sure what is wrong with Missy but it was very important that you called us. To be honest the other vet you called should have done something similar."
"Oh, I see." Mildred looked at Missy and could feel her hands shaking slightly. "I've not been without her for nearly three years now Sarah." Mildred could feel her eyes starting to well up and brought a hand up to wipe her nose.

Placing a supporting hand on Mildred's shoulder Sarah looked her directly in the eyes. "We will do all we can for her, she will be in the best place with the right people, we will find out what is wrong."
"I see, thank you." Mildred could feel that she was going to cry. "Please be careful with her, she's my friend."
"We will Mildred; honestly she will receive great care. I need to go to my car as there is some paperwork that I need you to sign and I'll get a carrier for Missy so I can take her straight away. I'll leave you with my personal mobile number and you can call me anytime. As soon as we can establish what is wrong we will call you of course."

Sarah was still holding Mildred's shoulder "Is that okay with you?"

Mildred couldn't speak and nodded.
"Okay, I'll just be a minute" she gently smiled.

Mildred watched as Sarah walked towards her front door and she went over to Missy and crouched down and placed a hand on Missy's head. With tears in her eyes she ran her other hand down Missy's body stroking her. "Please don't leave me Missy."

Sarah walked down Mildred's pathway to her gate and pressed the remote for her car to unlock itself. The sound of the boot opening automatically disturbed a wood pigeon in the tree above as a couple of loose leaves fell to the ground. She went to the boot and removed a carrier and placed it on the pavement next to her and started sorting through the paperwork that Mildred would need to sign. She glanced over and could see in the car opposite that someone was still reading a very large newspaper, although it looked to be the right way around now. Closing the boot and relocking the car she put the paperwork inside the carrier along with a blanket and walked back to Mildred's gate. As she opened the gate she turned around again looking at the other car and could see that someone was fidgeting behind the newspaper. "Strange people around" she muttered to herself and walked back up the pathway.

Jessica pulled the newspaper back down and looked down at Khepri. "Right, she's obviously taking Nahla away, we must be ready!"
Ever since the phone call Khepri had been sitting upright. "Well, whatever she said to you I hope it works out and you know what you are doing!"
She paused momentarily and placed a hand upon her cat. "Please do not take any risks Khepri, you are my cat and I love you; it upsets me that you are being asked to do this. What on earth I am going to do next I have absolutely no idea!"

They were both looking at each other although one was more confused than the other.

Having explained the paperwork to her, Sarah looked on at a very upset Mildred signing her name where she had been asked.

"These copies are for you Mildred." Without words she reluctantly took them from her. "I want to leave you with my business card as well; you can see my personal telephone number here at the bottom" she pointed out where her direct line was. "I know that you are upset so call me if you need to, she is going to be in the best place, I promise."

Mildred wiped her eyes doing her best to maintain some composure and just nodded. She crouched down to look inside the carrier "get well soon Missy please" and she reached out at the grill that her cat lay behind.

She stood back up and looked at the vet and nodded again.

Sarah put a reassuring hand on Mildred's arm and put her work bag over her shoulder and picked up the carrier and headed towards the door. Mildred opened the front door for her.

"I will call you Mildred I promise, as soon as I can."
"Okay, thank you Sarah."

The vet nodded at her and she watched as she walked down her pathway to her gate. "Do you need a hand with the gate Sarah?"
"No, I'll be fine, thank you Mildred. Goodbye for now."

Mildred closed the front door very gently and went straight to the front room to look out of the window. Sarah's car was parked on the bend just out of sight but then maybe that was for the best. She walked over to her sofa and sat down; looking at the cat cushion she picked it up and held it to her chest. Tears were running down her face. "Oh Missy, what has happened?"

Sarah placed the carrier on the back seat on the passenger side so she could keep an eye on Missy throughout the journey. Securing the carrier as best she could with assistance from the seatbelt, her work bag and the signed paperwork were now on the front seat next to her and she started the car.

Glancing at her sat nav that had come on automatically it looked like she could get out of Rocke Road at the bottom and indicated to move away. She looked directly to her right at the parked car opposite that clearly still had an occupant behind the held up newspaper and she pulled away.

Jessica peered from over the top of the newspaper. "Here we go Khepri" and threw the newspaper to the side and started up the engine.

Following the vet down Rocke Road she felt it best to leave a little bit of distance not wanting to give the game away. She had been so highly discrete so far, but for all of her thoughts about her new surveillance skills only one thing was paramount in her mind.

How on earth am I going to be able to get Nahla?

Chapter Twenty Three:

ACTIONING THE SWITCHAROO

FRIDAY MORNING APPROACHING MIDDAY

Raysmau left her office clutching the two security reports.

Closing the door behind her she passed by the security control room on her right. One of the Escarrabin jumped up upon seeing her "Ma'am."
"Don't worry I can do the gate for myself, unexpected meeting."
"Yes Ma'am, if you are sure Ma'am."
"I am." As she approached the gate and pressed the wall mounted button to release it, the familiar sound of metal upon stone filled the corridor. She walked through casually glancing at the reports until she reached the exit door. She brought her right shoulder down towards the illuminated crest as her pin badge connected and the heavy old doors started to open inwards.

She took a quick observation of those in the lobby area knowing that more Escarrabin were arriving within the next couple of hours. As she glanced around she could see those on shift were in their allotted places. Walking across the elaborately decorated floor she passed by the clerics on her right and could see their heads were down busy with administration. A couple of elders were also in conversation and they nodded to her as she walked past, the sound of her heavy footsteps was unmistakeable. As she proceeded to the stairway she could see down the grand walkway at the far end two Escarrabin were keeping a close eye on a watcher that was cleaning one of the far stairways. On the face of it everything appeared to be in order. She could hear her security doors closing behind her in the background as she reached the stairs. The lift on her left was where it was supposed to be and not below ground and, satisfied, she headed up the stairs for her meeting with the Reeve.

Deep in thought as she walked she knew that words would need to be chosen carefully about the events of the day before. The reports told their own story but she was apprehensive about the outcome of them. Being sent into the below was now a high probability and the Reeve may command such action.

This in recent history was an unprecedented act and as she walked down the corridors she considered what she would do if she were the Reeve. She hated to admit that if it had been the other way around she would probably send everyone below for a thorough search and investigate whatever the noise was that had come from the darkness deep below. What such a beast is, how it got there and if it is secured she had to confess to herself that she had no idea, all she knew was the warnings of her predecessor.

As she approached the Reeve's doorway she looked back to the quadrangle at the 4 clerics who, like the clerics in the lobby, seemed to be busy, with what she didn't really know as the curator seemed to keep them occupied.

Taking a deep breath outside the grand and scarred door of the Reeve she knocked three times with her knuckles and took a couple of steps backwards. She didn't notice that one of the clerics had looked up as she surveyed this grand old door, all of the scars and the stories it told went back generations of generations. The cracked and repaired old seal in the centre of the door was one of the stories that she did know of.

The door was pulled open and Raysmau was surprised to see the Reeve standing there having opened it herself.

"Good morning Ma'am" Raysmau nodded.
"It's almost afternoon Raysmau. I was surprised to hear from you, come through, I trust this is urgent."

They passed through the Reeve's corridors and Raysmau could see that the doorway ahead into the Reeve's office was already open.

"Come in, take a seat Raysmau" as she ushered her hand towards a chair already placed in front of her desk.
"Thank you Ma'am."
Raysmau gently sat as much as her big frame would allow in the seat next to the Reeve's desk.

"So, what's troubling you Raysmau, we have plenty to do today?"
Raysmau observed that the Reeve was shuffling papers on her desk and that her focus was elsewhere.
"I know Ma'am but I felt it prudent to bring something to your attention."
The Reeve looked up and took her seat opposite Raysmau without saying anything.

Raysmau, with confidence, looked directly into the eyes of the Reeve. "There was an event yesterday which in itself may not be remarkable but it led to an escalation."
The Reeve frowned, "An escalation; is this not something that you can handle?"
"On this occasion Ma'am no, it needs to be brought to you for your consideration and council."

The Reeve sat back in her chair and Raysmau could now see that she had her full attention. "Have a couple of the Escarrabin fallen out again?"

"No Ma'am." Raysmau gave a gentle smile. Drawing her breath she proceeded. "Yesterday two Escarrabin found a watcher around the great statue of Salma. As I say that in itself may not be remarkable but it's the second time it has happened and it was the same watcher on both occasions. He was not supposed to be there and was scheduled for duties over towards the lake."

The Reeve put her hands behind her head ushering the head of the Escarrabin to continue.

"It is the nature of this watcher that concerns me. He has been brought before me and is due to be disciplined, although I feel discipline would not have any effect to him, he is not like the others."

The Reeve brought her hands back down as she heard this. "Really, how so?"
"A feeling that I have. He's arrogant but there is something else about him; he has a deep distain for us."
"Well that's not uncommon among watchers."
"Indeed, but he's different...he's different."
The Reeve blinked upon hearing this "I see, presumably there is more to this?"
Raysmau swallowed. "Yes Ma'am, that is not all."
"Not all?"
"Two of the Escarrabin took him below after he had seen me and they claim that he threatened them."
"Threatened them, our Escarrabin?"
"Yes Ma'am, he has an effect on the other watchers as well, I have it here in their reports for you to see." Raysmau leaned forward and placed both reports on the desk. "The two Escarrabin felt they were in danger and they both felt compelled to draw their Scatterblades."
The Reeve's eyes widened. "You can't be serious Raysmau, drawing Scatterblades on watchers in the below?"

Raysmau sat in silence briefly letting the words sink in as she swallowed for the second time knowing that something needed to be voiced that is often not well received. "With the absence of cameras outside in the grounds Ma'am we only have the accounts of the Escarrabin to understand what the watcher was doing on the outside and why he was around the great statue of Salma."

"I get resistance on this from the Grand Council Raysmau. I agree with you on this matter and if it were solely my decision, security matters would be taken a great deal more seriously but in any event to my knowledge a Scatterblade has not been drawn within these grounds in a very long time!"

"Indeed, but there is also something else Ma'am."
The Reeves's eyebrows rose as she leaned back in her chair with her hands back behind her head again. "Well, let's hear it!"

Raysmau took a deep breath. "The two Escarrabin claim that they heard something in the deep, far in the deep, something of old and not of this place... it was moving."

The Reeve felt an instant rush of adrenaline pass through her, showing quizzical eyes at her head of security, "You sure of this Raysmau?"

"I must report to you of my concerns; I do not know the full history of events of the past and what has happened in days gone by in the below, but in any event something has awoken down there, something, not natural."

The Reeve took her eyes away from Raysmau and looked down to think; a watcher had been seen twice by the statue, something was moving in the deep and other watchers were becoming unruly. She picked at her lip with her right hand before bringing her head back up to look at Raysmau.

"I'm sure it's nothing!"

"Ma'am?" Of all of the reactions she expected, this was not one of them. "The watchers don't like being told what to do at the best of times. See that he is punished properly and if you can leave your reports here I'll read them through and come back to you."

"Well yes Ma'am; you don't want any further action to be taken at this time; Scatterblades were drawn?"

The Reeve smiled at Raysmau. "No, that's fine but thank you for letting me know."

Raysmau stared back at her superior at a loss for words.

"That will be all Raysmau." The Reeve raised her tone in authority and tilted her head down looking directly into Raysmau's eyes.

"Yes Ma'am." Raysmau stood up from her chair and nodded and took a couple of steps backwards before turning around to head for the door.

As she closed the door she lifted her head and could see that the Reeve was watching her every move.

She headed out towards the grand door of the Reeve as a scowl appeared across her face. What was all that about? No further action to be taken and she dismissed the noise from below as probably nothing.

She had never seen a Reeve throughout her working history fail to take decisive action. Something was not right and there was more to this, Raysmau was certain of that and she did not like being kept in the dark.

The Reeve watched Raysmau exit her doorway pulling the door closed behind her. As soon as she was certain that she had gone, she leaned forward onto her desk and brought a hand up to her mouth with worry. Taking deep breaths she bowed her head to let her hands move through her hair.

Highly unnerved she closed her eyes and continued breathing deeply. She suspected what may lie below but it moving - how can that be possible? With her hand resting across her temple she was considering everything that Raysmau had said, reading the reports would make no difference to the outcome of her suspicions.

Her deep breathing ceased, her eyes opened and she sat up as it dawned on her, she knew exactly what the watcher was up to. She leaned across her desk and grabbed at her phone. Looking up at her clock knowing that her head of Order would be one hour ahead of her she sat patiently listening to the phone ring at the other end.

Her pulse was elevating the longer she waited, hoping that it would be answered.

"Si buenas tardes."
She drew a deep breath of relief. "Ma'am, it's the Reeve of Loxley."
"Yes Reeve what is it?"
"I must speak with you...urgently."

Sarah Belloch turned to look over her left shoulder and could see that Missy was lying in her carrier; she could see the occasional paw twitching. Following her five years of training to become qualified as a vet, work placements and having worked for Castle Hollow for the last two years, she had never witnessed such an event.

As she drove towards the surgery she estimated with traffic permitting she could be there in 15 – 20 minutes.

David Fullerton the senior partner knew she was on her way and she certainly wanted a second opinion from him. With huge ambitions and her love for her job she hoped to be a partner of Castle Hollow in the future or, better still have her own practice. But this certainly was a mystery and she hoped to give some relief to Mildred later by way of good news.

As she approached the line of traffic waiting at the traffic lights her thoughts turned to Mildred. There could be no doubt how much Missy meant to her, as all cats do to their owners. A little shiver ran through her spine as she was still trying to get the tingling of the smell of fish paste out of her nose. Can't believe anyone still eats that she thought to herself as she stopped in the line of traffic and noticed a car closing up behind her in her rear view mirror.

"Khepri what are we going to do?" Jessica estimated from looking earlier on the internet that the vets practice was probably only around 10 minutes away. "If she takes Nahla into the surgery we are never going to get her out!"

She glanced down at Khepri who was still sitting upright in the front seat looking at her as she spoke. As the lights turned to green she maintained what she considered to be a reasonable distance behind the vet's vehicle.

The speed of the car got up to 30mph and Jessica knew that she was running out of time. With one hand on the steering wheel and the other clutching a lock of her hair, her hands were shaking and her teeth were chattering knowing full well that if she let Nubia down she suspected that it wouldn't be good. "You know Khepri I have no idea why this is so important. It must be devastating for Mildred that Nahla is so unwell, I would be if it were you, but why we are on 'this mission' (she took her hand off the wheel doing an inverted comers gesture) I have no idea. She was shaking her head trying to think of how to get to the cat in the car in front and more importantly getting away with it. She continued to follow the vet down the main A5 road knowing full well that Castle Hollow Vets was now only a few roads away.

They stopped at a roundabout and she could see there were two cars in front of the vet.

"Right, decisive action Khepri, we'll need to ram her." She looked down at her cat who had turned her head further towards her upon hearing this. "Well you got any better ideas?"
Khepri blinked and Jessica saw her tail curl and extend. "Well what was that, was

that an agreement to my plan or what, oh my days, what am I doing?"

Jessica looked in her rear view mirror and there were cars that had stopped behind her in a line of traffic. She looked ahead and out of her windows for Police and could not see any. Her adrenalin was spiking, her pulse was elevating further and she screwed up her face and almost closed her eyes. "Brace for impact Khepri!!" She took her left hand off the steering wheel and placed it on her cat to hold her.
She saw the vet's car move forward to the front of the queue.
"Here we go, we're going to ram her!!" Making a yelling noise she drove right at the vet's car hitting the bumper at probably all of about 3mph.

She felt the slightest tap as bumper hit bumper. "Phew, you okay Khepri?" She reversed the car back slightly.

"What the hell?" Sarah Belloch had felt a knock at the rear of her car. She looked in the rear view mirror and could see a car backing away from her slightly and the driver looked like she was flapping her arms and could see her lean over to her passenger seat. Turning around to check on Missy she could see that she was unmoved. She looked back in her mirror to see the driver getting out of the car.

Jessica leaned over and opened the passenger door of her car slightly "Right Khepri, do what you need to do." She saw her cat look up at her. "Please be very careful." A sad expression was all over Jessica's face as she undid the seat belt. "Right" she said getting out of the car. As she took a few steps forward towards the vet's car, not surprisingly there was no sign of any damage. 'Think, think, think' Jessica's mind was in a mental chatter.

She looked down at her heels and then up as she could see the vet taking her seat belt off obviously about to get out of her car. Quickly glancing around she could hear a car horn blaring from the line of traffic behind but no-one was watching. She lifted her right leg up and kicked her heel through the rear quarter light. She watched as the red bits of plastic fell to the floor and looked up upon hearing the vet getting out of her car.

"Well what on earth happened there?" the vet exclaimed.
"I'm so so sorry, I don't know what I was thinking, I must have just lost my concentration!"

Jessica looked to her left and could see Khepri walking past her towards the rear of the vet's car.

"I'm sorry, it was my fault, hands up" Jessica smiled.

"I'm not sure what you are smiling for?" Jessica watched as she saw the vet crouch down to look at her broken light on the floor.

"I'll just check this side" Jessica said and made her way to the left rear of the car and crouched down herself. She glanced around to the side and could see Khepri sitting staring at the car door.

"Is everything okay there?" Jessica said trying to make conversation with the vet whilst reaching out her left hand to open the rear passenger door.

"Well not really, you've done some damage."

"I'm sure it can be fixed" Jessica said whilst at full stretch pulling on the door handle. She was relieved to find the door was unlocked.

She looked at Khepri and tilted her head to the right as if to say 'go on then, get in.' She watched as she saw Khepri jump up into the vet's car.

Jessica stood back up to look at the vet. "I'm really sorry about all of this, what is your name?"

The vet was starring quizzically at her. "I don't understand how the light broke, I barely even felt you hit me."

"Yes, quite strange that, I must have been at an angle or something?"

Jessica looked through the rear windscreen of the car and could see Khepri pulling at the cat carrier.

Sarah was starring at Jessica. "Strange that there isn't a mark on your car don't you think?"

"Mmm, what, sorry?"

"Your car, there's not a scratch!"

"British car see, made of strong stuff!" Jessica smiled.

"I think you'll find these are made in Japan now."

"Oh really?" Jessica was looking around unsure of what to do next.

"Well I guess we had better exchange details then, I trust that you are insured?"

"Oh yes, please do not worry about that" Jessica offered a reassuring smile.

"Bet you don't have a no claims bonus though do you?"

Jessica noticed the look of displeasure all over the vet's face as she walked back to her car door.

Jessica's eyes flared with worry as she looked through the glass to see Khepri getting into the carrier. Placing a hand on her temple with frown lines etched on her forehead, she realised that if the vet looked on her back seat she would now see two cats in her carrier.

Swallowing heavily she could feel beads of sweat developing on her brow. Sarah leant into her car and reached over to her bag, dragging it onto her front seat looking for a business card.

Jessica looked at the floor at the broken plastic from the light and then looked back up again and could see the vet bent over looking into her bag on her front seat.

Looking around she could see that the cars from behind were now passing them by and their occupants were looking to see what had happened but no-one was really watching. With her right heel she started kicking some of the broken bits of plastic under the driver's side rear wheel and quickly retracted her foot as she saw the vet approaching her.

"This is my card with my details on it; I will of course need yours."
"Yes of course, I'll just get those for you but you know we should clear this plastic up from the floor, someone may get a puncture. I can see that some is under your car as well."
She watched as the vet couched down and frowned upon seeing broken bits of red coloured plastic around her wheel.
"We really should pick those up" Jessica announced.
She sighed "yes of course, you are right."
Jessica watched as the vet extended her arm underneath the car and she took a few steps to her left and leaned over to the slightly open passenger door. Quickly leaning in she could see Khepri in the carrier staring at her and her cat nodded at her. Jessica leaned in and gently lifted Nahla from the carrier and closed the passenger door and placed Nahla on her chest and tried to cover her with her black suit jacket.
As she closed the car door she saw a paw come through the cage of the carrier pulling the cage shut.

"Well okay, I'll get those details for you now."
The vet stood up holding bits of plastic in her hands and jumped seeing a cat's head resting on the chest of the woman who had hit her car.

"What the...well where did that come from?"

"I'm what, sorry?"

"The cat, I didn't see it there before."

"Really? Oh I always take my cat everywhere with me, as a vet I thought you would have noticed!"

"Wait a second!"

Jessica's heart was in her mouth as she watched the vet throw the bits of plastic to the side of the road and practically pushed her to one side as she opened the passenger door of her car and looked inside. She opened the gate of the carrier and could see that Missy was still in there, asleep, and she could see her paws still twitching.

Jessica gulping offered a smile "Now let me get those details for you" and she walked over to her car opening the passenger side door and gently placed Missy on the seat. "Oh my poor dear, you do not look well." Jessica was shocked at seeing Missy with her paws shaking clearly in some discomfort. She opened her glove box and took out a pen and a scrap of paper and closed the door behind her.

She leant on the vet's car and wrote her details down on the piece of paper. "I could pay you cash for the damage if that helps."

Sarah didn't doubt it looking at the expensive clothing the stranger was wearing.

"No, you know what, I think we'll do this officially, something is not right here!"

"Well, whatever do you mean? I'm sorry, I told you I was careless that's all."

"My last call, where I just came from, there was someone in a car outside acting suspiciously. Do you know where Rocke Road is?"

Jessica took a step back as her heart was pulsing again. "Erm, I'm sorry, Rocke Road, no I've never heard of there."

"Are you following me?" Jessica watched as the vet walked over to her car and peered in. She could see a cat asleep on the passenger seat as well as large glasses with a clown nose fixed to them on the floor. The vet turned around to look at Jessica with hands on her hips.

"As I say, something is not right here. For the second time I will ask you, are you following me?"

"I really have no idea what you mean, you must be mistaken!" Jessica had a pleading look on her face suddenly having a strong urge for needing the toilet, as the vet angrily walked back past her to her car and opened the driver's door to reach for her bag again.

Jessica took a couple of steps towards her car. "Well, I'll be on my way then."
"Not so fast!" The vet held her phone up and took a photograph.
"Excuse me what are you doing?" Jessica questioned whilst trying to hide her face.
"You tell that ex of mine to leave me alone and next time he hires a private investigator to hire one that actually knows what they are doing!"
"Well, I really..."
"And what's more, what sort of a responsible pet owner drives around with their cat in their arms mmm? Maybe if you concentrated more you wouldn't have accidents. If you don't care for yourself then think of your pet, am I clear!"
Jessica blushed. "Mmm, yes."
"You'll be hearing from my insurance company."
Jessica watched as she saw a very angry veterinarian get back in her car and pull away.

Wiping her brow and putting her hands on her hips she let out an almighty sigh and then looked to the sky; that was close!! She was distracted by a car horn that reminded her she was standing in the middle of the road and creating an obstruction. Quickly gathering her thoughts she checked her heels were not damaged and walked back to her car.

As she got in she looked at Nahla and placed a hand on her head "I have no idea what Nubia has in store for you but I hope that she can make it all better and this was worth it."

She started the engine and drove the length of two streets before pulling over to make a phone call.

Her heart was just about back where it should be as she reached for her phone and hit redial.
Pleasingly the phone was answered quickly.

"Lady Nubia, I've done it, I've completed the mission objective and I've done the switcharoo!!" Jessica was ecstatic with pride.
"You've done a what?"
"A switcharoo!"

"A switch a what?"

"I've switched the cats."

"Well why on ever didn't you say that? Right get over here immediately, I'll send an instruction to your navigator."

"Lady Nubia you are a good hour plus from me and I need to get back, I'm supposed to be taking Mildred to the Gathering in a few hours."

"You'll make it; I trust you have your pin with you for the gates?"

"Yes My Lady, I always carry it with me. I'm not sure if I will have enough fuel."

"Well get some! When you get here the car will bring you to the back of the house again. I'll also have something for you that you can take away with you."

"Take away with me?"

"Well yes of course, you want Khepri back don't you?"

"Well yes My Lady."

"Well when the time is right you'll need to switch the cats back again!"

She hung up the phone.

Jessica put her head in her hands not having thought any of this through. The very idea of having to even possibly encounter the angry vet again made her feel nauseous.

No thanks and no nothing for her efforts as she looked down at poor Nahla.

She was distracted by the navigator flashing and her car peddles moving as she sat back in her seat. It would appear she had little choice; it looked like she was off to headquarters again.

Chapter Twenty Four:

THE GREAT STATUE OF SALMA

FRIDAY APPROACHING MIDDAY

Although her head of Order, Lady Berenike, spoke fluent English, the Reeve didn't speak a word of Spanish. Regardless, she chose to speak slowly all the same as some words were not easy to say in any language.

"Can you talk privately my Lady?"
"Yes, I'm in my office, what is troubling you Reeve of Loxley?"
"I've been informed about a worrying development. We have a watcher that may be becoming active and he is disruptive and not like the others; ordinarily my head of security would not bring this to me. However, on two occasions the same watcher has been seen around our great statue of Salma. Now this in itself is one thing but he is causing unrest below with the other watchers and there is reason to believe they may be becoming hostile, possibly he is trying to unite them."

She could hear her superior breathing down the phone "Please continue."

"It just came to my attention that yesterday there was an incident below and defence weapons were drawn but during this process a noise of something moving was coming up from very deep below."

"This is indeed unsettling. What sort of a noise do you think was heard?"
"I was not present my Lady but it was described as unnatural and an assumption is being made that it could be something from the past, from long in the past."

The Reeve could only hear breathing through the phone receiver.

"There is something else. One of our own has become very ill, and our curator believes it could be the first sign of the prophecy. The timing of a gathering of everyone around the world is suspicious and my concern is the timing is not a coincidence. Is it possible the actions of this watcher has brought something back from the past, his actions around the statue concern me?"

"This is a very worrying development Reeve and of course you know what lays protected beneath the statue. As unlikely as it is that he has somehow discovered what is below it, potentially trying to access it would be of immediate concern and a security priority. One of our own becoming ill at the same time as well... this does not sit well with me and you were right to call."
"That is why I seek your council on this matter My Lady."
"It would be an unlikely event that a watcher could have gained access as they do not know or should not know about these things. If this information has come into his possession then we have a serious issue of security."
"Yes, someone may be helping him."
"Has the watcher been assessed through the usual protocols?"
"He has but the manner of his arrival here was unusual as well. He was found not far from our main gates, we have cameras outside, and the Escarrabin caught him and brought him in."
"So this is a watcher who knew the location of your headquarters as well!"
"Yes, putting it together it is becoming a little unnerving."
"It does, I've never heard anything like it before, he wanted to be caught. Reeve tell me what of his hands especially the right hand, have you seen any discolouration especially of a turquoise colour?"
"I'm not sure of the answer to that, we are very wary of their hands of course and measures are taken as is usual."
"I see, well that may well be needed to be looked into but Reeve you must find out if he has gained access below the statue. If he has I know what he is trying to do with everything that you have told me."
"Please continue My Lady."

The Reeve could hear deep breathing down the phone in this moment of silence.

"I know that your predecessor would have told you much about the days of old especially the dark ones much of which like to be forgotten. What she may not have told you is that a great many things were buried below Loxley, well more sealed away, if the truth be told; they were very dark days indeed."

With a very dry throat the Reeve adjusted herself on her seat, her left hand moving through her hair in concentration.

"In the very deep a wall of iron was built, hundreds of years ago. It was built to close off everything that lay beyond to ensure that what lay behind it and secrets of old would never resurface. Now if what you are telling me is that a noise from beyond there has been heard and you have potentially a watcher who is trying to unite them, this is of grave concern. The prophecy has spoken about three events and you have already described that one of our own is very ill, presumably she is suffering the pain of two hearts?"

"Yes my Lady we believe there is a potential for that."

"Then it is vitally important that you get to the statue immediately. You know where the room of keys is once you are inside?"

"Yes My Lady I do."

"Once inside you should see two very old large bronze keys that have no place with the others; they are both four sided keys that were designed with extra security in mind. Both will be needed to open an access point within the wall of iron. That doorway within the iron wall will not have been opened for hundreds of years and there is no guarantee that it will open at all, it is so old. The watchers do not have the strength to challenge us but if this one of whom you speak is gifted and can unite them, what lays beyond that wall of iron is what he will need to set them all free. That is a presumption on my part unless there is another goal that we are not yet aware of."

The Reeve sat back in her chair considering this sudden mass escalation of events.

"Reeve, however, our foremothers would have taken exceptional precautions and I know this, no one person alone would be able to open that doorway whether they are exceptional or not. There would be a third key and for safety's sake there would be no reference to it within your grounds. I will need to refer to the ancient archives here to establish where that key is."

"I understand My Lady."
"It is doubtful but if your watcher has somehow found the third key this will need to be escalated to the Grand Council immediately."
"Yes My Lady."
"For now, go to the statue and establish if the keys are still there. If they are matters may not be as bad as they may appear. Once you have done that call me straight back as I now have some work to do in the archive."

"Yes My Lady, of course, I shall go there straight away."
"Reeve, whatever you do, be very careful. If this watcher has gained access someone is helping him. Do not trust anyone or discuss these matters with anyone but me at this time."
"I understand fully and I will come back to you as soon as I can. Thank you for your council My Lady."
"I'll speak with you soon Reeve of Loxley."

The Reeve heard the phone disconnect at the other end as she placed her phone back in its cradle.
She stood up in the silence of her room and paced up and down with her hands on her hips deep in thought at what might be. Looking at her clock pendulum swinging back and forth, she was forced to consider if Nubia, the paranoid curator, had been right all along.

Having parked her car, Sarah walked in to the reception area with her work bag over her shoulder and holding Missy in the carrier. She looked at the receptionist who smiled at her as she answered the phone "Castle Hollow Veterinary Practise how may I help you?"

She walked straight behind the reception desk and through a door marked private to look for David the senior partner in the practice.

"Is David in his office?" she asked Julia as she passed by her - Julia was also a partner.
"Yes he is, he tells me that you may have an interesting case."

"I certainly have, you are not kidding."
"May I join you I would like to see?"
"Yes of course please do, another opinion couldn't hurt."

Julia followed Sarah towards David's office and they could both see that his door was open. Sarah peered her head around his door and saw that he was sitting at his desk typing on his computer.

"David I have the cat with me that I told you about."
He looked up with a smile. "Excellent, it sounds most interesting Sarah. If you can take her through we'll have a look straight away."

As she left his office Sarah could hear his voice from behind her.
"How you holding up Sarah?"
She stopped in her tracks and turned around to look at him and took a deep breath. "You're not going to believe it; he hired a bloody private investigator to follow me."
"You're kidding!" exclaimed Julia.
"And that's not all, she was wearing a clown nose and drove into the back on my car, broke one of my lights!"
Julia raised an eyebrow and was looking at David who looked in shock.
"You can't be serious" David said with his mouth aghast.
"Yep and she was driving around holding a cat."

David and Julia were both looking at each other.
"A private investigator wearing a clown nose driving with a cat and she crashes into you!" David didn't know whether to laugh or not and was pinching himself on the side of his leg to make sure he didn't.
"Well that's about the mark of the man" Julia said.
"Total looser" Sarah shared her thoughts as all three of them nodded their heads in unison.

"Well let's take her through" David said ushering his hand towards the doorway of the next room.
"I took her photograph; the investigator."
"Good for you" David said following Sarah into the surgery. "If she continues to harass you, you should call the Police."
Sarah placed the carrier with Missy inside gently onto the counter. "Oh don't

worry about that, I intend to. Really strange, all of her clothing looked designer as well."

David shook his head. "Right let's see what we can see" he said walking over to the side and taking a pair of disposable gloves from their box. "Tell me a little about her please."

Sarah took her notes from her bag although she didn't really need them. "The cat's name is Missy, and she's a nearly three year old British Shorthair. Doesn't respond to any stimulation, in considerable discomfort and has been this way for over 24 hours. As you know I detected a bizarre heart rhythm." Sarah took a step forward towards the table where David was leant over Missy studying her. "I detected two possible heart beats."
David looked up to Julia's frowning face and then to Sarah with a half smile. "Two heart beats you say?"
"Yes Julia, I've never experienced anything like this."
"And there has never been any history of any heart abnormality in the past?"
"No, apparently not, although we have never seen Missy before. She called some other vet first called Fennaway." Sarah shook her head slightly as she said this.
"I've never heard of a vet called Fennaway around here, have you David?" Julia asked her business partner. "Nope, never heard the name must be someone new, too many coming out of college now" he said with a mischievous smile whilst looking at Sarah.

David looked down at Missy watching her paws occasionally twitching. "It's almost as if Missy is unconscious, how strange." He walked to the side and picked up his stethoscope. "Samantha" he yelled placing it around his neck. All three of them turned around as the receptionist came into the room. "Just in case can you prep the room for surgery please."

Khepri's ears twitched immediately as she heard this.
"Right then Missy; let's see what is going on."
Khepri could feel the presence of the vet standing over her.
"Mildred will be devastated if the cat needs surgery."
David looked up "Mildred?"
"Yes, the owner, she was almost beside herself, sad really. It's almost as if Missy is all she has in the world."
Julia shook her head slightly upon hearing this. "It is sad but I get it, I really do."

David had shifted his attention to Julia.

"Well I'd much rather have my cats than a boyfriend any day of the week."

"I can relate to that!" Sarah said instantaneously.

"We are not all bad you know."

"Rubbish!" Sarah and Julia said at the same time, "you're all as bad as each other!" Julia added.

David smiled placing the ear buds into his ears.

"I think the news of any surgery upon Missy will come as a blow to her" Sarah said.

Upon hearing the word 'surgery' for the third time Khepri was done with her Oscar winning performance for today and opened her eyes.

"David, her eyes have opened!"

David took a step back looking down at the cat. "Well so they have. I didn't imagine that, they were closed before?"

They both nodded.

All three of them watched as '*Missy*' extended her paws and straightened her tail and sat upright.

"Well I never." David brought his head down to look at Missy a little closer. "Hello Missy, this must be very confusing for you but I just want to check your heartbeat." He put the chest piece on the side of the cat and listened intently. A considerable frown appeared across his face as he looked up at Sarah. He removed the chest piece and performed the same movement three times before pulling the ear buds out and letting the stethoscope rest on his neck.

Taking a couple of steps backwards he looked at Sarah. "There is nothing wrong with this cat, well certainly in terms of heartbeat, the rhythm is fine, not abnormal in any way. And I most certainly can't hear any signs of two heartbeats Sarah!"

Julia frowned and shook her head slightly and looked over at Sarah.

"That's not possible David, I know what I heard and I know what I saw." She walked over to him and snatched the stethoscope from his neck and placed the buds in her ears.

He took a couple of steps further back. "You should have gloves on Sarah" as he looked at Julia who looked at the floor with further shakes of the head.

"I'm telling you, I know what I heard!" as she placed the chest piece on the side of Missy. She closed her eyes upon hearing a completely regular heartbeat coming up through her ear buds. "It's not possible..." She pulled the ear buds out and stepped back and looked up at Julia.

"You've been working a lot of hours of late Sarah" Julia said taking a step towards her as she then looked down at Missy. "With everything that has gone on and now you have a private investigator following you, it hasn't been easy."
"That has nothing to do with my professional capacity."
"We are not saying that Sarah" was the voice from behind her as she turned around to look at David.
"David please, I'm telling you what I heard."
"See it from our point of view; you now have Magnum PI on your tail wearing a clown nose."
"But you could see that when I brought her in she looked unwell."
"Indeed and for that reason we will keep her in overnight to monitor her but ask yourself this, does that cat look unwell to you?"
Sarah looked down to see Missy sitting upright staring at her. "I don't understand it, I just don't."
"Sarah." She looked at Julia. "Look why don't you take the afternoon off, we'll call Mildred later and give her an update. Just leave the client notes with Samantha and come back in the morning so you can take Missy back to her. It's for the best."

Sarah starred at Julia with her mouth open in shock and turned around to look at David who offered the slightest of smiles and then looked at the floor.
"I see, I see." She removed the stethoscope from around her neck and gently placed it on the side and picked up the client notes and her bag. "Well, I'll see you tomorrow then."
"See you tomorrow Sarah" Julia said watching her leave the room as she turned to look at her business partner with some concern.

She dropped the client notes on the receptionist's desk as requested. "Here, these are for you, I'm having the afternoon off."
"Really, are you doing anything nice?" Samantha enquired as she saw Sarah turn around looking quite angry.
"No, car repairs" and with that she pushed the exit door open as hard as she could.

Reaching into her bag in the car park she stopped walking and pulled out her phone. Entering the password she went straight to her picture file and pulled up the picture of Jessica. She stared at it angrily for longer than she meant to.

"I'm on to you!"

The Reeve had made her way to the security wing of the Escarrabin having been reasonably undetected so far. Although members of the security arm of the Order seeing her was not an issue in the slightest, she did want to keep out of view of the elders and especially the curator.

Much was on her mind and the thought or even the very consideration of an insider had her deeply troubled. She needed to be sure of her facts and did not want to be responsible for the creation of any panic.

As she approached the side exit doors that would lead her out to the gardens at the front she turned around to check that no-one was following her and then placed her pin badge to the scanner logo for the doors to open.

Waiting patiently as the heavy wooden doors opened inwards she looked over her shoulder continuously and stepped through as quickly as she could into the fresh summer air. Once outside she waited for the doors to reclose before moving forward. Keeping against the wall of the house as she moved forward whilst still checking behind her, she could see a couple of watchers in the distance tending to the gardens, wearing their goggles to protect their eye from direct sunlight.

Treading as carefully as she could across the gravel, she reached the front of the building and looked directly ahead down the main driveway and gardens and could see the great statue of Salma in the distance directly on her left. With her right arm resting on the corner of the house she peered round and could see there was no activity out of the front of the house and boldly started to walk forward cutting across the grass. Being as careful as she could to keeping at an angle, hoping she couldn't be seen by her own security from the lower front windows of the house, she increased her pace watching as the huge statue came closer to her.

The great statue was an impressive sight as a shrine to her past and everything that she did for the Order a long time ago. Under her leadership, she shaped not just how the Order functioned but also moulded the relationship with the Reeves and their need for privacy and security. The Order had been in peril in days past and her diligence and intelligence had sought to rid that from any future events.

The Reeve upped her pace as the statue became ever closer still being very vigilant, watching behind her and looking back at the great house checking that she was not being observed. As she passed the pyramid shaped bushes she could see the stone cats at the feet of Lady Salma coming into view, there were eight of them in total. As she made her way to the foot of the statue, the Reeve looked up at the enormous size of the figure above her and she ran her hand along the top of the huge stone plinth that she stood at the base of. Lady Salma was cradling her beloved Alliaa in her left hand and her right hand was held aloft with her palm facing forwards as a symbol of resistance against the watchers and the darkness that they stood for.

The Reeve took a couple of steps backwards looking up at the statue as she needed to compose herself. Her pulse had elevated and although it was a warm day in the height of summer she was becoming unnecessarily clammy with anxiety.

She took three deep breaths and walked back towards the statue.

Knowing that Nahla was now on the way to headquarters Nubia was preparing her couch to make it as comfortable as possible for her. She plumped up the couch under her main window in her office as best as she could and went into her private quarters to obtain some more bedding and pillows. Her constant standing on the couch to look outside had taken its toll.

If she were truthful with herself she was not sure of the next steps to take. She had done the right thing in ensuring that Nahla was not taken away for assessment by anyone other than Fennaway but she was not going to be able to solve Nahla's pain. Fennaway would probably have to be called to headquarters to oversee her. These are trying times she thought to herself dumping the extra bedding and pillows on to the couch. In any event it was stuffy in here and some fresh air couldn't hurt as she stood on the couch and leaned towards the window.

Bringing the window off the latch she opened it outwards welcoming the fresh Welsh air into her room. She closed her eyes and took a deep breath and inhaled. Enjoying the clean air, making a change from the smell of musty old furniture, she reopened her eyes to see a figure standing in the distance next to the great statue. She rubbed her eyes and squinted in the sunlight and focused at the figure that was unmoved looking upwards at it. Judging by the misplaced suit the figure was wearing it was a reasonable assumption that it may be the Reeve. Well what was she doing over there? She jumped down and ran to her desk pulling open one of the large drawers, taking the bottle of whisky out. She leant to the back of the drawer and pulled out a set of binoculars and flipped their protective caps off and ran at the couch and leapt upon it.

Practically throwing the binoculars to her eyes she focused pretty well everywhere except where she really needed to see. "Come on!" she chastised herself before the statue came into view. Looking around the base she grimaced that she couldn't see anyone. She pulled the binoculars from her eyes to rely on normal vision and frowned as she rested them down on the windowsill and leaned forward out of the window. Shaking her head puzzled she knew that she had not imagined it.

"Well where the hell did she go?"

After taking her three deep breaths the Reeve walked towards the statue and stretched her arms up against the stone plinth and pushed up onto her toes. She was almost at full stretch as she felt her way around the paws of the cats set in stone at the base of Lady Salma.

There were four cats on either side of the great lady's legs. The four that the Reeve was running her hands over were against the left leg of the huge statue and only three of them unlocked what she suspected Duat had been trying to access.

Taking a deep breath she pressed down with her left hand onto the left paw of the first cat. She felt it depress into the stone work and took a couple of steps to her right ignoring the cat next to the one she had just pressed down upon. Now was the tricky bit as the left and right paw of the next two cats needed to be pressed at exactly the same time. Stretching like she was about to do a star jump, she pressed down upon both paws at the same time and immediately heard a loud echoed thud from underneath the statue and the sound of moving stone.

She was immediately flatfooted again as she peered around the corner of the statue and could see the stone plinth to her right hand side had moved inwards. As she moved around she looked over her shoulder for the last time and back at the house and pushed against the stone. She heard the expected secondary click as the very heavy stone found its way onto the runners underneath and then pushed it over to the right and climbed into the very dark hole that had appeared.

The Reeve could feel her heart pulsing as she had only been in here once before and didn't care for being locked in the pitch black that she knew was about to happen.

She reached out to the large handle that was set into the reverse side of the stone and took a deep breath and gathered her strength and pulled the stone back over to close her in. As the stone moved on the runners she placed both hands against it and pushed until she heard a loud echo of the sound of stone sitting back into place and the cats claws above her outside resetting.

In the darkness she crouched waiting knowing that she could not stand yet for fear of banging her head on the heavy stonework above her.

She started to count down from ten, hating every moment of the darkness, when she heard an old motor start up from below and flickered light started to appear. She could now see the old staircase directly to her left and let out a huge breath of relief as the beads of sweat fell from her forehead.

At the bottom of the staircase the symbol of the Reeve lit up to the right hand side of the steel door and she looked at the old wheel that she would need to turn to open it. Still crouched down she stretched her left leg out and shuffled towards the stairs until she had descended enough of them that she could stand up fully.

Taking some thirty of so stairs, she went deep below the statue. Her mind had lost focus from the possible missing keys and was now concerned about what she would do if the old release mechanism to get out didn't work. No-one other than the Reeves knew of this place and of course that was the real reason why there was no CCTV on the grounds in order to protect the secrets of the hidden vault from the prying eyes of others. However once inside there was no form of communication whatsoever and potentially she could be trapped here. This was something that she would need to address at a later stage.

At the bottom of the steps the illuminated symbol shone above the protective casing of the scanner and there were no visible signs of anything forced. Unclipping the casing so it fell forward, she put her right hand against the scanner and pressed with her left hand on the symbol and watched as the scanner started and moved up and down her palm. As the scanner proceeded to read her hand she looked behind her at the ancient lighting system and shook her head slightly. If her predecessor had installed this level of security to gain access you'd think a light switch at the top of the staircase would have been a consideration.

The scanner stopped and the illuminated logo of the Reeve turned green. She replaced the protective cover and took hold either side of the large wheel built into the centre of the door and put her body weight against it and started to turn on it.

The old wheel took some effort to move as she could hear the locking mechanism working from within. She continued to turn until she heard the sound of multiple locking points giving way and she took her hands from the wheel and took a deep breath. Putting both of her hands on the door, she leant against it with her weight and pushed from her shoulders until the old steel door started to steadily move forward across the stone floor.

She heard a clicking noise as the lights of the vault flickered on one by one revealing its various chambers and she could hear the humming of electricity echoing from the far end of the vault from the sealed temperature controlled rooms.

The huge expanse of the vault and its eight chambers were the treasures of the Reeves that had been collected and stored for centuries. For all the steps that had been taken for their preservation, it was highly disorganised and priceless items would appear to have been left here in the past as if in a hurry. If the Reeve of Loxley had any part of this in the future the varying chambers and its treasures would be logged and separated. Organisation is something the Reeves pride themselves upon. Why Roman, Egyptian and other relics were stored in the same chambers she had no idea.

As the Reeve walked forward her footsteps echoing in the coldness of the vault, she headed for the room of keys glancing at various artefacts on the way. Some she recognised from archaeology programmes on television, which was painful to watch at times knowing that they were wasting their time looking for them.

She looked up upon her approach to the chamber on the far left, the only chamber with its own unique archway; the centre keystone of the arch had an old faded image of an ancient key engraved into the sandstone.

Below ground the heat of the summer afternoon bypassed this place and she shivered as she entered the key chamber, the sweat from her previous excursions now making her cold. The keys were not hidden and did not need to be. This was an area of private storage and she walked over to an old desk in the right hand corner of the chamber, seeing lines of keys hanging on the wall above it.

There were a couple of heavy ornate eight foot long gold carrying rods propped against the desk that she carefully moved to the corner as she studied the keys looking for the two keys that had four sets of teeth.

There were hundreds of keys from the old system that opened every door of the mansion. The pin badge door entry system had been installed a few years before making all of these old keys redundant and here they now lay discarded to the cold and dark of the key chamber.

She recognised many of the keys that hung on the hooks that were crudely embedded into the wall as keys that opened old chests and small keys that opened lockable books. She ran her left hand along the multiple lines of old brass and iron keys, some of which would have been centuries old, but none of them were close to what she was looking for.

Taking a couple of paces backwards she brought a hand to her chin in thought and bit on her lip and looked around the rest of the room of keys.

Her eyes were drawn directly to her left where she could see a couple of keys hanging in the far corner.

Pulling her suit jacket together in the chill she took a few paces over to them and bent over to look at them. They were old, very old, but not what she was looking for but her eyes were distracted by a word above them to the right. It had been scratched into the wall by hand and was very faded. She leaned in closer allowing her eyes to focus on the barely readable word 'Ferius'. "Ferius?"

Her eyes went upwards to her left trying to access her brain and she shook her head, it had been a long time since she had spoken the language of old. Screwing up her face in thought her eyes never moved from the faded singular word as she brought her right hand to it and rubbed gently across it as tiny particles of old stone fell to the floor. She gulped immediately as two more characters came into view 'Inferius!' As her eyes tried to access her brain again, she let out an audible gasp and only one spoken word "below." She looked down at the two empty hooks on the wall "Oh No!" as the realisation dawned on her that the keys were missing.

In the coldness she felt the hairs stand up on the back of her neck as her breathing became agitated knowing full well that their security had been breached. Stepping back and breathing heavily she looked at the floor knowing that she would need the help of her superior and the Grand Council would now need to be informed.

Thoughts of self preservation ran through her mind, knowing that this security breach had happened under her tenure but how anyone could have got in here and bypassed the scanner that was only accessed by her hand she did not know.

She clung onto the wall of the archway listening to her heart beat and the humming of the electricity. She had better check the doors of the temperature controlled rooms to ensure that nothing obvious was missing from there as well.

Still breathing heavily, she walked over to the two sealed caverns and looked through the heavily fortified screen doors of both of them. Truth be told, as it was only her second visit here, and unless obvious, she would not know if anything else was missing. The cavern on her left had rows of books and protected artworks but there was no sign of any forced entry. The second cavern had an old chest with a white sheet draped over it and she bent down slightly and could see it had what looked to be gold legs. There were also a couple of sarcophagi, scrolls and other artefacts. This temperature controlled chamber bared more resemblance to a tomb than anything else but in any event, it did not look like it had been disturbed.

Taking one final look around, she headed out of the exit door and pulled heavily against it until it rested and spun the locking wheel around until it would turn no more.

Knowing full well that in a moment she would be back in darkness, her anxiety was increasing again as she reached the top of the stairs, taking hold of the iron lever to release the stone to allow her to exit.

Taking two deep breaths she took hold of the lever with both hands and pulled down as the electricity was cut. In the dark she heard the stone move towards her and the cracks of daylight started to make its way through.

Exiting this place was one thing but her troubles had only just started.

Chapter Twenty Five:

THE KEYS OF INFERIOUS

FRIDAY APPROACHING 1.45PM

Having made her way back to her offices as quickly as possible the Reeve was sat at her desk behind closed doors. There was going to be no easy way to explain what she had discovered. If her head of Order was correct and the four sided keys were supposed to be in the vault they certainly were not now. She would have explaining to do, knowing that fingers would be pointed at her.

There were no guarantees that Duat had them. There were no guarantees they were even there. Let's face it they could have been missing for a long time. She needed to get her story straight and in doing so try to protect her own reputation at the same time. Other than her first visit to the vault following her appointment at Loxley, no-one had been below the statue for a long time, well to her knowledge anyway. Her predecessor may have even removed them, but she had to be honest with herself, that would be highly unlikely.

She had to prepare herself by way of explanation, not easy when you are not in possession of the facts. If they had been there, the Reeve's security had been penetrated but how could that possibly be. No-one should have known about the vault, let alone how to access it from above and below.

Drawing her breath she picked up her phone and hit redial and waited to hear a

Spanish greeting at the other end.

She closed her eyes knowing that security measures being breached had not happened at any headquarters the world over in a very long time. It would get talked about throughout her Order with much detriment to her personal reputation.

After listening to the phone ringing at the other end for thirty seconds or so she gave up and slowly put the phone back down. Her head of Order must be busy and she didn't mind that as it gave her more time to think.

Approaching 2pm

The car hurtled around the bend into the dead end road that she now recognised; this time there would be no faffing around looking for secret entrances. Jessica reached inside her jacket pocket and pulled out her pin badge and fixed it to her lapel.

She felt the brakes of the car depress beneath her feet as the car pulled to a stop at the semicircle at the end of the road. Time being of the essence, Jessica jumped out quickly and went straight to the scanning post and bent over so her pin found the mark of the scanner.

She looked around to ensure that she wasn't being watched as she heard the sounds of moving metal from beneath her feet as the trees in front of her gave way. With a few steps she was back inside the car making a mental note not to bang the car horn as she went down the driveway this time, it didn't matter what she saw.

Glancing across at Nahla and watching her paws twitch, she hoped that she may get some answers as to exactly what was going on. The car sped forward towards the grand archway and as she passed through she could see the trees behind in her rear view mirror were moving back into their original place.

Staring at the expanse of the mansion house as it became ever closer the building and their gardens were beautiful; when she has her own office here she hoped that she would be able to enjoy them more. The statues looked fascinating telling stories from the past presumably. It may even be that Lady Nubia may not be quite so rude if she was here more often but she doubted that somehow.

As the main entrance came into view for the second time this week, her car pealed round to the left of the building and she could hear the gravel beneath the wheels being disturbed in, what would appear to be, the most silent of places deep in the countryside of North Wales.

As the car veered to the right at the end of the building she could see that Nubia was already at the door waiting for her.

Jolting forward in her seat as the car abruptly stopped and dust came up from underneath the wheels she sat in her driver's seat waiting to see if Nubia would come forward to her. After a few seconds it didn't look like she was going to. Jessica released her seat belt and opened the door to get out.

"Good afternoon Madam Nubia" she said without response as she walked around her car and opened the passenger door. "Come on Nahla, let's take you inside." She very gently pulled Nahla to her chest, holding her with both hands and supporting her head and swiped at the car door with her backside to close it.

Why Nubia had a frown across her face she had no idea as she walked towards her.
"There you go, that wasn't so difficult was it?"
"Well it was quite challenging actually if I'm honest Madam Nubia."
"Pass the cat to me."

It was not lost on Jessica that yet again there were no please or thank you.

As Nubia took Nahla from Jessica, she studied the cat and the pain it was in was very evident. "Oh my poor dear" she said whilst stroking Nahla's head.

It was only now, in their second meeting, that Jessica had witnessed any emotion from the curator of the Order; maybe she was human after all but the jury was out on that one.

"Right, we need to know when Khepri is coming back from the vets so you can change the cats around again. Mildred of course will know straight away that Khepri is not Nahla."

"Well yes My Lady but how on earth am I going to do that?"

The frown was evident again as the curator looked up at the face of Jessica and sighed with a shake of her head. "Well you are seeing Mildred later aren't you? Ask her about the wellbeing of her cat, she's bound to tell you. They will probably keep Khepri in overnight for observations."

"You don't think they will do tests on her do you?"

"Let's hope not, that could cause another problem, so monitor it will you, let me know if you hear anything untoward."

Nubia turned around to walk back into the mansion "Step in; I have something here for you that may help."

Jessica followed with a little dip, as her heels slipped on the gravel, as she went through the archway into the dimly lit room and heard the door closing behind her.

"Over there." The curator nodded at an old table on the left hand side and Jessica could see what looked to be a very old camera. "Take that, just in case you need it."

Jessica walked to the table and picked up what she guessed to be a very old Polaroid camera. With confusion on her face she turned to the curator and shook her head. "I don't understand, a camera it looks ancient?"

"Far from it, 30 years or so is very young in our time line and besides you should never mock the old, Jessica."

Not for the first time Jessica felt like she was being told off.

"That may buy you some time, you just press the red button with it pointed directly at your target."

"My target?" Jessica said with some shock.

"Yes, your target. The flash will disrupt the brain for approximately 8-10 seconds and no more."

Jessica looked back at the camera as she heard this.

"It may help you do, what was it called, a switcharoo did you say?"

Jessica looked down at the floor with a little embarrassment.

"I assure you it works; I took it from the security wing of the Escarrabin earlier."

"The Escarrabin My Lady?"
The curator closed her eyes at the slip of the tongue and looked upwards. "Yes, the Escarrabin, our security officers, you will come to see them in time when you settle."

Jessica watched the curator as she stroked Nahla and turned to walk away. "Let me know if there is anything that I need to be aware of Jessica."

"Um, yes I will do. Lady Nubia may I ask something?" Jessica watched as she saw the short stature of Nubia turn around to face her. "What is wrong with Nahla?"
"We don't know but we can't have outsiders assessing our own, it's as simple as that."

Jessica nodded. "I see" (she didn't) and was reasonably sure that she was not being told the full story.
"Well off you go then, you have a gathering to attend and you'll be a degree level 6 next time I see you."
Jessica smiled upon hearing this and she watched the curator disappear with Mildred's cat. "Let yourself out, your car is ready for you" is all she heard echoing throughout the old room.

Standing there holding the old camera, looking at the flickering candlelight, she felt a wave of discomfort in this creepy old place and quickly made her way to the exit.
The symbol of the Order was lit next to the door and she lifted her pin towards it and was relieved to see the door opening in front of her.

Her car was already running *(how do they do that?)* as she got in and took her seat watching the doorway to the mansion close. Pulling her door closed, the car immediately moved away and she looked at the old camera on the seat that had taken the place of Nahla. Her thoughts were of Mildred and the worry she must have.

As the car pulled around to the front of the house she looked up at the imposing frontage as she moved down the driveway. She could see a couple of floors up that a tall lady in a business suit was watching from above.

I wonder who that could be. Not giving it any further thought she turned back around and the car took her back towards the archway.

"Hello, is that Mildred?"

"Yes, it's Mildred speaking."

"Hello Mildred, I'm Julia one of the partners at Castle Hollow Veterinary Practise."

"Oh yes, how is my Missy please?"

"Well I'm very pleased to say that she has made a full recovery and everything is well."

"She's awake and has stopped shaking?" Mildred said with excitement and glee.

"She seems completely normal Mildred, quite odd actually if I'm honest. When she came here she just seemed to make a miraculous recovery. Her paws were shaking and they just seemed to stop and she opened her eyes and has been fine since. Funny really, although we did not know what was wrong, we were talking about possible surgery and she just seemed to wake up. I'm sure our cats understand us some times!"

"Well my Missy is a very special cat."

"I'm quite sure she is" responded Julia quite positive that she could hear clapping coming from the other end of the phone. "I can tell that you are happy Mildred and so are we but to be on the safe side we would like to keep her in overnight just for observations."

"Oh, really?"

Julia could hear that the clapping from the other end had stopped.

"It is customary Mildred as in truth and I must be honest with you, we didn't do anything but Sarah had mentioned to us about an abnormal heart beat so for that reason it's best to be safe. I hope that you agree?"

"Well yes I guess so if you think its best, I thought Sarah was going to call me?"

There was a brief pause at the other end of the phone before the voice resumed. "She wanted to but has had to go out on another call. However she will bring Missy back to you tomorrow morning."

"Well that is good news Julia, I'm so happy I cannot tell you!"

"I'm glad to be the bearer of good news and you have our telephone number if you need to call us and you can email us if you would like."

"No, just phone thank you as I don't have a computer."

"Oh really, that's quite rare these days but as you wish Mildred. Call us if you need to, if not and everything is okay overnight Missy will be back with you tomorrow."

"Yes I'm quite old fashioned and do without technology but I'm so so pleased Julia, thank you very much for calling."

"You are welcome, goodbye Mildred."

"Goodbye, thank you!"

She put the cat phone down with something to finally smile about and clapped her hands together with joy. Thank goodness for that, what a scare Missy had given her and she raised a hand to her chest and took some deep breaths.

"I think a celebration cup of tea is in order!" she laughed realising that she was talking to herself with no Missy to listen to her. She went into the kitchen and turned on the gas and filled the kettle. As she turned around her eyes immediately latched onto the cat birthday cards on the side.

She bit her lip in thought. Well I guess there is no reason for me not to go to the gathering now.

Looking at her clock she could see that it was approaching 3; Jessica was due to pick her up around 6ish.

A rush of excitement came back to her now knowing that she was going out to meet her own kind, lovers of cats, enthusiasts of cats and having a lovely evening at the same time.

I guess I had better start to get ready she considered and kicked her shoes off across the kitchen floor. There was much to think about including what she would wear. She had better check her wardrobe again.

Approaching 4pm

The Reeve was back at her window having heard the disturbance outside of other Escarrabin arriving at Loxley. It was scheduled for them to arrive today but her mind was now on the use of them other than their usual ceremonial duties. With troubling events of potentially missing keys and a rogue watcher, they may have a more serious role to play while they are here.

She watched them filter off to the side to their entrance into the manor house. She had no idea why the near 6th degree elder called Jessica had been seen here again. She suspected that it had something to do with Nubia again. But for now her thoughts were focused on the below and that could wait until later.

She went over to her phone to try her head of Order again.

The phone must have rung at least twenty times and as she was about to hang up she could suddenly hear a muffled voice from the other end.

"Hello, My Lady?"
"Si Reeve I am here."
"I did try to reach you earlier."
"I have only just returned from the archives. These things take time; I had to look very deeply into the past. Now tell me, did you go the statue?"
"Yes My Lady I did." The Reeve swallowed and looked around her room to check she was alone. "The keys, I could not find them. I found two empty hooks that were below the word inferious, I suspect that is where they should be." The Reeve could sense the discomfort at the other end of the phone upon hearing this.

"Reeve, this is most serious!"
"I know My Lady. Is there any way that my predecessor may have removed them or they were moved to somewhere else?"
"I think that to be highly unlikely and we must assume not."

They were both silent for a few seconds.

"Reeve, if those keys have been taken that is one thing but how could that watcher have got down there and furthermore provided a successful scan of your hand? It is only your hand that allows for the vault to be opened."

There was a pause as she thought further...

"We have to assume that someone is helping him, someone who can access certain information. In any event it would sound like this watcher is well informed and this may have been planned for some time. His showing up outside your main gates and now with the keys missing confirms that he wanted to be caught."

"Those thoughts had occurred to me as well My Lady."

"Reeve of Loxley your security has been breached while you are in control and you have not been in post for very long, this does not bode well for you."
She swallowed as her face drained of colour. "Yes I am aware of this My Lady."
"The first thing to do is to find out if the third key is missing, the iron wall will not open without it."
"I understand; have you been able to find out anything from the archives?"
"Si I have been able to. This is a two part process and first you need a key to open where the main key is hidden. If the watcher had got to this key you would probably already know about it so it may well be safe."
"I understand; where do I find it My Lady?"
"It should be safely with Lady Safiya your head of house. She however will not know the significance of it."
"She has no idea?"
"No, however if process has been followed, she will have it."
"Will she tell me where it is and how I can get to it?"
"No, she will show it to you."
The Reeve was surprised by this answer "She will show me?"
"It is a small ring and she should be wearing it. Within the ring is a key and that will open the door that contains the main key and the priority key to the wall of iron."
"I see My Lady, however once I have the ring key, where is this door that is to be opened?"

"You are sitting on it Reeve of Loxley."

The Reeve's eyes flashed and she quickly jumped up and took a few paces backwards from her chair.

"Claim the key and find within the chair where the master key is stored."
The Reeve didn't offer a response other than a silent nod of the head.

"Reeve listen this is very important. Whether the key is there or not, what lies below will need to be investigated and action taken but as yet I have not been able to find what this creature is and I need to return to the archives to see if I can find anything that will help you. Do not, under any circumstance, go down there until you know what you are facing. I would suggest for now speak to your head of the Escarrabin to keep vigilance as you do not want to cause a panic but do not go below until you have the facts to hand."

"Yes My Lady, I understand."
"Go and see your head of the house and I will call you when I can find out more."
"Yes my Lady, I will do that."
"Find the key Reeve and put a stop to whatever this watcher is trying to do!"
"Yes My Lady I will do my very best."
"I must go."

The Reeve heard the phone disconnect in Spain and she placed her phone down not taking her eyes off her chair. She pulled it back from her desk and circled it a couple of times and crouched down to look underneath it. How could this possibly be, she only bought it from IKEA a few weeks back and assembled it herself? She was feeling her way along the arm supports when she suddenly stopped and shook her head and looked up at the ceiling. "Idiot!" as she kicked the chair to the side and she watched it glide across the floor on its wheels.

She let out a deep sigh as she went into one of the adjoining rooms and stared at the ancient chair that she had replaced as it was so uncomfortable to sit on, no matter how many cushions were put upon it. She couldn't bear this thing, it was heavy and cumbersome and looked more like a throne than something you would sit on in your office.

As she dragged it away from the wall it had been discarded against she felt along the heavy oak arm supports for anything that resembled a key hole. Her elder had said that it was a tiny key so she felt her way carefully but nothing was obvious. Crouching down to look underneath the elaborate chair design, the dark oak wood made it very difficult to see. She took both of the back legs of the chair in her hands and lifted it upwards feeling the weight of it on her back in an instant and spun it over so she could see the underside clearly in the light.

"Well I never." In the top right hand corner there looked to be a small keyhole. She pushed at the panelling and nothing moved, it was sturdy and clearly well made. Wrapping her knuckles on the wood all around the keyhole listening for a hollow sound of a hidden compartment, she considered that a sledgehammer would probably do the trick, as unethical as it may be to some in destroying this grand old uncomfortable chair. Taking a couple of steps backwards she was giving this serious thought but she knew the Order of old do not do things in half measure and there could be a security mechanism inside that could damage the key, even if it were there in the first place.

It was no good and she couldn't delay any further. She would have to see the head of the house, there was no way around it. She knew full well that Safiya would be asking questions of her and she didn't want to give answers at this time, not that she had many anyway. A security breach was very serious and if Safiya didn't need to know then she would avoid the questions completely.

It was troubling but she would have to face up to it along with any other action that may be taken against her in the future. She needed to prepare for an awkward meeting.

Having got out of the shower Mildred raced for her phone with an old towel wrapped around her. "Number 1 Rocke Road" she answered with a couple of puffs of breath.

"Mildred, it's Daphne."
"Oh hello Daphne, lovely to hear from you." She was indeed pleased to hear from her elder.
"I'm just checking in, I trust that you are going to the gathering later on?"
"Oh yes, I'm very excited about it, although it was a close call I very nearly wasn't going to go."
"Heavens Mildred, why ever not?"
"Oh it's Missy, she has been terribly unwell. I've been very worried about her the last couple of days."
"Did you call Fennaway?"
"I did but I was not very impressed with her level of service so I called someone else."

"You called someone else Mildred?"
"Yes, I called a vet at Castle Hollow, much better."

There was silence at the other end of the phone.

"Daphne, are you still there?"
"Where is Missy now Mildred?"
She could sense concern in her tone of voice. "Well I'm very pleased to say that she is much better but they are keeping her in overnight, just for safety, procedure apparently. Kamilah Fennaway tried to talk to Missy down the phone, can you believe it?" Mildred was in fits of laughter as she spoke.
"Err that is indeed unusual." Daphne gave out a small fake laugh.

Mildred continued to laugh before realising that her laughs were not being matched from the other end.

"Mildred, do you know whether this other vet will run tests on Missy?"
"Tests Daphne? Well I have no idea; I'm guessing not and hope not. Apparently as soon as Missy arrived there she got much better, strange isn't it?"
"Yes that is indeed very odd Mildred."

It was not lost on Mildred that Daphne's voice had become more serious the longer the conversation went on. She sat on her bed as the water drops fell from her hair somewhat perplexed with this sudden change of tone.

"Anyway, I'm glad you are going Mildred so I shall see you later on."
"Yes Lady Jessica is collecting me a little later; we should be there for around 7.30 I would think."
"Yes I know. I saw her a couple of days ago and she did mention it. She's never given me a lift anywhere so I'm guessing she has taken a shine to you Mildred."
"Oh really, well that's nice to hear" although the use of the word 'shine' again was perturbing.
"Yes, isn't it."
Mildred noted the words coming from her elder were still somewhat odd.

"Well must dash, I was just checking to see that you are okay and I look forward to seeing you later Mildred."
"Thank you Daphne, I look forward to seeing you to, goodbye for now."

"Goodbye Mildred."

Daphne terminated the call very concerned with what she had heard and pondered for a few moments.

Flicking through her phone book she found her elder's phone number and dialled. It only took a few rings to be answered and instantly from the background noise Daphne could tell that her elder was in a car.

"Lady Jessica its Daphne."
"Yes I know, your number flashed up on my phone; I'm driving at the moment you are on speaker."
"Okay, I shall be brief. I don't wish to talk out of turn but I've just spoken to Mildred, the one on Rocke Road that is and she tells me that another vet has her cat Nahla."
"Yes we are aware of it, it's all in hand."
"Oh, you already know My Lady?"
"Yes apparently Mildred didn't get along with Fennaway but we have taken precautions. It was quite the security operation but it would appear I'm a natural!"
"I see" Daphne had no idea how Jessica could already know about this. "I just wanted to bring it to your attention just in case any tests had been undertaken; I thought it prudent to let you know."
"Thank you and we do appreciate that but it's all in hand Daphne. I saw to it personally but please do not tell Mildred!"
"Well, okay, that's good then and no, I will not say anything."
"I'm just driving back from North Wales but I should make it back in time to collect Mildred for the gathering so I'll see you later tonight then."
"Yes okay My Lady, I look forward to it, thank you."
"Thank you Daphne, goodbye for now."

As Jessica disconnected the call her thoughts immediately turned with some concern to Khepri hoping that no testing had been undertaken on her. She swallowed at the thought of it in worry, shaking her head to clear her thoughts. "She's too smart, she'll be fine."

Glancing at the navigator it was still probably going to be an hours drive home dependent on traffic. "Car, can't you go any faster?" It didn't and stuck to the speed limit as she crossed her arms and sat back letting the car do the work for her.

The Reeve had ensured her old fortified door was secured as she walked towards the lobby area.

The four heads of the clerics were looking down at their work in an all too familiar pose. As she passed them she looked over to see what they were doing; shuffling papers and writing notes. The Order, and especially the curator, certainly seemed to keep them busy. She passed by two further corridors before joining one of the grand staircases that flowed throughout the centre of the house.

The red carpeted staircases and their viewing balconies in-between offered views directly to the glass dome at the top of the house and the grand lobby below.

The quarters of Lady Safiya could be found on the fourth floor, this was the most opulent part of the house. The quarters themselves were not open to other elders and visitation was strictly by invitation only. As one of the most senior elders in the United Kingdom Lady Safiya enjoyed peace when she could get it and disliked being disturbed at the best of times.

As the Reeve headed across the fourth floor towards her quarters two of the Escarrabin were guarding her entrance door. Upon them seeing the Reeve approaching, their backs became immediately straighter and their chins were lifted.

They both nodded together "Ma'am" as she arrived at the doorway and she nodded back to them as the Escarrabin on the right opened the door for her. She followed the security officer into the waiting area and reclosed the door behind her.

The Reeve walked forward to a solitary cleric sat at a desk who handled administration for the senior Lady of the house.

"I would like to speak with Lady Safiya please."

The cleric looked up at the Reeve and from underneath her hood she could immediately see the paleness of her skin and her white eyes.

"Do you have an appointment Lady Reeve as I'm not aware of it? The Lady of the house is very busy today."
"I do not but it is very important that I see her and if possible straight away."

The cleric stood up. "Wait here My Lady Reeve, I will see." The Reeve nodded for the second time and took a couple of steps backwards to survey the grand surroundings of Lady Safiya's chambers.

The walls of the room were covered in wooden panelling but no artwork was affixed to any of the walls throughout. Only one solitary painting was hung on the wall behind the cleric's desk of the Lady herself. The Reeve stepped forward to the ticking from the grandfather clock. It was much older than hers and had discoloured slightly over the years. The pendulum was sealed within and it's swinging back and forth could not be seen, only heard.

The heavy wooden door to the left of the Reeve opened. "Please come through, she will join you shortly."

She watched as the cleric stepped forward and ushered her to enter the sitting room. "Thank you" the Reeve said whilst passing her. The door closed behind her and she took stock of the room whilst she waited.

She was stood on a wooden floor with a huge rug that covered most of the room. The chairs were very old and no doubt very valuable and a huge chandelier hung above her. There were old candle holders that were fixed into the wooden panelling on the walls but the panelling only went half way up the height of the room. A stone layer rose above those up to the mahogany coloured panelled ceiling.

Her eyes were distracted by a long yawn of one of Safiya's cats. The Siberian cat looked at the Reeve and, with disinterest, immediately closed her eyes and went back to sleep upon a cushion on one of the grand old chairs. Alicia her eldest cat did not enjoy her sleep being interrupted, she suspected Safiya would not welcome the interruption either.

The creaking of floorboards could be heard coming from another room as Lady Safiya walked in dragging her supporting stick with her; she used this on occasions when out of public view. Two of her cats followed into the room with her.

"Reeve, I was just made aware that you wanted to see me, the cleric tells me it's urgent."
"Yes Ma'am, I'm very sorry to disturb you."
"Well as long as it is important. We haven't spent much time together, I hope that you are settling in well?" She ushered her cane towards a chair directly in front of the Reeve directing her to sit.
"Yes and thank you Ma'am."
"Truthfully I'm glad of the break, gathering days are tiring days Reeve. So much going on at home and abroad, too much to organise." She gave a faint smile. "I feel old."
The Reeve having sat perched on the end of the chair with her legs together, offered a faint smile in response.
"So what is troubling you?"
"It may be something and yet it may be nothing Ma'am."
"Isn't is always."

The Reeve watched as the senior elder took a seat and propped her cane against her chair and one of her cats jumped up upon her lap.
"I don't wish to trouble you with much of it but today I spoke with my elder in Spain."
"Yes I know of whom you mean, Lady Berenike of the Order of Reeves."
"Yes Ma'am." The Reeve swallowed as she gathered her words. "She informs me that you have something, a key to be precise."

The colouration was instantly drained from the face of the head of the house of Loxley.

"I can tell that you know of what I speak Ma'am." The Reeve watched as she saw Lady Safiya move her right hand over her left.

"Why do you ask this of me Reeve?" Her tone had changed and was now of caution and concern.
"Because I'm told that I may need it Ma'am." She watched as she saw one of the

most respected elders look towards the floor in thought.

There was silence between them before she looked up to the Reeve again. "Understand this, this key was passed to me by my elder whom was hugely respected and it was passed to her by her elder and so on and so forth. I was told, as was she, that if the day comes that the key is ever asked for, it would be because of times of great peril. So I ask you this, is this a time of great peril Reeve?"

The Reeve thought long and hard about her answer. "I can only hope not but there is something that I need to check and that key, the one that you wear on your finger, can help solve part of a problem."
The senior elder smiled slightly but it was not one of happiness. "So you know that it is on my finger, you Reeves are very well informed."
The Reeve was without words and could only offer a slight smile by way of response.

"I know that even an elder of my level is never aware of all of the facts and I know how secretive the Order of the Reeves is. If I pass this to you it's not because I want to. I pass it to you hoping that whatever it is that you know that you do the right thing."

She removed the old ring from her finger and studied it and placed it in the palm of her right hand and held it forward. "I've worn this for a very long time. It is a tradition of times past so please do bring it back to me if you can."
The Reeve stood up and walked over to the sitting elder and bent down to her open palm and reached out to take the ring. "Not so fast Reeve" as she closed her palm again. "Are we in trouble, do the Grand Council need to be informed of what has happened here?"

"All I can offer you Ma'am is that I'm investigating something and if the time comes that decisive actions need to be taken I assure you that I will inform you as soon as is practically possible but for now I do not want to be responsible for alarm if it need not to be."
"You are still asking a question of something that has been kept secret for hundreds of years Reeve and seeing as I'm not an old idiot, your being here asking me what you are, I have to conclude that the matter is serious!"
"I will endeavour to find out Ma'am."

The palm was opened again and the elder nodded her head for the Reeve to take the ring that she had worn for so long.

The Reeve slipped the ring into one of her jacket pockets not wanting to examine it in front of Her Lady. "Thank you Ma'am."

"You had best go and do whatever it is that you need to do Reeve as I do not know what that key opens."

The Reeve looked on as Lady Safiya lent on her cane and stood back up as her cat leapt to the floor.

"Do come back with answers Reeve, you all have your secrets but we have some of our own too."

The Reeve gave the slightest of smiles and nodded and headed for the door.

As Lady Safiya watched the head of security leave she slumped back into her chair again. She had told the truth, she did not know what the key opened but she knew that potentially peril may not be far away.

Chapter Twenty Six:

THE SERPENT'S WHEEL

FRIDAY AFTERNOON 4.40PM

Nubia stood propped against her desk having smuggled Nahla into the mansion house. The black cat with the white tipped tail lay upon her couch but she was far from peaceful. Nubia had made her as comfortable as possible but her discomfort was clear to be seen to the most untrained of eyes.

Leaning over to her phone she dialled the vet, the one she trusted that is.

"Kamilah just to let you know that Nahla is here with me."
"Really, how on ever did you do that in the end?"
"Never mind, I know people as well you know." She spoke with smugness in her tone.
"Of that I don't doubt Nubia." A small ripple of laughter came from Kamilah. "But what is her condition?"
"Not good, she is still as you described and if her condition does not improve I may need to call you over but in truth I don't know what you would be able to do for her."
"It is difficult Nubia, no doubt; the last time this happened to one of our own events did not play out well."
Nubia chewed at her fingers again. "Yes, I am aware of this despite how long ago it was."

"And what of Mildred?"

"She thinks her cat is at the other vets right now so it has bought us some time, how much I can't be sure of but I should be able to find out more later."

"My phone is always open for you Nubia if you need me, you know that."

"Thank you my friend, I will come back to you if there is anything to update you with."

"Okay Nubia, we'll speak later on."

The call had ended and Nubia looked over at her clock. Jessica should be picking up Mildred in a couple of hours or so and hopefully she will be able to find out how much time they have and how long she can keep Mildred's cat at Loxley before further potential problems arise. She was certain that she had done the right thing in protecting one of their own but it was never far from her mind that in doing so she may have created entirely new complications.

It had been a few years since Mildred had worn any makeup. She hadn't worn any at the last two gatherings but today was different. After the long week and the stresses of Missy and her mystery illness she needed some pampering and, importantly, to feel good again.

There were no fixes in her dresser for the wrinkles across her forehead or the crow's feet around her eyes but she did have one lipstick and an old brush for her hair that had become somewhat unkempt of late.

Reflecting on her earlier call with Daphne, her tone had certainly changed when she mentioned about another vet being called. She shook her head slightly, there were some strange things about the cat club. Maybe this evening may offer some more answers or maybe she should start asking more questions.

Hair still a little damp from her shower, she tugged at it with the brush and screwed up her face as she pulled through knots of her thick curly shoulder length auburn hair. It was usually tied up but this evening she would try something different. She had new(ish) clothing and wanted to impress so her hair would be worn down and that was that.

The thickness of the matted knots would mean slow progress, just as well she allowed a couple of hours to get ready. With a deep puff of her cheeks she let go of the brush as it hung there tangled swinging in her hair, this was going to be much more difficult than she realised.

Her doors were firmly closed behind her as the Reeve stood over the heavy, cumbersome and now upside down chair.

She reached into her jacket pocket and pulled out the ring key and in the privacy of her office it was the first time she was to examine it. Her predecessors at Loxley had probably never seen it or even known of its existence.

She held the small ring up to assess it; it was of a crude design, very old and looked uncomfortable to wear. She doubted it would fit many of her fingers and smiled slightly imagining Raysmau trying to put it on.

She could see there was a tiny fold in the design that allowed the key to be worn flat against the finger. Using both hands she very gently pulled at the ring allowing the key to extend but even at maximum extension it would have only been an inch or so in length.

As the Reeve knelt down on one knee she took a deep breath and placed the small key into the keyhole on the underside of the chair and gently turned it. It was stiff and unmoving as she applied more pressure; her tongue unbeknown to her hung out of her mouth slightly as she concentrated. The key started to turn to the left and she heard a click come from within the chair. In the centre of the panel of the overturned chair a small perfectly cut square of solid wood fell backwards into a hidden compartment that had appeared as soon as she heard the lock giving way.

The Reeve's hand shook slightly with anticipation as she put her hand into the newly appeared hole to pull out the fallen piece of wood from the hidden compartment. Taking the perfectly hand cut square of wood out and placing it on the floor she peered inside the compartment that was surrounded by dark stained wood, it was impossible to see into it.

The tongue had gone back into her mouth as she bit at her lip. Much like closing the door behind her in the darkness underneath the statue, placing her hand into something that she could not see into filled her with some trepidation. As she was right handed and in case there was some sort of 'protective measure' she sacrificed her left hand and pushed it forward and felt around with the tips of her fingers. The hole was not very deep and her eyebrows lifted upon feeling what felt like a cloth bag and she immediately dragged it out.

Standing back up and walking into her office she sat at her desk and opened the folded cloth bag. She could smell a waft of dust as it opened and the object fell onto her desk with a heavy thud.

A perfect circle of about six inches round made of what she guessed to be iron, now lay upon her desk having been hidden away for hundreds of years. There was a centre piece that was fixed from multiple points around the circle. The thickness of the centre piece she estimated to be probably around two inches wide and the way the centre piece was secured made the key look like some form of small steering wheel. However the head of the creature in the centre of the circle she recognised straight away as one of the feared creatures of old - cats feared them as much as they feared rats.

She stared at the head of the serpent and knew straight away that she had found the hidden key.

She looked up now certain of knowledge and knowing; the wall of iron could not be opened and the watcher was bound to fail.

Friday 5.06 pm

"Mildred it's Jessica, are you okay?"
"Oh hello Jessica. I'm really good thank you, feeling much better now, it's been a trying week."

Mildred was mostly dressed and ready, just a few finishing touches needed to be applied. She was still due to investigate an old tube of mascara she'd found.

"Really?" Jessica tried with her most *'I'm surprised to hear that voice.'* "Well I've been out all day so I should be with you in around an hour or so I would think."

"Great, thank you Lady Jessica I'm very much looking forward to seeing everyone."
"You're welcome; see you in a bit then."

Mildred put the phone down and returned to the bathroom to assess herself.

Her shoes were the cleanest out of the three pairs she owned, her stockings were a little creased in places but they would have to do as it had been some time since she had bought new ones. Mr Franks did not sell them but in any event that would never be a conversation that she would contemplate having with him, so charity shop one's sufficed.

She had ironed her brown pencil skirt and as she turned to look at herself in the mirror she could see from behind that her stockings were really quite baggy at the back of her ankles. Her eyebrows rose upon seeing them; she could not wear them of course but that would mean bare legs and in places she could see that hairs were jutting through the old stockings so she discarded that idea straight away.

Her white floral shirt was neatly buttoned and she admired her hand made creation of quite possibly one of the best cardigans she had ever seen. It would certainly be talked about.

Her long heavy jacket had been lying on her bed in readiness and she slipped it on. It was the height of summer but she had been saying to herself all week that first impressions counted so the fake fur stole would need to be added just the same.

As she wrapped the stole around her neck and un-tucked her now brushed long hair there was still one remaining item, the piece de resistance. The beautiful black cloche hat with the red outline of a cat that she had paid £4 for would be worn with pride. And with the exception of her bag she was ready; although she mustn't forget the invitation and the cards.

And of course the fish paste sandwiches.

Since unlocking the chair the Reeve had barely let go of the secret key. Reasonably heavy with a pattern of teeth throughout on the one side, she had not seen a wheel shaped key before and had to presume that it naturally sat into a slot and you turn it like any other traditional key. She held it out in front of her pretending to place it into something. By gripping the head of the serpent that came forward from the centre of the iron wheel you could get leverage of sorts.

She placed it gently on the desk and picked up the phone and redialled. Her head of Order had said that she would call her but, given the circumstances, it could not wait.

Listening to the phone ringing in Spain it remained unanswered as she placed her phone back down. Her Lady must still be in the archives. Finding such information quickly was never going to be a straightforward process.

As the clock in her room struck 6pm, darkness would be falling in a few hours and irrespective of what her head of Order may discover, going into the below after dark would not be a consideration. If this one watcher was uniting them, it was too much of a risk after the light had fallen when they were at their most active and when their strength was at its highest.

Feeling around her neck, she released the clasp of her necklace and removed the charm that had sat on it and placed it into a drawer of her desk. Her silver necklace was reasonably sturdy and she hoped that it would take the weight of the key that contained the serpent.

If no-one is to be trusted then for now she would have to wear it.

Friday 6.09pm

Jessica arrived at Mildred's and this time parked directly outside her gate and switched the car engine off. Memories of earlier surveillance flooded straight into her mind and she looked at the floor well next to where Mildred would sit.

She let out a sharp 'ah' upon spotting the huge glasses with the clown nose on the floor and unclipped her seat belt and leant over and threw them onto the back seat along with the binoculars and the newspaper.

She felt a tinge of guilt knowing full well that Mildred had no idea that she had been there earlier and that her beloved cat Missy was not where she was supposed to be. Play it cool Jessica, play it cool she was repeating in her mind as she banged the horn of her car.

Jessica was looking around the road and missed Mildred instantly bob up at her window at the sound from the car outside.

The blue door of Mildred's house started to open and Jessica saw an arm appear and place a huge bag on the path outside. Jessica watched with a puzzled expression when she saw the back of Mildred as she locked her front door.

"Oh my days, whatever is she wearing?" Jessica muttered as she saw Mildred struggle a little as she lifted the bag and waddled towards her gate. Jessica pushed at the button to lower the passenger window as Mildred approached and leaned her head right inside. Jessica was momentarily startled looking at the shocking peachy/pink lipstick Mildred was wearing and, as she smiled, she could see that lipstick was caked over some of her teeth as well.

"Hello Lady Jessica!"
Jessica's wide open eyes acknowledged an overexcited and highly enthusiastic Mildred.
"Can I put my bag on the back seat?"
"Er, yes of course Mildred, please do."
Mildred opened the door and immediately spotted the glasses. "Ha! What do you have those for?" Jessica looked in horror as Mildred picked up the glasses with the red nose.
"Oh, I went to a children's party a few days ago" was the best that Jessica could come up with off the top of her head.
"He he, bet you looked a right clown in those!"
Jessica looked back towards the road and frowned. "Yes, quite."

Mildred tossed the glasses to the side and placed her heavy bag down and got in the car.

"You will have to excuse the state of my car Mildred; I'm not much of a car person."

"That's because you are a cat person!"

Jessica tried her best to smile but found Mildred's pink teeth quite the distraction.

"That's okay Lady Jessica, I have bits and bobs around my house as well. We have to live comfortably don't we!"

"Yes we do." Jessica watched Mildred get in and she immediately looked Jessica in the face and beamed a smile of pink. Awkwardly returning the smile, she spoke trying to avert her gaze. "Please just call me Jessica Mildred, no need for Lady."

Mildred leaned forward to her and clapped her hands with excitement. "As you wish Jessica" and she put her seat belt on.

A slightly bemused Jessica started the car and pushed down with the clutch. Mildred glanced down at the very shiny black heels that Jessica was wearing and noticed the amount of leg she was showing.

Mildred coughed under her breath "well you look er...nice Jessica."

"Thank you Mildred, it's just a little black number. It's not often that I get out."

"Yes I know what you mean" as Mildred looked down at her wrinkled stockings and scuffed shoes, she waited for Jessica to return the compliment but it didn't seem to be coming any time soon.

Jessica's nostrils flared as she looked around the car. "Can you smell that Mildred, what is it?"

"Oh, ha ha, it's fish paste sandwiches, I have three plates of them!"

Jessica started to open her window slightly. "Oh I see, that's nice."

"Well it's not far from here Mildred; I think we should be there in about 20 minutes or so."

"I've never been to Dovecote Manor before, it sounds very grand indeed."

Jessica looked over and smiled. "I've been a couple of times, it's quite nice."

As they left Rocke Road Jessica bit at her lips knowing full well that she would have to ask the question fairly soon. "So how is Na..." she corrected herself "how is Missy?"

Mildred started waving her arms around speaking at a hundred miles per hour

"Oh I've had the most traumatic time Jessica I can't tell you. Missy has been very unwell, called the vet that Lady Daphne recommended, she was useless, then had to call another. It's been a terrible couple of days."

"Oh, that sounds upsetting; I would be lost without my cats." Jessica's mind had started to wander off worrying about Khepri.

"Something about an irregular heartbeat."

Jessica took her eyes off the road to look at Mildred as she said this. "That sounds troubling." Jessica returned her gaze to the front, deep in thought.

"They've kept her in overnight to observe her."

Jessica took a deep breath. "Well that's good." Her heart was racing as she tried to figure everything out. "So when does Missy come back then?"

"Tomorrow morning."

"What time?"

Mildred looked straight at her driver. "Excuse me?"

"Oh, I'm sorry Mildred, what time are you expecting Missy back?"

"Erm, I'm not sure, does it matter?"

Jessica smiled. "No, not at all, I just wondered if it were likely to be early. If so we had better not keep you out too late tonight!" Well done, not bad, Jessica thought to herself.

"They didn't say and I guess they would have done, so I would presume mid morning so there is no rush. I do hope my Missy will be okay."

"So do I Mildred, so do I." Jessica's mind had wandered off again.

"I know, it's the strangest thing, never seen a layout like it."

Thomas and Brooke both shook their heads in some form of agreement as they set the tables.

"Only 45 guests, the bar will remain closed and no food service."

"Maybe this cat club is broke!" Thomas quipped at his supervisor at Dovecote Mansion as they studied the seating plan that had been provided in advance.

"Well they paid the hire rate for the room in cash, want eight urns of hot water to be provided for tea and alcohol is only on the tables with the fewest guests, never heard of anything like it! And get this, as soon as they are here they insist on not being disturbed and all of the curtains are to be drawn."

Thomas and Brooke both looked at each other with some astonishment and laughed.

"The crazy cat ladies roam among us" Brooke giggled, prompting further laughter from Thomas and Mary their supervisor.

"You know, get how weird this is." Brooke and Thomas walked over to Mary to listen as she looked over her shoulder and then lowered her voice. "Its ticket only right, for this cat meeting and they are bringing their own security!"

"What! Ha ha, you serious?"

"Very!" Mary responded instantly with laughter.

"Security for a cat club meeting, that's the state of the world now!"

Mary looked at Thomas upon hearing his remark. "And what would you know about that, you are barely out of school!" she smiled.

"You'd be surprised!"

"I don't think either of us want to know thank you" Brooke replied as she finished setting one of the tables.

"Tom, can you check the projector is working okay please? Apparently they are giving some sort of talk."

"Pictures of cats probably, God can you imagine the boredom."

Mary smiled and shook her head at Tom. "No, not really" and ushered her arm at him to switch the projector on and that it aligned to the projection screen. "Anyway, they'll be arriving soon so let's get a move on."

Mary stepped back and looked around the vast room that only held nine round tables, save the tables where the tea and food was going to be; whatever food it was they were bringing with them of course. Her eyes were distracted as she looked through the windows and the doors that led to the patio area outside. She could see cars starting to arrive and double blinked in shock at some of the beautiful vehicles that were parking up.

"There must be some money in this." She turned her head to look at her staff and nodded towards the outside. "Maybe I should join this cat club!"

Shula and Kassia from the Escarrabin Order walked through the grand entrance of Dovecote Mansion towards the reception desk where they were politely greeted by Michelle.

Michelle could not help but notice the two smartly dressed ladies approaching her, who wore suits and what looked to be sensible shoes. "Good evening ladies, how may I help you?"

"We are from the United Kingdom Kat Chamber. We are here to provide assistance for the meeting this evening." Kassia informed the receptionist with a short and succinct smile.

"I see; your meeting is in the Dogpole Suite further down the corridor. You go past the bar area and you come to two double doors. Go through there to a reception area and then it is the doorway to the left that will be directly in front of you. The room is set up ready for you I understand."

Kassia nodded. "Maybe you can show us all the same."
"I'd be happy to, can you sign in here please?" she asked as she passed the register of visitors book towards them.
"You do it for me" Shula said to Kassia.
Michelle smiled and looked on, noticing that the one that had just spoken hadn't made any eye contact and was constantly looking everywhere except towards her and the reception desk.

A frown appeared across Michelle's face as she read the names of Sharon and Tracy being written in and the remaining boxes on the visitor's book left blank. She politely coughed and looked up at the writer as she put her pen down. "You have surnames?"
"No, just Sharon and Tracy, we are security you see."
"I see, then you will not mind if I ask to see your security licenses then please." Now the one that had ignored her was looking directly at her. "It's for my records, just in case something, well, something went wrong."
The rude one, who she guessed may be Tracy, continued to look at her. "They talk about cats, it's not a boxing match and besides we are more of a concierge service for the elder members, they are quite old so we help them."
"I see" she said with some suspicion. "Well then you had best follow me and I'll show you where to go." Michelle looked down again at the book. "Sharon and Tracy is it?" She was met by two short smiles without words. "This way then."

As Michelle walked the length of the corridor hearing the footsteps behind her she was speaking to herself 'Sharon and Tracy; I wasn't born yesterday.'

"This is impressive, don't you think Jessica?"
Jessica turned towards Mildred. "It is a lovely building. We have never gathered here before but I think I mentioned to you earlier I have been here for smaller meets a couple of times."

Mildred was looking all around in her excitement as the car rolled down the driveway slowing on a couple of occasions to go over speed bumps. The manor house stood majestically in front of them on this beautiful summer's evening. She glanced over at a small lake as the car veered around to the left where other cars were parked.

"Wow, have you ever seen cars like this Jessica?"
Jessica smiled back. "I have. They belong to some of our senior members and they have been involved within the club for much longer than you and I."
"Well, you've been involved for longer than me Jessica."
"This is true but as you see, I do not have a car like those and I don't really care for it. Have you never noticed the cars at the other gatherings you have been to?"
"No, guess the parking area must have been somewhere else."

Jessica watched Mildred looking through the glass and could sense her excitement about being here as she parked the car.

Jessica undid her seatbelt. "Well let's go inside Mildred."
"Well before we do, I have something for you Jessica."
"Oh really?" Jessica smiled as Mildred reached behind and lugged her heavy bag to her knees and placed a hand inside and brought out a card.
"For you!" Mildred passed the card to Jessica with a beaming smile.
"Oh, why thank you Mildred, that's very sweet of you."
"Well aren't you going to open it?"
"Yes of course." Jessica smiled as she tugged at the envelope that revealed a picture that she recognised from earlier on in the shop. As she opened the card she could see the clumsy writing inside. The printed words of 'Happy Birthday' had a line drawn through them to say 'Happy Gathering!!' Jessica smiled. "That's really very lovely Mildred, thank you very much."
"The cat on the front looks just like my Missy."
"And looks like my Khepri."

They briefly went quiet with concern for both of their cats.

"You have a cat called Khepri Jessica?"
"Yes, that's her real name."
"Real name?"
Jessica closed her eyes instantly knowing what she had said and had to think quickly. "Yes, her real name, I have two names for her, ha ha."
"Oh okay, think I would get confused with that. Anyway I'm so pleased that you like it."
"Do you mind if I leave it in here Mildred, I can take it home later?"
"No, not at all."
Jessica could see, as Mildred undid her seatbelt and her bag fell open, all of the other cards in there. Jessica smiled realising that Mildred was the one that the man in the shop had referred to earlier, the one who had bought 44 birthday cards.

As they got out of the car, Jessica picked up her bag and noticed an arm waving at them directly to her left indicating that they should proceed that way.

Jessica led the way with Mildred dragging her bag in tow as they approached the two officers of the Escarrabin.

"Your tickets please ladies."
Jessica put a hand into her small clutch bag and passed the ticket over as she watched Mildred fumble with her jacket.
"Are you not hot Mildred wearing all of that?"
"No, I'm fine Jessica, it's here somewhere." The three of them stood patiently as Jessica observed the two security officers watching intently over Mildred's movements.
"It is here, I didn't forget it" as she bent down to look in her bag. "Here, hold these will you" as she passed both of the Escarrabin a plate of fish paste sandwiches. Shula looked at Kassia as they both turned to look at Jessica who offered a small smile of embarrassment.
"Ah ha, it was here all along!" as she checked her jacket pocket again and took it out. She couldn't help but notice that they did not look very impressed as she put the invitation in her mouth and took back the plates of sandwiches and craned her neck forward for them to take the invitation.
As she put the plates back into her bag Mildred wanted to make amends. "Would

you care for a sandwich?"

"No" was the matter of fact response.

"Oh...okay." Mildred turned to Jessica and flashed her pink teeth as both invitations were read over and checked.

"I wondered could I keep mine as a memento please?" Mildred asked.

"No" was the very short response.

"Oh, okay."

"Thank you ladies, please go through."

Jessica stepped gracefully into the main room as Mildred trundled in behind her. "Jessica, the last couple of times I've been to one of these the people at the front have not been very friendly, are they members of the club?"

"No, well kinda, they just help out with security I think; they won't be part of the meeting. I don't know much about them, above my level you see."

"Oh, okay." Mildred was distracted as she glanced around recognising a couple of faces instantly from her local group. "Why on ever would we need security Jessica, we are here to talk about cats?"

Jessica smiled. "And that we will Mildred, it's just a precautionary thing. It's supposed to make you feel more comfortable."

Mildred wasn't sure that it did.

"Well let's go and get you a cup of tea and say some hellos."

"Yes please Jessica." Her tone was one of excitement again.

"Oh Mildred, just a little thing please. Now that we are in front of people again it's Lady Jessica. It's just a procedural thing."

Mildred looked at Jessica's smile and beamed one back herself with a shrug of the shoulders. "As you wish Lady Jessica!"

"Come on, it looks like the tea urns are over here."

As Mildred walked over to the tea area still with her large bag dragging behind her, she glanced over and noticed Mildred from Merewood Close was walking around the tables and taking out small cakes from a large white box that she was carrying. Mildred studied this as she watched Mildred, the cake supremo, gently place an individual cake next to the name cards indicating where everyone was sitting.

Jessica reached the tea urns first but had said a few 'hello's' on the way there. "What would you like Mildred?" She noticed that Mildred was looking the other way.

"Oh, urm, tea please Jessica."

Jessica coughed.

"Sorry, Lady Jessica."

"What type of tea, there are many."

Mildred looked at the huge variety of different teas but was far too distracted by the other Mildred's cakes looking so good. "Oh, whatever comes to hand, I don't mind, thank you."

She turned back around biting at her lip considering whether she should add her cards next to everyone's individual cup cakes as well.

"Well hello Mildred."

Mildred had not seen that Mildred from Alpine Grove had approached her.

"Hello Mildred, how lovely to see you." The other Mildred had clearly arrived there a little earlier as she already had tea in hand.

"So, did you bring your fish paste delights with you?" She took a sip of her tea and gave a patronising smile.

"Yes, I have them here, 3 plates of them. Do you know where I should put them?" She watched as the other Mildred looked at the floor smiling with some form of other answer in her mind.

She looked up still with a smile. "Yes over there" and nodded towards a table with other food on it. "You'll see mine; the crusts have been cut off and they are on my finest bone china plates."

Mildred watched her beam in pride; her fish paste sandwiches came fully loaded with crusts and did not sit on expensive plates.

Mildred looked uncomfortably at the floor. "Well, that's good then."

"Here we go Mildred, try this herbal tea, I like this one." Mildred looked up to see Jessica passing a cup and saucer towards her and beamed a big smile in the direction of the other Mildred that a senior Lady had made a cup of tea for her.

"Hello Lady Jessica, I'm Mildred from Leamington Spa, we met briefly once before."

Jessica turned around to see an outstretched hand from a lady she didn't seem to remember very well but couldn't help but notice that she was dressed similarly to Mildred.

"Ah yes, hello Mildred." Jessica smiled and took her hand to shake it.

"So you both know each other very well then?"

"Lady Jessica gave me a lift here." Mildred beamed with pride trumping the other Mildred and her perfect sandwiches.

"Yes that's right; I'm the elder of Daphne who is Mildred's elder so we are getting to know each other a bit better."

"Oh I see, well that explains everything then. May I ask Lady Jessica, how many cats do you have?"

Mildred looked surprised by this question.

"No, I do not mind, I have three" Jessica responded politely.

Mildred's eyes widened; she knew that Jessica was above her level but with three cats that would make her a degree level seven elder. "My my Mildred, you do know some important people."

Mildred continue to smile although she was somewhat confused by the conversation.

"Well I must mingle, not often we all get together, it was lovely to see you again Lady Jessica and don't forget to put your fish paste sandwiches out Mildred, I'm sure they will be a delight."

The sarcasm in her tone was not lost on Mildred as she watched her turn around and walk off to talk with others.

Jessica looked at Mildred and they both smiled.

Standing at the entrance doors, Shula had paced up and down a couple of times now. "How many we at now?"

"36, there has been one cancellation so just 8 more to arrive."

Shula nodded at Kassia and looked inside the room. They had made the arrangements so all the members of the gathering could enter through the side doors next to the patio area so they didn't have to pass through the main part of the hotel. As she looked inside, the ranks of order were easy to distinguish and not just by age alone.

"You can see who's who, they don't blend together too well do they?"

Kassia smiled "They never do, the ranks don't mix and the same could be said of us."

Shula returned the smile only slightly as she looked at the variety of styles of dress. Those who were 8th and 9th degree elders all seemed to dress in a similar way, heavy coats, large bags and hats even in this heat. But one did stand out albeit dressed in the same way as the others. Shula watched her and her confidence as she worked the room. "That's the one who introduced herself isn't it?" Kassia poked her head around the door and looked to where Shula was nodding. "Yes definitely, said her name was Mildred, Leamington Spa I think she said she was from."

"She looks like she is trying hard." Shula turned around and looked towards the parked cars. "Someone must be after promotion."

"It's possible; there is a naming ceremony tonight so someone will be."

Shula sighed. "Standing on doors, could do without it."

"Could be worse, at least it's not raining" was all Kassia could offer in return.

Mildred was glad to be free of the weight of the fish paste sandwiches as she laid them out on the table next to the other Mildred's perfectly hand cut ones.

There was much to survey, sandwiches a plenty and Mildred's amazing cakes. She looked in some dismay at the curled up corners of her own and prodded at one, the texture felt somewhat wooden.

Mildred hadn't lied; she did indeed own some amazing plates. In comparison to Mildred's own that were different colours and different sizes, her sandwiches were standing out for all of the wrong reasons.

The chomping of her teeth was only disturbed by a voice from behind. "Hello Mildred!"

Mildred turned around to see the smiling face of Daphne.

"Oh Lady Daphne, how lovely to see you."

"And you Mildred, what have you brought with you then? They look like some fancy plates."

"Erm yes Lady Daphne, I have brought some sandwiches."

"Well they look hand cut as well, how lovely, not sure about those ones though."

Mildred followed Daphne's eyes as she looked at her fish paste sandwiches.

"I wonder who brought those; anyway at least yours look lovely Mildred."

Mildred responded by way of a smile deciding that she would take some of the credit for the perfectly formed sandwiches.

"I brought something for you as well Lady Daphne."

Daphne smiled as she watched Mildred pick up her bag from the floor and passed a card to her.

"A card Mildred, it's not my birthday!" She laughed as she opened it and read the scrawled words.

"They didn't have happy gathering cards at the shop!"

"Well I guess they didn't, thank you very much Mildred, the cat looks just like your Missy."

"And Lady Jessica's Khepri."

"Oh, Jessica told you her cat's real name then?"

"Yes apparently her cat has two names."

Daphne smiled but decided to add nothing further to this.

"Well, it's a big evening for Lady Jessica with it being her naming ceremony as well."

"Naming ceremony, what on ever is that?"

"Oh, she didn't explain that to you as well?"

"No, that hadn't been mentioned." Mildred looked a bit bewildered and not for the first time, with the unusual processes that seem to be involved in this club.

"Well, I was surprised when she offered you a lift; she must have plenty on her mind."

Mildred nodded in agreement not understanding a word of it.

"Come over here and sit with me Mildred, I'll explain a couple of things."

Mildred watched on as Daphne turned around heading for a table. She reached out with her left foot to slide her bag under the sandwich and cake table and picked up her herbal tea and followed.

Mildred watched Daphne pull a chair out for her. "Please do sit Mildred."

"Thank you Lady Daphne" she responded as she pulled at the chair and sat down.

"It's like this Mildred. Naming ceremonies do not happen very often and it only happens when one of our ladies are promoted, I guess is a word you could use for it."

Daphne could see that Mildred was studying her intently.

"From this evening, Lady Jessica will not be Lady Jessica any further."

Mildred tilted her head in a confused state towards Daphne. "Well what will she be then?"

"I don't know and I'm guessing that she does not know yet but in any event she will be given a new name and that is what she will be known as forever more. It's quite an accomplishment."

Mildred looked across the floor at Jessica talking away to some very elegantly dressed ladies.

"I'm confused Lady Daphne."

"Well we can't all be Mildred's, Daphne's and Jessica's for ever more can we!"

Daphne looked at Mildred's face in a state of some perplexity.

"I know this seems daunting to you Mildred and it was for me at the start but the longer you are with us the more things are explained."

"I just like cats."

Daphne smiled. "Mildred, yes you do and we all do, we adore cats but there is a lot more to the UK Kat Chamber than you realise. It will all become clear in time. Who knows you may have a new name in the future."

Mildred recoiled slightly in her chair. "But I like being called Mildred."

"And I like being called Daphne but it's not my real name. I hope to discover it in the future as you may as well. Has it never occurred to you that we all have the same names?"

"Well, I thought it was just a coincidence."

"Nothing is by coincidence Mildred, they never are and your invitation to join was predetermined a long time ago."

Mildred watched Daphne nod at her as she said this and had a smile across her face by way of reassurance.

"It will all become clear my friend, don't you worry."

Daphne stood up with her eyes looking towards the food table. "Let's go and try some of your sandwiches, they looked like bone china plates you have there Mildred."

Mildred smiled and looked at the floor as Daphne walked away. This was odd, far too odd as it dawned upon Mildred what she had gotten herself involved in. Her concentration was disturbed as she heard the doors close from where she had come in and the curtains were pulled across. The two rude ladies who had taken her ticket walked across the floor and they both nodded at some of the more elder ladies and she watched them leave the room via another doorway.

She looked on as everyone in the room was chatting away. Some of the ladies who were dressed similarly to her, looked as if they were talking about cats. The other ladies that Jessica seemed to be conversing with looked to be talking about something completely different.

The room was now closed and she was here now. I may as well hear what they have to say but she would have to reconsider her membership of this club; there was clearly something not right about it or the ladies involved within.

The Reeve reached for her phone somewhat relieved to hear it ring.
"Reeve, are you alone?"
"Yes My Lady I can talk."
"Do you have the key, have you found it?"
"Yes My Lady, I believe that I have it. I've never seen a key quite like it."
"Is is safe?"
The Reeve put her hand to her sternum and instantly felt the iron weight press against her. "Yes it is safe. Do you have news?"

The Reeve could hear deep breathing from down the phone.
"Tell me Reeve, does the key bear a symbol on it or have a creature of some significance?"
"Yes My Lady, it does. There is a centre piece which I think you need to hold on to, to turn the key."
There was silence and more heavy breathing all the way from Spain in her ear.
"Is it a serpent?"
The Reeve closed her eyes and spoke gently. "Yes it is the head of a serpent."
She could hear coughing from the other end of the phone; she knew that her head of Order was worried. Words of concern were muttered in Spanish.

"My Lady, you know what this is or what it means?" She could hear swallowing from the other end of the phone as her head of Order gathered her words.
"Whether it travelled here or was brought here I do not know. I have had very

little time and the archives are not easy to navigate from such times. I need more time but I suspect we do not have it."

The Reeve could hear the shakiness of her voice.

"It is a keystone species from long ago. It has but one purpose and this watcher may, and I repeat may, have been able to bring it back to being. How I do not know but it is to be feared and it is enormously destructive." The Reeve could hear sadness in her tone as she spoke slowly and clearly.

"It is from a place, a guardian of the underworld from the time of the Order Of Ancients."

"So, you have been able to determine what it is my Lady?"

"It has had other names but more commonly it is referred to as the Hydra."

The mouth of the Reeve fell open with an audible gasp. "But how can that be, the Hydra was a myth?"

"No Reeve, it was not, it never was. It is a true being from darker times."

She could hear her Lady taking a deep breath. "Your superior knew much of this as you will in time, not all myths are myths. The myths were created as a cover, they were to conceal the real and save people from fear. The Hydra is just one small part of that cover and it is quite real I can assure you."

The Reeve was dumbfounded and placed a shaky hand over her mouth. She swallowed as she spoke. "And it has been here for all of this time?"

"So it would appear. I know of some of the referred myths and what belong to legend but that is not to say that I know it all as this afternoon has proven. Why it was brought or travelled to Loxley I have no idea but our own ancients thought it wise to keep it there and so the wall of iron was no doubt built to ensure it would never rise again. Who knows what else may be down there. It requires a thorough investigation now that those secrets may be about to be exposed."

"Do we know more exactly about this Hydra, can it be defeated?"

"Oh yes, it certainly can but the documents I have studied does not discuss or detail its condition."

"Condition My Lady?"

"Yes, its condition. We do not know whether it fought before it was laid to rest."

"I'm sorry, I do not understand?"

"I can only quote from what I know and not from what I see here, as those details have been omitted or are at another place. The Hydra will have a centre core and multiple heads, nine to be exact."

The Reeve looked towards the ceiling and shook her head. "Nine."
"Yes the number nine is not lost on you and nor should it be. It has been a number associated with our Order from the beginning of the time of our existence. The number here is not a coincidence, it was meant to be. Look at the key Reeve; I presume that the serpent head you mentioned is supported by nine individual spokes to hold the head in the centre."
"Spokes my Lady?"
"Yes, I think that may be the English word for it."
"Please bear with me."
The Reeve put the phone down on her desk and unclipped her necklace to look at the key in more detail. She held the centre core and counted the supporting rods that held the serpent in place in the centre. There were nine, her head of Order was right. Lifting the phone back up and nodding her head. "Yes, there are nine spokes, but you mentioned condition?"

"Well yes, we do not know whether it fought. We do not know whether it fought at Loxley or was brought there from its natural domain in Greece where it lay under earth at Lerna, the place often referred to as a gate to the underworld. As I said before, I have not had the time to establish these things, if indeed I can at all. Remove the head of the Hydra another two will form. If it fought we have no way of knowing how many heads it has."

"Oh, my word." The Reeve had to take stock quickly, "I have to ask again, can it be beaten?"

"Well firstly you have the key and without that it should not be able to get out. It is strong and of enormous power but it has a weakness, but it is a weakness that you cannot control or beat, it will be of its own doing."
"I'm sorry My Lady I don't understand."
"It will need access to water. Unless there is some form of labyrinth beyond the iron wall with a watercourse, it will need water and it will need it soon. That is its weakness and can be its undoing."

There was silence between them as the Reeve considered everything she was being told.

"If it is freed, if the watcher somehow succeeds to release it, you and the Escarrabin will not win, not down there, not in the darkness of the below, it will be a slaughter."

The Reeve's eyes closed and her throat was dry. "May I ask why my Lady?"
"You cannot fight the un-fightable within the confines below ground. Its rage will destroy anything you put in front of it and will tear through your security doors and anything in it's path, without mercy."
"Are our scatterblades useless?"
"As a firing weapon yes. It would need precision shooting to remove the heads; if the heads are not seared quickly two more will grow. The use of pulse fire in the below may bring the whole lot down on top of you. The scatterblades would have to be used as their original intention from the past as a sword weapon; the steel would have to be heated in order to sear the heads and that alone is far from easy. The blood of the Hydra is highly toxic and its own blood can be used to sear the heads but that is hardly recommended and to try so would lead to certain fatalities."

The Reeve ran a shaky hand through her hair.

"And that is not all Reeve. Poisonous fumes come from the mouth and that is why it is not beatable in the darkness of the below. It would be a slaughter unlike any we have seen in a very long time. Combine that with your watcher and, if he has united the other watchers, the seriousness of this is now of paramount importance."

"So you are saying that we have to let it escape?"

"In part; your watcher will know that it will take all of your efforts to destroy it and that it provides cover for him and his kind. He will not care for the beast. He intends to sacrifice it so they can all escape. All of this and the first sign of the prophecy having shown do not bode well."
"No My Lady, it does not."
"If it escapes it will head for water."
"The lake?"
"Yes, it will destroy everything inside it and that is not to say that new serpents may come from it but afterwards it will not like the above and will need to go back below. It is on the outside that you may have a chance to destroy it with

your pulse applications but your Escarrabin must be ready."
"I understand My Lady, well - at least I think I do."

"I will need to refer this to the Grand Council for their views and you will need to hold tight. It is darkness where you are in a couple of hours and you will not have the time to prepare. I suggest you go at dawn when the watchers are less active and find this one that is called Duat. Find him, find the missing keys and put an end to this. Let's hope the second prophesised sign does not show. If it does you may have no choice but to act quickly."
"I will need to consult with Raysmau My Lady."
"Do so. She is a good soldier and trusted but, at this time, do not tell her everything until we know more and I've spoken to the Grand Council. Use your judgement as to what to do but keep that key safe at all times!"
"Yes My Lady."
"I will call you soon Reeve. Do your job and execute a plan and contain this as best as you can. I will be in touch soon."
"Thank you for your council my Lady."

The Reeve put the phone down and with shaking hands struggled to reattach her necklace. The key was safe but if the watcher knows about it he may directly come for her. She opened her desk and took out a pair of gloves in preparation for carrying her own modified spear.

There was much to consider, much to fear and lives may be lost. They would need to be ready.

Chapter Twenty Seven:

WELCOME TO THE KAT CLUB

Making the best of it having decided to stay, Mildred had to concede that Mildred's cakes were very nice, although that would come as no surprise to anyone.

At the food table the cheese and ham sandwiches were being demolished at an increasing rate, the same could not be said for hers.

With a casual glance over her shoulder she could see the two Mildreds were in conversation much like everyone else, so it would appear that she had the food table to herself momentarily. She bypassed the cheese and ham as a silent protest and added some of her own fish paste sandwiches onto the other Mildred's bone china plates. At least it made it look like hers were going down.

Turning around with the third cup cake in her mouth she could see that Jessica was talking with some of the other members. Mildred had seen them before at the other two gatherings that she had been to but had never spoken to them. As she chewed away it occurred to her that they had never spoken with her either. For a club that adored cats they seemed to keep themselves to themselves.

Putting her plate back down on the table and picking at her teeth considering the garb that Daphne had been talking about earlier, she was paying more attention than she had at the last two gatherings. Not so far away there were huddled groups with lots of smiles but the group that Jessica was talking to seemed to be absent of any humour. Their conversation looked serious as were the group behind her, almost like little splinter groups, strange to say at the least, as she picked chocolate bits out of her teeth.

She was dressed in her best and yet no one had complimented her as she reached for just one more cake; was that the forth or the fifth? It didn't really matter, she wasn't dieting and could not care anyway. Mouth full she was drawn to a couple of small groups over at the other side of the room, the ones who dressed more *'elegantly'*. They wore jewels that hung from just about everywhere. Only one thing unified them other than their lack of smiles, a small pin badge that all of them wore, it was worthy of closer inspection.

The cake was woofed down as she bent down below the table to reach for her bag and took out some of the cards. Let's go and see how friendly they would be.

As she walked over to the group that Jessica was talking to, she glanced over to her right and could see that ham and cheese Mildred was eyeing her suspiciously, not that it was any of her business in any event.

Jessica saw her approaching and lifted her right hand slightly indicating to whom she was speaking with to stop talking.

"Ladies, you may well have seen her before and I know that one of you of course is in the local meets but if you've never met may I introduce Mildred from Shrewsbury, just down the road from here."

Mildred beamed a big smile of discoloured teeth with cake stuck to them, along with fading pink lipstick. "Hello ladies, it's nice to finally meet some of you!"
A couple of them winced but could not help but keep staring at what looked to be the remainder of many cup cakes gleaming back at them.
"Well, I've brought you all something!"
Jessica smiled on as she watched Mildred with all of her enthusiasm distribute the cards. "It has a picture on it, just like my Missy!"
"Well that's nice then, thank you Mildred" one of them said although Mildred noticed that she was not given their names.
"So how many cats do you all have then? I only have my Missy."

"Yes they know you only have one cat Mildred, you haven't been a member for very long. We all have three," Jessica added.

"You all have three, that's a coincidence!"

Jessica met Mildred's smile but there were no words exchanged and there was suddenly an air of some disquiet as conversation stopped.

"Erm…well….okay, I hope that you all like them." Mildred nodded with an awkward smile as she felt uncomfortable being here.

"Some of the ladies over there have six cats or more Mildred."

"Jessica!" One of the ladies spoke in a serious tone looking at Jessica in such a way as if to say 'stop talking.'

"Six!!! Wow, how lucky. I would struggle to remember all of their names, ha ha ha."

"You definitely would Jessica as one of your cat's has two names!"

The group all looked at Jessica as she winced and looked at the floor.

The ladies watched Mildred's fits of giggles peter out to an uncomfortable cough.

"Well, I guess that I should be going then, plenty of people to see, much talk of cats."

Jessica gave her a smile but was the only one of the group that did.

"Well, enjoy the cards then." She gave a forced smile and looked over to one of the groups that had lots of cats 'apparently'.

As she trundled off she could hear murmurs from behind and what sounded like Jessica saying something like *'she's still new, give it time'*.

Mildred glanced across into a mirror on the wall to her right and, in the reflection behind her, she could see a couple of the cards had already been put down on a table, unopened. A deep frown had stretched across the length of her forehead with a lack of understanding as to why so many here seemed to be somewhat rude. It hadn't escaped her notice that there were other clubs that cat fanciers could join.

She would try again by approaching the small group in front of her. Their faces looked very serious and she overheard them talking about something called *'watchers'* whatever that meant. They could do with someone watching them for attitude problems Mildred considered with a slight smile. There were only four in this little huddle that went immediately silent by Mildred's interruption. "So how many cats do you have then?" as she thrust a card towards each of them. Mildred noticed they were all drinking red wine and yet again conversation seemed to cease instantly.

"What's this may I ask?" one of the lady's said to her.

"It's just a card to say hello." Mildred decided not to display so many smiles this time as she looked closely at the pin badge the lady was wearing. "Well that's nice of you, thank you." The lady in question noticed that Mildred was not looking her in the eye and seemed more focused on what she was wearing.

"Well, I'm guessing that you must be Mildred then?" another lady voiced to her direct right. Mildred turned and was instantly close up to her pin badge and stared at the logo on it that matched what the others were wearing. "Well yes I am. I'm fairly new, only been a member for a few years," Mildred said with an excited smile that someone actually knew her.

"I see" was the response from another who appeared to be studying what Mildred was wearing who followed up with "that's a nice cardigan."

"Thank you, I made it myself."

"Ah ha" the lady nodded.

"Ladies, ladies please take your seats" was the voice over the microphone as the lights came up over a staged area that had been hidden. Mildred looked up at the huge crest of the United Kingdom Kat Chamber LIV that was now displayed proudly in the lights and there was a podium in place ready for a speaker.

"Well I had best take a seat then, enjoy your cards!"

The ladies politely smiled back as she walked off.

"Rehema, how did you know that her name was Mildred?"

"I didn't, it was a one in three guess."

They sniggered among themselves as they took their seats.

"Jessica." Mildred had cupped her hands to her mouth conscious that the room had now gone very quiet. "Lady Jessica." Jessica looked over to her. "Yes Mildred." "There is a seat over here if you want it?"

"No, Mildred, I'll be sitting here. I'll see you later though."

Mildred was disappointed. "Oh, okay" as she looked at rude Mildred staring at her.

She went back to her table, still with cards in hand and smiled at the other eight that were sat at the same table as her.

"Did you enjoy my cakes Mildred; I saw that you had some?"

"They were a delight you must teach me some day!"

"I'd be happy to; we'll work that out, cake and cats day!"

"I'd love that, will give you a call to arrange."

They both smiled together as they were interrupted.

"Did you try Mildred's sandwiches?"

Both Mildreds looked at expensive plates Mildred. "Yes I had one Mildred, I quite like fish paste." The response was met by a scowl as Mildred looked at her new cake making friend who gave a smile back and leant in to her. "Ignore her Mildred, she's always like this. I've got used to it and just ignore her."

Mildred pursed her lips and nodded as she watched the other Mildred turn in her seat to face towards the stage.

They all started clapping as Lady Skylar took to the stage. Mildred recognised her as she had spoken at the last two gatherings that she had been to. She was much older and had been a member for some years apparently. She was told last time that apparently she was the owner of seven cats.

"Thank you, ladies and honourable members of the United Kingdom Kat Chamber. I welcome you to this gathering of the middle sector of the UK Chapter. I give special appreciation to our elder members who have been with us for some time." There was further applause as Lady Skylar waved her hand towards the table at the front. The five ladies sat there, looked over at the other members and nodded with appreciation for the applause.

Mildred looked at the speaker and what she was wearing; her long flowing black gown, jewels around her neck, jewels in her immaculately styled hair and she even wore black gloves that went to her elbows. Lady Skylar's appearance could not be more diverse from her own. Her style of dress was more in keeping with the ladies on the front tables. It was not the first time that she had noticed this as she surveyed the members on her own table and the one in front of her.

"Ladies as some of you may know, I have some formal announcements to make later on as well as some sad news to deliver to some of you but I will come to that shortly. As is customary we have a presentation for you to enjoy and I'm very pleased to say that Daphne from Stow-On-The-Wold in the Cotswolds is going to give a short slide presentation of her two cats, so let's give her a round of applause."

Mildred looked over to her Lady Daphne who was clapping at the table in front of her as she saw another lady stand and take to the stage. Mildred shook her head slightly 'so many Mildreds, Daphnes and Jessicas', she was still confused about the *'real name'* conversation she had had earlier.

"Thank you Lady Skylar for your warmth, it is always a pleasure to see you and my esteemed fellows."

Mildred shook her head yet again upon hearing *'esteemed fellows'* with a smirk. "As we all know, we are brought here today for our love of cats but also our love of order. It is through our strength and our determination that this great organisation still exists to this day." There was rapturous applause from around the room as Mildred looked at those sat at her table clapping, nodding and beaming smiles. Mildred the miserable had even stood up for this comment. Two of her own table were looking at her as it dawned on her that she was the only one in the room not applauding. Mildred looked at them, nodded and starting patting her hands together, what for she had no idea.

"Our love and our unity brings us together as one on this most important of days." *(There was further applause)*.

"And this evening I am going to show you a short snippet of my home life and that of my two cats Tale and Lilly."

Mildred, upon hearing this and the somewhat diverse names for cats, blew her lips together sounding like she was making some form of repetitive farting noise as the lights dimmed and a screen lit up behind.

Daphne went into her presentation with much enthusiasm that was met warmly from her own table and the one in front of her. Elsewhere however, especially towards the front, they were whispering to themselves with complete disinterest in the presentation.

The presentation was not dull; Daphne owned two beautiful cats and she had the same interests as her. Quite why she had called her cat *'tail'* was anyone's guess. Mildred crossed her arms looking at the other tables with further confusion. Much did not add up here and to describe some of the members of this cat appreciation club as rude would be an understatement.

In her private quarters Raysmau had changed from her ceremonial robes and armour examining them for any marks, blemishes or dust. The old house was a dust magnet and like all Escarrabin, took great pride in her presentation. She unclipped her neck chains and placed them gently upon her dresser. There had been no reports of any note from her officers that were at the five gatherings that were currently taking place across the UK and Ireland, so no news is therefore good news.

The buzzing of her intercom sprung into life as she reached over and pressed the button to talk. "Yes what is it?"
"I'm sorry to disturb you Lady Raysmau but the Lady Reeve is here and would like to see you."
"Please send her through into my office, I will be there momentarily."
"Yes Ma'am."

Good. Finally we may have some answers to explain the Reeve's lack of decisive action from earlier on. The matter of what happened below needed to be fully investigated even if her own officers had overreacted and required disciplinary action to be taken against them.

In her underwear, she reached for her gown and slippers. The Reeve had arrived unannounced and she was signed off for the day, so she would have to receive her dressed as she was.

On occasion Raysmau had disagreed with some of the decision making of the previous Reeve. It was the same with her first placement as a chief security officer of the Escarrabin in Italy. Her disagreeable views were always kept to herself. It was a delicate balance and all she could do was offer guidance and subtle views that hopefully may carry some influence. But what she saw today was a blatant lack of process and inability to make decisions when they needed to be made.

She made sure that her gown was fully drawn as she walked down the corridor that would lead to the rear door of her office.

The Reeve had her back to her looking at framed pictures of elder Escarrabin from the past as she opened the door into her office.

"Thank you for seeing me Raysmau, I appreciate you are off duty now."
"A head of security is never fully off Ma'am."

The Reeve turned to her with a smile. "No, I guess not."
"Please forgive me for how I am presented."
"Not at all." She was still smiling as she nodded her head towards the chairs for Raysmau to sit down.

Raysmau drew her heavy chair from behind her desk and sat down, curious to know what was so urgent that this conversation could not have waited.

"I would imagine that you are surprised by my reaction earlier on today when you brought me news about the watcher and what happened below."
Raysmau tilted her head slightly to the right with her eyes looking directly at the Reeve.
"It was more of a statement than a question; I would have been concerned or confused if I had been you."

As she took a seat opposite, the Reeve recognised the familiar pattern of Raysmau in thought, as she noticed her hands were bound together over one of her knees, twiddling her thumbs.

"I will level with you Raysmau. My actions earlier were because I needed time to think and I also needed time to consult."
"Consult Ma'am?"
The Reeve nodded. "Unruly watchers do not concern me, they can be dealt with and the drawing of scatterblades is indeed a serious matter and that we can deal with. It is the other matter that concerns me and I needed to take council with my head of Order."
The Reeve looked Raysmau directly in her eyes as she continued. "Let me ask you a question that I have never asked you and please be frank with me. Have you ever been in the below, right to the very bottom?"
Raysmau took great pride in never showing expressions, irrespective of outcome, but this question concerned her and she felt that she had swallowed upon hearing it. "I have been below but not for some time but never to the bottom, never into the depths, there has not been a need for it."

The Reeve got to her feet again. "That is as I thought." She flashed the slightest hint of a smile as she looked at Raysmau and then put her hands in the pockets of her suit trousers. As she looked around the office at the old pictures on the walls she took a deep breath. "In my Order we know a lot of the secrets of old and they are kept secret for good reasons, many matters are known about this place and what may lie below."

Her thumbs had stopped turning on her knee. "You know what it is?"
The Reeve took a couple of steps towards the desk and nodded. "I suspect what it may be."
"But this noise, this roar, the sound from below has never been heard before."
"No and I very much expect anyone who lives has ever heard it, it's something of old that has woken."
"Or brought back?"
"Indeed."
"You have a course of action Ma'am?"
"I'm taking it now by informing you but I'm also hopeful of further information later. But in any event darkness will fall soon and we cannot risk going below in the hours of darkness to investigate. Please remain vigilant and have officers guard the lift that goes to the below. Anything suspicious, no matter how small, please inform me irrespective of the hour."
Raysmau nodded. "Yes Ma'am I'll arrange that right away."
"Dependent on what I am told in all likelihood we may have to be battle ready for a dawn search of the below and if so we have to go right to the bottom as far as it takes us."

The Reeve looked upon the huge frame of Raysmau as she stood up. "Ensure the Escarrabin return here immediately from the gatherings they are at, we may need all of the help we can get."

"Yes Ma'am I'll see that a message is sent out."

The Reeve turned to walk to the exit door. "Oh one more thing and for now, do this as quietly as you can."

Raysmau could see that the Reeve looked uncomfortable as she spoke. "Collect all of the body armour we have to include the biological suits, full face protection with breathing apparatus without exception."

Raysmau nodded with concern that didn't require any words.

As the Reeve opened the door she was stopped by the voice from behind.
"Ma'am, may I ask one thing?"
The Reeve stopped and looked over her shoulder and gave a slight nod of the head.
"What is it, what are we potentially dealing with?"
The Reeve was still looking over her shoulder but did not look directly at her head of security. "The Hydra." The Reeve left and closed the door behind her; she didn't look at the face of Raysmau as she spoke and presumed it was just as well.

Well it was fair to say that there was a small ripple of applause albeit somewhat muted as Daphne finished her presentation. Mildred clapped along with the others from her table and the one in front but the forward tables were still in some conversation and it was a lacklustre display of appreciation.

"Thank you Daphne, we very much appreciate you welcoming us into your home and the lives of your cats." Daphne left the stage and retook her seat before Lady Skylar continued.

The membership looked on as her body language changed and her face took a more serious stance. "As some of you are aware you may see that we are missing a beloved member this evening. For those of you who do not know, it is my very sad duty to inform you that Lady Tempest regrettably was taken from us a few weeks ago."

A confused Mildred leaned over to her right. "Where has she been taken?"
"I think Lady Skylar is saying that she has passed Mildred."
Mildred looked with shock towards the stage at this news. Not knowing who Lady Tempest was it was clear that others did as many heads bowed and in the silence of the room you could have heard a pin drop.

"Lady Tempest was much admired and, even for her level, she was known outside of this chapter and respected further afield."
Mildred's quizzical eyes remained forward, hanging on every word that made

little sense.

From the table in front of her a lady, who she did not know, spoke up quite loudly. "What happened?"

The question was not lost on the speaker as she looked towards the table in front of her and took a nod from the lady who was sat in the centre.

"She was most unfortunately involved in a road traffic accident. At this time that is all I can say but we are looking into it."

Mildred bobbed her head back like a parrot and leant to her right again. "We are looking into it, doesn't she mean the Police will be looking into it?"

Mildred on her right shrugged her shoulders obviously not understanding this odd statement either.

The room was distracted as one of the security guards that Mildred recognised from earlier opened one of the closed doors. She leant her head in and looked at Lady Skylar with a nod and reclosed the door again.

Mildred frowned and did the parrot bobbing again and leant to her right. "I don't mean to speak out of turn but Tempest?" She shrugged her shoulders. "Tempest, why do they have such odd names?" Cake creation Mildred offered no response.

"However what this does mean is there is a gap in our ranks. It doesn't happen very often I'm most pleased to say but order must continue and the Grand Council have made their decisions."

They all looked on as she adjusted herself. "But first we will have one minute's silence for our beloved friend Lady Tempest."

The room fell silent and everyone looked to the floor in contemplation. Mildred however couldn't help but notice the one cupcake left on her table. She eyed it and flexed her fingers wondering if she could nab it with the same stealth as she had removing the flyer about the woman who can talk to animals from the café a couple of days before. Her tongue poked slightly from her mouth when she noticed Jessica was looking at her with disapproving eyes.

Mildred leaned forward and put her elbows on her knees and rested her head into her palms 'grand council, honestly….' Her words were in her head which was probably for the best as everyone else looked somewhat gripped with anticipation prior to this moment of mutual silence. Lady Tempest, - will Lady Macbeth pop up next and she let out a deep breath.

She was distracted as the minute passed and bolted upright again. "Although it is with regret that this event has happened some time before it was due, I therefore announce to you all that this evening is Jessica's naming ceremony. Please stand Jessica." There was rapturous applause around the room and Mildred felt somewhat compelled to lift her chin up as she put her hands together gently mimicking a light effort of clapping.

She looked on as Jessica looked around the room with a smile and politely nodded accepting the appreciation from her peers.

"Jessica please do join me on the stage."
The applause continued as Jessica walked up only three steps that lifted her above everyone else and stood next to the podium.

"My Lady, if you would be so kind?" came across the microphone as Lady Jomana got to her feet from the front table holding in both hands what looked to be a large and heavy old sword.

"Well, what the bloody hell is going on here?" The words had slipped out (and not in her mind this time) as a couple from her table looked directly at Mildred with some disbelief. Her hands shook fearing she was about to witness some bizarre beheading ritual and her own mind surprised herself as it questioned that without Jessica it would be a long walk home.

As the sword was passed from Lady Jomana to Lady Skylar they both bowed their heads slightly at each other and everyone watched as Jessica went down on to one knee. Mildred looked on as her chauffeur for the evening showed far too much leg for her liking as the sword was placed on one shoulder and then another. Words were exchanged in this action but they were unheard as far back to where Mildred was sitting.

The sword was passed back in both hands to the lady who had carried it as they both nodded to each other again.

Lady Skylar retook her place back at the microphone. "Please rise."

Mildred stood up and was quickly pulled back down. "Not you Mildred, she means Lady Jessica!"

Still in thought but feeling rather terrified she took her seat again and watched Jessica stand back up.

"Lady Jessica has passed, from now on she will be known as Lady Suzanna!" Everyone in the room stood up cheering and applauding and Mildred could see a huge smile on Jessica's face.

Mildred was the only one who remained seated but that was short lived as she could feel eyes were being set upon her. "Yeah, woo woo" she joined in giving something that resembled fist pumps in the air. It somehow seemed appropriate, as she looked around the room, to establish exactly where all the exit doors were.

There was no speech given and it didn't look like one was expected. Lady Skylar leaned forward to the new Lady Suzanna and kissed her face on both sides and presented her with a certificate.

The only words that Mildred thought she could discern across the microphone were "can I check please, is that spelt with one Z or two?"

Lady Skylar didn't look impressed, so Mildred guessed that she had heard correctly.

The clapping continued as Lady Suzanna *(with one Z)* returned to her seat and received many pats on the back from her table and Mildred watched as her elder, Daphne, walked over to her to congratulate her.

"Yes congratulations to Lady Suzanna, although you are now sat at the wrong table!" Lady Skylar was in laughter as Suzanna stood back up smiling with more pats on the back and moved to the table in front of her where she received handshakes and applause.

"Ladies this does of course mean that we need a replacement for Lady Jessica." There was stunned silence around the room and Mildred looked at the table in front of her whose members had suddenly frozen as if it was an awards ceremony on television.

"The Grand Council have agreed that Lady Daphne from Housman Rise in Staffordshire is promoted to degree level seven, let's hear it for Daphne!"
The ladies at Daphne's table all stood up and congratulated her. Mildred could see that she was practically in tears at this apparent promotion as she turned around and looked directly at her. Mildred smiled back and gave little hand claps and nodded to her friend, the same 'friend' who had introduced her to this cult of lunatics. Mildred had made the decision; as soon as those doors were opened again she was off – not worrying if she had to walk home. At least Jessica *(now Suzanna)* kept her head, God knows what happens if you get on the wrong side of this cat club!

Everyone looked on as Daphne went to the stage and received a kiss on either side of her cheeks from the speaker and was presented with a certificate; there was no sword needed for her.

She was beaming smiles all around the room as she sat back down but this time at the table in front of where she had been initially sat.

Mildred was picking at her teeth again and opening and closing her mouth when she returned her eyes to the lone cup cake on the table. She looked at it and grinded on her teeth and wondered if anyone would mind if she nabbed it. Well I'm leaving afterwards anyway so who cares as she leant across the table and stuffed half of it into her mouth.

"Our final announcement for this evening, ladies before we all head off. As is customary, we have one more promotion to make from our ninth degree elders."
Mildred was looking at the half eaten cup cake. It was a conundrum as she really would like to know how to make these but suspected after this evening she wouldn't be seeing Mildred again, shame really.

"The Grand Council has spoken and they have made their decision, the new degree level is awarded to Mildred, congratulations!"
Mildred was distracted from her eating as Mildred from Alpine Groove stood up with a huge smile and shook the hands of those on either side of her.
"Oh, I'm sorry I do apologise ladies I didn't say, the award is for Mildred from Rocke Road." Two of the three Mildreds froze for completely different reasons.
"Mildred it's you!" as she felt an arm on her shoulder still chewing on what had been left of the cup cake.

"Eh, you what?"

"It's you, well done. You'll get a new cat now!"

Mildred looked up at the other Mildred who was red in the face and looked furious as she slumped into her chair and stared at her.

"Well go on then, collect your award!" Mildred swallowed the remaining contents of her mouth and looked into the face of the cake master who looked thrilled for her.

"Erm, okay." Mildred stood up to applause around the room. In all of her time she had never been awarded with anything before and for that very moment she looked across the room of smiles (well except one) grateful that she was being appreciated and meant something.

She shuffled forward and could see that her Lady Daphne gave her what looked to be a thumbs up and Jessica on the table in front of her was also full of smiles. For the first time in a long time she felt happy momentarily putting it to one side that she was going to run off as soon as she possibly could. She approached the stage and the three steps that would take her up to the imposing figure of Lady Skylar.

"Congratulations Mildred, very well done" as a certificate was passed to her. It was similar to the one she had at home except on quick inspection the markings were different. She would need to look at it further, later on, after she had left this place which would probably be very soon she suspected, undecided whether she would be walking or running.

"Thank you Lady Skylar, would it be possible to say a few words?"

"That's not the usual protocol Mildred but yes if you would like."

Mildred looked across the room and the tables with seated occupants and could see that she also had the attention of the ladies that sat at the front. She looked nervously at the sword that lay on the table as she gathered her words.

"Well, fellow ladies and cat enthusiasts, this is an honour. I've never won anything before so this is a surprise."

She could see the glaring face of Mildred at the back of the room and Daphne, now in her new seat, was giving an expression of 'go on'.

"I love cats and I love my Missy. It's been a difficult week as she has been so

unwell." Mildred noticed that Jessica *(Suzanna)* suddenly took her eyes off her and looked at the floor. "So this is very welcome. I would like to say that I also enjoyed the presentation that Daphne gave about her cats. They are very beautiful and I hope to have more cats in the future."
Mildred noticed that two of the ladies on the second table had leant in to speak to each other.

"She really hasn't got an absolute clue has she?"

Mildred could see they were sniggering to themselves but continued undeterred. "Yes I hope that one day I will get a Tom cat and have lots of kittens."

There were gasps around the room and the sound of a wine glass smashing as it was dropped to the floor. Mildred froze in the silence and looked at all of the opened mouths and looks of horror that were fixed upon her.
"Erm..."
A muffled sound could be heard across the room as Mildred put her hand over the microphone and turned to Lady Skylar. "Did I say something wrong?" She leant in to Mildred and put a hand on her shoulder and whispered into her ear. "I think it would be a good idea if you stayed back afterwards. A few things need to be explained to you, there is much that you do not know yet."

Mildred removed her hand from the microphone. "Erm, okay well thank you ladies er...world peace I guess," she shrugged.

She could see Mildred the miserable doing a face palm as Lady Skylar gently pushed her to the side "Let's hear a round of applause for Mildred." There were a couple of muted claps as she walked back to her chair and looked around the room to plenty of stares. As she went to sit down she heard the voice over the microphone. "Mildred" as she turned around to see Lady Skylar pointing that she should sit at the table in front of where she had been. As she sat at the seat that Daphne had been in minutes before she did not get the appreciation from the table that Daphne had received at hers. She looked behind to see expensive plates Mildred shaking her head staring at her. As she watched Lady Skylar continue to speak, the words were drifting away as she read her certificate. She looked up. There was somegood news however, there were more cupcakes on this table.

Their phones had been set into silent mode but they both felt them vibrate within their suit pockets.

They read the message simultaneously. "Not usual that we are sent a reminder to return back to headquarters is it?"

Shaking her head Kassia looked at Shula. "Not that I recall, must be something going on. Shu how much longer do you think this is going to take?"

She watched as Shula gently opened the door into the gathering and quickly reclosed it. "The speeches have finished so shouldn't be too much longer now."

"We could encourage them of course," Kassia had a mischievous look in her eye, "now that we've had a message to return and all."

Shula nodded in response. "Okay, let's go inside by the exit doors, it may help them make up their minds."

The two members of the Escarrabin walked through the room towards the doorway that would lead the visitors out over the patio to the awaiting cars.

"You hungry?"

"A little, not really supposed to eat on duty."

"I know" said Kassia "but look around; no one is really paying us any attention."

"Alright go on then pass me a couple of those sandwiches will you."

Kassia grabbed them two sandwiches each that they tried to hide behind their backs as they stood next to the exit doors and opened them, letting the summer evening air drift through.

Kassia put one to her mouth as discreetly as she could and took a bite and then put her arm behind her back.

"You okay?" Shula had a slight smile across her face watching her fellow Escarrabin's face screw up in some apparent discomfort. She leant forward to the table and put the half eaten sandwich and the spare one back on the plate.

"Whatever you do, do not eat those, stale fish paste."

Mildred was the last one sat at her table, some had already left and others were talking among themselves. The ladies who had been sat on the front table all rose together and spoke to some of the other 'smarter' dressed ladies on their way out. Mildred got up and walked over to the window to see that car doors were being opened for them, and that was the nice looking expensive cars of course. They travelled separately and all had their own drivers - *'alright for some I guess.'*

She retook her seat and looked over at Daphne and Jessica, or should I call her 'Suzanna' now, as they were in their own little clusters chatting away as she shook her head.

Looking around at the empty tables were tea cups, the occasional wine glass along with the one that was broken on the floor and she noticed that her cards were mostly left on the tables of the ladies she had given them to. She shook her head at the rudeness and had no idea why she had wanted to impress these people.

Talking of which, she thought to herself, watching Mildred approaching her with her fish paste sandwich plates in her hands. "Well you've got plenty left to feed your cats Mildred" as she dropped them with a loud clang on the table.
"I only have one cat Mildred as you very well know."
The response was met with the slyest of smiles, "Not for much longer."
She turned around to see if anyone was listening in and bent down to Mildred who was still sat down. "You don't deserve this you know, this rank of elder that you now have."
"I do not know what you mean Mildred?"
"That is my very point, this award is beyond you and way beyond your skill set."
"If you intend to judge me on my sandwiches then you really do not know my skill sets Mildred," *(not that she had any idea what they were herself.)*
There was silence between them but the anger on Mildred's face was not going anywhere anytime soon.
"And besides, the Grand Council has elected me!" Mildred had no idea what she was saying but it seemed to do the trick as Mildred's face fell with more redness, before she turned around and went off sulking.
Not sure of what to make of anything that was going on, she leaned forward and grabbed one of her own sandwiches off the plate and proceeded to chomp away before stopping and pulling what hadn't gone into her mouth away. Looking at the half eaten sandwich she had to concede, they really were bloody awful.

"Ma'am, do you require our service any further this evening? I only ask as we have received a message to return to headquarters."

"No, thank you for your help." Lady Abrielle Suzanna's elder nodded at Shula.

"Is everything okay?" she asked with some curiosity.

"Ma'am?"

"Well why would headquarters want you back quickly?"

"I'm not sure, the message didn't say, probably just another training exercise." Shula smiled.

"No doubt, you Escarrabin work hard, thank you again."

"Thank you Ma'am."

Lady Abrielle watched the member of the Escarrabin Order walk towards her colleague and they both left via the patio doors. She noticed that one was carrying all of the invitations. There were only a few members left in the room now, the three that had been promoted including her, Suzanna and a couple of other elders who would need to explain the new responsibilities that came with such promotion within the Order.

She looked towards the far table at the lady wearing the cloche hat and the fake fur stole who sat alone engrossed in eating something. In all of her days she didn't recall being at a gathering where one of their members talked about cat breeding on the stage.

She went over to Suzanna who was in conversation with two other elders more senior to her. "Have things been explained to you so far Lady Suzanna?"

She smiled. "Yes My Lady, everything is in order."

"Good, good to know" she looked over at Mildred again. "In view of what happened earlier I think she is ready for the chat now." Suzanna turned to look at Mildred who seemed more interested in the food on the table than anything else.

"Yes my Lady, I think you are probably right."

"I know that strictly speaking you are considerably above her degree but I know that you know her and a friendly face will help. Take Daphne with you, I understand that she is her elder and I know that you are hers."

"Yes that is correct. I'm very pleased that Daphne has moved up as well, she will be a great asset in the future, I'm positive of that."

Lady Abrielle looked at Suzanna with a smile. "The Grand Council always chooses wisely."

"Yes My Lady." Suzanna could not help but grin in agreement.

"Congratulations on this evening, I will see you soon. I'll leave you to your chat."

"Thank you My Lady, its lovely to see you again."

Suzanna walked over to Daphne. "Everything okay?"

"Yes we are fine thank you. It will take a while for me to get used to calling you Lady Suzanna from now on."

They both smiled as Lady Sherine, who Daphne had been talking to, said her goodbyes.

"It looks like we are the only ones left now."

"That's probably a good thing Daphne, we need to have a chat with Mildred similar to the one I had with you a few years ago."

They both looked over to Mildred who was now looking at them both. "Yes after her speech this evening I think that is a very good idea."

Raysmau picked up her mobile phone and read the message. Her security officers in Scotland were the last to report back and she now knew that, with exception to those on driving duties, all members of the Escarrabin who were working this evening were making their way back to headquarters. It would be some hours before some of them returned as she mentally prepared herself for how to brief them all in the morning.

Some will not have had much sleep but a show of ranks and strength will be important. There would be much fear about going below and there was no shame in admitting it. The question of whether to inform all about the possibility of an encounter with the Hydra did bother her however, how could it not? But her team were far from stupid and with the protective measures that they would have to wear, would be indication enough that this was far more than a search and detain exercise. She would have to consult with the Reeve, but her feeling was that her team would need to know the facts or the facts as they may appear.

There was much to consider and darkness was starting to fall outside. The dawn of a new day could be a test that her kind had not seen in a long time and it was not a test that she was looking forward to.

They both pulled chairs next to Mildred noticing the crumbs all over her.

"I must say, I do love your cardigan Mildred." Daphne said, that was received with some suspicion.

"I guess I need to call you Lady Suzanna from now on then?"

"You do" Suzanna said gently with a smile.

"Did you figure out how many Z's there are in your name yet?"

Suzanna laughed. "Yes it's just one apparently."

Suzanna and Daphne both laughed together but Mildred just looked at the both of them.

They regained their composure when it was obvious that Mildred appeared far from amused and Suzanna decided that it was time to press on with 'the talk'.

"You must be a little confused Mildred about some of what happened this evening, in fact it's written all over your face."

"Confused would be one word for it; is this some version of the Freemasons or a cult or something, as to be honest I just want to join a club that appreciates cats?"

Daphne and Suzanna gently laughed. "No Mildred, I can assure you that it's nothing like that, in fact it is a great honour to be part of this." Mildred heard the words and looked directly at Daphne.

"And what exactly is THIS Daphne?"

Daphne looked at Suzanna with a request in her eyes that she resume the lead.

"I know this will not be easy for you Mildred but we, and that also includes you, are members of the Horde Of Light."

Mildred, who was looking directly into the eyes of Suzanna, just blinked and then looked to her left at the seriousness in Daphne's face and then back to Suzanna again and started snorting with laughter. She put a hand to her eyes to rub at a couple of loose tears that had run down her face. "Is this like one of those hidden camera shows or something?"

They both looked on as Mildred was turning around mimicking a camera crew coming in as she giggled to herself. Her laughter silenced when she could see the seriousness in both of their faces.

"I reacted in a similar way Mildred when I was first told, with exception to the hidden camera thing mind."

"I bet you did Daphne. Well that is your name isn't it or will that be changing any time soon?"

Daphne's face provided the briefest of smiles. "It will probably change in the future Mildred yes as indeed will yours. I have told you of this."

"Excellent I have always wanted to be called, well now let me see, erm, Mary or Joanna. Yes I like that 'Lady Joanna' or lets go the full hog and I'll be called Douglass, yes Douglass. Now that's a solid name, you can both call me that from now on!"

Suzanna did not care for the patronising tone coming from Mildred. "We do not take names from the world of men."
"I'll bet, what about Steve, everyone loves a Steve."
"That's enough!"
Mildred jumped at the tone of Suzanna's voice.

Suzanna took a deep breath and lowered her tone and resumed with a more passive voice. "One does not simply join our Order Mildred and we are an Order that goes back over many centuries. You were selected to join us and you always were going to. You came of age a few years ago when Daphne, who is your elder, first visited you."

She tilted her head back slightly and her eyebrows came together with bemusement or amusement, she wasn't sure. "Came of age! I became of age for many things and that was some years ago, quite a few in fact!"
"This is different, this requires maturity and our numbers are exacting and your time was right. You were brought into the fold when a member passed on, we are always replaced you see?"
"No Suzanna, I really don't see at all."
"As you know from this evening we recently lost one of our beloved members."
"Lady Tempest" Daphne interjected.
"And with her passing it allowed her position to be filled and that was taken by me and Daphne has now taken my position and you have taken hers. That leaves a new position to be filled and for the lady who will be selected you will now be her elder.

Mildred shook her head "I'm sorry, but you what?"
"You will be responsible for her Mildred and you'll need to go and see her as I did with you."
"Well I'm sorry Daphne but I thought you were barking when you first came

round."

"Barking is a strange choice of word Mildred, cats don't bark now do they!" Suzanna and Daphne grinned together.

"No I guess they do not." Mildred's voice had become very quiet in all of the confusion.

"Look, I know this is a lot to take in but you are now what is known as a degree level eight member, Daphne is now a seven and I'm now a six and the roles that we play are very, very important."

"What has this to do with cats and my Missy Jessica?"

"It's Suzanna from now on if you please and it has everything to do with cats Mildred. Missy was brought to you as she is one of our own. All cats are important, very important, but our cats are special and you are their protector."

Mildred shook her head again. "I think she does a perfectly good job of looking after herself, well except for this week of course."

They both watched her as she looked towards the floor in worry.

"She'll be back tomorrow Mildred and I'm sure that she will be fine; I also have something else to tell you and it's very important."

Mildred looked up at Suzanna.

She took a deep breath and looked Mildred directly in the eyes and nodded as she spoke. "Every cat has a name Mildred, every cat without exception, whether they are one of ours or not."

Mildred raised an eyebrow and looked at Daphne who nodded supporting this statement.

"Well of course they do."

Suzanna smiled. "But they really do Mildred, they really do. Your cat who is one of us, is not really called Missy, her real name is Nahla."

Mildred looked back at Daphne who continued to nod.

Mildred snorted a little. "What?"

"Nahla."

"Well what on ever does that mean and why can't I call her Missy?"

"You can look up the meaning should you choose but ask yourself this, have you ever called out the name Missy and she doesn't come to you or you think she doesn't even hear it?"

"Well yes, quite a bit actually but cats can be like that sometimes. I don't think that is unusual, they are very independent."

"Indeed they are, as are we, including yourself Mildred, when you think about it. You are very independent too and always have been, but they prefer to be addressed by their real name. Try it when you see her and you will see, I guarantee it!"

Mildred was at a loss for words, or polite ones at that, and those words do no usually fit her style of vocabulary. "Well okay, answer this please. If that is the case, why did you not tell me her name at the start?"

"If it's of any consolation Mildred I asked the exact same question when I was told!" Daphne reached over and put a hand on Mildred's knee and nodded.

"I'm not sure that it is but can you explain that to me?"

"I can, well, in part. When a kitten is brought to you it takes time to discover the world and what surrounds her. She has to find her own way in life and when you come of age you are presented with her name. You have earned the right to know her name and for the future you can address your cat correctly as you bond further. You are one, does that help a little?"

Mildred was shaking her head. "I have no idea to be honest Suzanna."

Suzanna had noticed that Mildred had not been addressing her correctly throughout the conversation but this was clearly a lot for Mildred to take in. She would remind her to use her title later on.

"Your cat will gather its own mould and through the early stages of its life it is also independent until the time is right. Nahla's time is now right and the Grand Council has decided that your time is also now right. It's a tradition that has gone back through generations of generations and we are not looking to change that any time soon."

"So if I understand all of this correctly and I'm not sure that I do, you are going to give a cat to me that I need to give to a complete stranger?"

"Well she won't be a stranger now will she Mildred, as she has been selected, thereby she is known to the powers above if you will."

Mildred watched Suzanna do the inverted commas sign as she said this; she looked at Daphne who still resembled some sort of daft nodding dog when a further question came to mind.

"So okay then, where do the cats come from?" she looked at both of them "the one you are going to give to me?"

For the first time in this oddball conversation Daphne looked at a loss to answer as she looked immediately at Suzanna.

"I can't tell you that, I'm sorry."

"Well why ever not, Suzanna?"

"Because I do not know the answer."

Mildred frowned again and tilted her head a little to the side with some disbelief.

"Convenient don't you think?" she mumbled.

Suzanna shook her head and sighed "But I do know this; our cats are brought to us by a senior lady called the Keeper but how they come to her or from whom is unknown to all of us. It is a closely guarded secret and in our Order there are many secrets Mildred."

"Such as?"

"Well they wouldn't be secrets if I told you and I still have much to learn but consider this. Throughout history events that you may have read about or things that you see on TV such as the news for example, whenever something happens, someone 'important' *(she was doing the inverted commas again)* addresses the nation or nations through the media and often tries to give answers even if they do not know them."

"Well you mean like politicians or something?"

"Yes they are one vessel of information or misinformation dependent on things but ask yourself this, has there ever been a cat far away?"

Suzanna sat back in her chair confident she now had Mildred's attention and that her speech was going quite well.

"Well, I..."

"Think about names that are considered as great names in history; poets, authors, composers, heads of state, many many of them were devoted to cats. Even here in this country do you think it's a coincidence that you often see on the news that there is a cat in Downing Street?"

Mildred shrugged.

"They are our own Mildred, all of them and always have been. We are never far away and stay there to ensure that order is maintained, well at least where possible. We are always suspicious of key people who do not have a cat close by them but it's always only a matter of time."

Mildred watched as two heads were bobbing in agreement again.

"Well what order, what balance is needed, I don't understand?"

"This is a good question Mildred and you are asking the right ones." Daphne put a hand on Mildred's knee again.

"Mildred, regrettably not everything is good and it never has been. Out there on the outside of this place there are some who want to cause chaos and seek to poison the race of men."

'Mildred raised her eyebrows and shook her head "eh, what's that got to do with me?"

Daphne smiled but there was no laughter and Mildred looked at the seriousness of Suzanna's face.

"These creatures are vile and want to create a world of darkness and disorder and that's where we fit in; we are the light that prevents the darkness."

Mildred could feel her lips trembling as she stifled a laugh that was trying to escape but she contained it for now. She would have a giggle later over a cup of tea at home.

"So we are the great protectors then!"

"Something like that Mildred yes."

They watched Mildred look down at the floor, she was obviously amused.

"Mildred, look up please."

She lifted her head to face Suzanna.

"They are called watchers and they are a poisonous cast, a breed apart and we stop them from achieving their ideals."

"So at weekends do I go watcher catching or something?"

Daphne sighed. "Mildred, I accepted a lot of this better than you are, you will need time to think and adjust as I did. Did it ever occur to you that you get paid by us every month? Did you think cat clubs like you thought you'd joined, pay their members?"

"Well yes I had thought about it actually, thought it was kinda strange."

"Well now you know and in fact you will be paid more now that you are an eighth degree elder."

"I see; is there like hazard pay or something as some of this sounds a bit dodgy?"

Suzanna gave a short and succinct smile. "Well I think that is enough for today, we can talk again soon after you've been able to take it all in."

Suzanna went to stand. "Lady Suzanna, you haven't mentioned the new addition."

Suzanna looked at Daphne. "Oh yes, sorry Mildred there is one more thing" as she settled back into her seat again.

She looked at Mildred's confused face. "I do have some good news for you though, something I know that you will be very happy to hear."

Mildred had no words and just nodded a couple of times.

"When the new kitten is brought to you for our new member, you will be brought one as well and it will be Daphne who brings it to you."

For the first time, Mildred sat upright, focused on what she was hearing. "I'm going to have a new cat?"

"Yes Mildred that is correct," said Daphne as they both watched a smile erupt over her face for the first time since they had sat down.

"As Lady Suzanna has explained, now that you are an eighth degree elder you have responsibilities and one of those is being presented with a new cat. We both will have a new one as well."

"So you will have three now Daphne?"

"Yes and Lady Suzanna will have four."

"Four!" Mildred smiled. "You'll look like a crazy cat lady Suzanna." Suzanna looked on as Mildred cackled to herself. "That's not a term I care for Mildred but I'll let you have that one this time."

Suzanna stood up. "And besides Mildred, from what you have learnt this evening, we are no ordinary ladies and far from crazy for that matter. We are owed a great debt from those on the outside." Mildred felt her shoulder being patted a couple of times with Suzanna's hand.

"Time to go, much to do."

Daphne stood up and gathered her things.

Mildred, who was still sat down, turned around hearing Suzanna's voice. "Don't forget your sandwiches Mildred; it looks like there are quite a few left. I'll meet you outside."

Mildred looked on as Daphne and Suzanna left the room and she slowly stood up to look through the opened doors they had just left through. She could see they were talking to each other outside on the patio; Mildred was 100% sure that it was about her.

She looked across the abandoned room and heard the doors from the other side open as staff came in to clean up.

She grabbed at her bag and collected her plates. Suzanna was right, there were plenty of sandwiches left but she was more disappointed as she looked around the tables and could see that many of her cards were still there either unopened or had just been left behind. She clenched at her teeth as she walked around the tables to collect them and walked back to her bag and bent over and threw them in as she heard muffled voices from behind her.

"Look that is exactly what I mean, if you were ever going to describe a cat lady that would be it." Tom nodded at Brooke as they both looked at Mildred's baggy stockings as she bent over. They both giggled to each other as she stood back up and turned to stare at them, she didn't look too pleased.

Mildred looked at the two waiting staff as their laughs became muted. She knew they were making fun of her as she stared back defiantly at them. One day this fun and this mocking of her would stop, she was done with it. Tonight had reaffirmed it and her days of being the subject of ridicule were over.

Chapter Twenty Eight:

THE CLEAR SKY ABOVE ROCKE ROAD

FRIDAY LATE EVENING

Other than generalised pleasantries hardly a word had been expressed between them in the ten minutes or so that they had travelled together.

Mildred estimated they were only a couple of miles away from her home and she would be glad to get back there. The evening and the week overall had taken a somewhat turn for the surreal.

Clearly the newly named Suzanna had much to consider as well as she sat in silence. Mildred had noticed that documents had been passed to her by an elder earlier on in the evening after she had been *'named'*, presumably something official or more of their 'secrets', whatever that meant. If she were truthful Suzanna, like Daphne, were nice enough but clearly spent too much time in the company of catnip.

"So a new cat will be delivered to me then?"
Suzanna glanced across at Mildred. "Yes that is the way it is, probably sometime tomorrow or the day after I guess. It usually happens pretty quickly."
"I see. So what will be the name of my new cat and the other one for the new girl?"
"Lady, Mildred, she is now a lady as are you."

There was silence again and Suzanna knew that Mildred wanted answers. "I will not know the names of either of the cats. That is not my role and at this early stage, as they develop from kittens to adulthood, I'm not sure who does, the Keeper I guess. A lot of practises are time of old and their secrets are maintained and guarded. As you can tell, there are still matters of procedure that are beyond my knowledge."

"So what will I call it then?"

Mildred was surprised to hear laughter from her driver. "You can call her what you like Mildred; it's a temporary name for you. In time the real name will be presented to you when she and you are ready."

Mildred looked at the street lights and recognised they were only a few roads away from home.

"Does that all make sense to you then?"

Mildred shook her head. "I'm not sure Suzanna; it's a lot to take in."

"It certainly is and some adjust better than others but you have responsibilities now, you are a protector of cats."

"Like you?"

"Exactly, just like me. I've just been involved for longer shall we say."

Silence ensued as they pulled into Rocke Road. Suzanna looked up to the sky. "Well it's a beautiful summer's evening Mildred, not a cloud in the sky." There was no response forthcoming although she noticed that Mildred did peer forward to take a look.

The car stopped outside Mildred's home and Suzanna looked over to her. "You know my phone is always on for you if you need to speak with me. Daphne is your direct elder and that is the usual process but you can contact me if you wish. I want to take a keen interest in you Mildred as you adjust to things - we are like family."

Mildred nodded a couple of times in thought and the 'bad forces' that existed apparently out there somewhere. Quite what that had to do with her and Missy she had no idea.

She looked at Suzanna. "Is that why Fennaway was recommended, is she one of us this Horde Of Illumination?"

"Light Mildred, Horde Of Light." Suzanna saw Mildred shrug her shoulders and let out a deep breath.

"She is one of us, yes."

"You know I called someone else?"

"Yes I am aware Mildred. Our cats are very special and Fennaway understands them, please do not call others in the future."

"She can talk to them as well apparently," she said with a shake of the head and looked towards the floor.

"That's as maybe; it's not a gift that I possess."

Mildred looked back up raising her eyes. "A gift?"

"That's right, some of us are more gifted than others and you will have your own, you may just not know yours yet."

"I suspect it's not sandwich making," as she looked back down again. "My Missy is back in the morning."

Suzanna looked on as Mildred glanced over to her empty house.

"I'm sure she will be fine, let's hope so!" Suzanna looked away with some guilt in the part she played in switching the cats earlier on. How she was going to switch them back she hadn't figured as yet as her thoughts started to dwell on Khepri.

"Well I guess that I had better go." Mildred pulled at the door handle.

"Yes tomorrow is another day, another day another dollar."

"Oh yes, apparently I'll be having more of that as well."

"Sorry Mildred?"

"Dollars, money, although quite what I need it for is anyone's guess. Maybe I'll go on that game show I've been watching."

Suzanna smirked "And which one is that?"

"Bang Goes Your Money, I quite like him."

"Oh yes, I know the one you mean."

"There is something oddly charming about him, well, for a man anyways."

Mildred looked at Suzanna's smile. "Goodnight Mildred."

Mildred stepped out of the car dragging her heavy bag still full of cards and sandwiches. "Thank you Lady Suzanna."

"You are welcome, Lady Mildred."

They both smiled at each other as Mildred stepped back to watch Suzanna drive off.

She was right; it was a beautiful evening as Mildred looked down her road, alone, in the peace and quiet. Even the bus stop was empty; the kids must have gone elsewhere this evening. She looked up at the sky as she unclipped her gate. It was cloudless and the stars shone more so than usual. She was distracted by a noise coming from her neighbour's garden. She walked across her overgrown lawn and peered over to the rustling noise that she could hear. Sure enough she was greeted by the sight of a huge badger nosing away at Mr Jenkins garden. The badger hadn't seen her as she watched this beautiful creature making an unwelcome mess. She couldn't help but smile. I'll leave him to it she thought and walked towards the darkness of her home.

There was much to think about and she hoped a cup of tea would solve it but in her heart she suspected it wouldn't. It would be her first night alone in three years and she didn't like it, didn't like the thought of it at all. She had missed her game show of course, she realised as she opened her front door and switched the lights on. Maybe she would invest in one of those video recording devices as apparently she would be a lady of some wealth now, and then what, a computer, a car?

There was a world of possibilities but if she were honest with herself, she was delighted that she would have a new cat, but that was all and she wanted no further part of it.

Nubia sat at her desk transfixed by her clock, her elbows and palms were supporting the weight of her chin; it was approaching 10.30. The midnight hour was rapidly approaching and she hoped that Lady Ebony's predictions were not right.

She ran her tongue over her lips in thought and bit down on her lip as she looked at Nahla who was still away in some other painful place. No matter what happens Nahla would need to be removed from here tomorrow as Mildred was expecting her back. She had only given the briefest of thoughts to Khepri *'standing in'* but Mildred, like all cat owners, would know the difference and explanations would need to be made. Some things can be very difficult to explain. She hoped with Mildred's elevation to degree level eight earlier this evening that matters of her rank and title would have been explained to her. She didn't know Mildred and had not met her, or at least in this time, but she knew that some new members struggled with the realisation that their former lives pre coming of age were nothing but blips in the past. Being brought into the Order was not a choice, it was a duty and she would have duties in the near future.

She reached down into her desk for the bottle of Scotch and collected a glass;

her nerves were being tested as she listened to the tick of the pendulum and that reassurance of time. She never really understood the 'shall it be one finger or two fingers' drinks measurement. She poured as she felt and she felt that it was probably somewhere around three fingers that would suffice. She enjoyed the peaty taste from the Scottish Highlands and put the glass back down and went over to Nahla who twitched in pain as her heart raced back and forth. She contemplated...the 'Great Nubia', Curator of the Horde of the United Kingdom drunk in charge of a cat that had two apparent heart beats, - she could not help but shake her head.

She leant against the windowsill, over where Nahla lay, and looked out of the open window studying the beautiful gardens that were surprisingly visible in the Welsh moonlight. It was a clear sky, maybe the clearest she had seen in some time as she looked out at the stars as they flickered so very far away. They were different worlds and not all of them for good but at least there wasn't a storm brewing so there would be no flashes of lighting or a blinding light and that was positive. It didn't look like there would be a sign from above as had been foretold.

The Escarrabin would be returning throughout the evening and into the early hours from their duties away from here and nothing untoward, at this time, had been reported.

As she sat back down looking at Nahla with concern she hoped that she would recover, recover after midnight that is. Anytime before then would be of concern; an hour and a half would tell.

Duat sat at the end of the carved rock that he used as a bed, focused on the grains of sand falling steadily through the huge hourglass. After nearly 24 hours of time passing it wouldn't be long before they ran out completely.

"Bellator, come."
He could hear his servants robe moving towards him as he approached the cut out area that resembled his chamber.
He entered with head bowed. "Yes Master how may I serve you?"
Duat was still leant forward focused on the hourglass. "It's nearly time, everything

is as planned?"
"Yes Master."
"Go to our brothers and see that they are ready."
"Yes Master."
"How many are there of us?"
"27 Master."
Duat took his eye away from the sand and drew a deep breath and stood up as the steam emitted from his mouth. He looked at Bellator. "Your time in chains in this place is nearly over, it is as foretold."

They were both disturbed by the banging coming from below in the deep. Bellator quickly turned towards the noise and pulled down his hood and then spun around with a nervous gaze to see Duat's smile. "My friend grows restless." Bellator stared at his master in confusion. Duat closed his eye and counted the multiple bangs that could be heard against iron. He smiled throughout and then looked up to the above. "Nine, it is untouched and perfectly formed."
He returned his gaze seeing the concern in Bellator's eye. "It is the sound of life behind iron; it too wants to be free. Like you it does not belong in this place and wants to be outside and to be beside water, not imprisoned by rock or iron and the will of others."
"I have dreamt of water Master."
"You have dreamt of lakes of fire, what it seeks is something quite different."
He stepped forward and his servant lowered his head again. "When it comes keep clear of it, it means harm to the others that live above but stay away from it. Let it carry out its will and determination and you shall be freed."
"Yes Master."
Duat turned around to look at the hourglass again. "The bumbling efforts of the elder to disrupt the inevitable were somewhat misjudged," he smiled.
"Master?"
He turned back around to look at the bowed head. "Her who was called by the name of Tempest; it needn't concern you as it is no more, I saw to that."
"Yes Master."
"Now go, ensure all are ready, we move in the early hours."
"I will do that now my Master."
He turned back towards the falling sand.
"Serpents and rats shall be free again to roam as shall we, it is foretold and inevitable; I have foreseen it."

Having just returned from the armoury and taken the opportunity to carry out an inspection, Raysmau was satisfied with what she saw. The battle armour was where it needed to be and in close proximity if the call from the Reeve was made.

Slight adjustments would need to be made to the night vision goggles if face masks and extra eye protectors were to be worn. That would be a decision that the Reeve would need to make in the event of the unthinkable.

As she entered her chambers and her ceremonial dressing room she knew that it had been some time since she had worn full battle armour. Some years, if she were honest, and it had never been worn since her tenure at Loxley.

She removed her loose clothing that she had worn in the armoury and walked to the glass case that contained her battle armour. She assessed the mannequin that wore it against her own frame and knew this may be a little tricky. Taking the key from her dresser she opened the glass door and started to disrobe the mannequin. The sheer weight of the armour was hardly a surprise and how it restricted her movements could not be forgotten. The reality is that wearing it now may be more difficult than before. As she placed the various layers on the chair next to her dresser, she started to apply the protective undergarments and the steel framed leggings. There was a short smile as she looked down at her size twelve feet and her socks with multiple colours as she drew the protective mesh over both of them. She was satisfied that her socks could not be seen by anyone before she summoned much needed assistance.

"Layla come into my quarters will you, don't bother knocking." She let go of the intercom button knowing that the guard in her security office sealed into her part of the building, would be with her in a matter of seconds. She squatted up and down a couple of times knowing that she could not be seen yet and stretched the protective leggings as much as she could as Layla walked into her chambers.

"Yes Ma'am, how may I be of assistance?"
"Help me with this will you."
The Escarrabin looked a little confused. "Yes Ma'am, with the battle armour?"

"I realised that I haven't worn it for a while and wanted to check it would still fit."

"Yes Ma'am, of course."

"Put on a bit of weight since the last time I wore it."

"Well if you have I cannot tell Ma'am."

Raysmau looked at her security officer with raised eyebrows.

With a nervous smile knowing that compliments were not being looked for she walked over to the chair that the battle armour laid upon. "Yes Ma'am."

"Just lift that up will you, it needs to be secured at the back."

She could see the look of shock upon the face of the security officer as she felt the weight of the main armour that would cover Raysmau's upper body. "My arms need to go through together so if you can lift it up in front of me."

The Escarrabin's shoulders shook from the weight as the armour was held aloft from underneath the armpits in front on her as Raysmau placed both arms inside. "You will see fasteners at the back that should secure it on to me."

Layla let go of the armour as it fell upon Raysmau's torso instantly gaining many kilos of weight.

In the mirror Raysmau could see the struggling face of Layla trying to pull it together as it pulled across Raysmau's chest and stomach. "Nearly there Ma'am."

"You won't break me just pull on it!"

It was a struggle but the fasteners were finally secured and Raysmau breathed out and could feel beads of sweat forming on her forehead from the weight, discomfort and how noticeably tight it was since the last time she had worn it.

"There, it fits no problem at all Ma'am."

She frowned, feeling like a robot. "Well I wouldn't say that."

Layla watched her head of Order walk (*of sorts*) up and down the room accustoming her body to the rapid weight gain.

"Thank you Layla, that will be all for now, I'll keep it on for a bit."

"Yes Ma'am."

Raysmau acknowledged the bow and watched her leave the room before blowing out as she leant against her dresser. "Who makes these things!"

She could hear the phone ringing in her office and sighed as she hobbled as quickly as she could in discomfort.

"Yes hello."

"Raysmau, it's Lady Nubia."

"Yes My Lady, are you okay?" Raysmau looked at the clock and could see that it had just passed quarter to eleven. It was a bit late to be calling and rare to hear from the curator in any event.

"Yes I'm fine are you; you sound a little out of breath?"

"Yes Ma'am...sorry I was just doing some cleaning." She frowned a little saying the first thing that popped into her head.

"I see...I've looked out of the window and not seen any of the Escarrabin return yet this evening from the gatherings."

"No My Lady, I'm not expecting them for some time yet." She puffed as she spoke, with no idea why she was being asked a question like this.

"That is as I thought but just a question for you please. When they are all here how many will there be?"

Raysmau went to sit down and realised that she couldn't so remained bent over the desk with the weight of the armour on her back. "Well it will be 36 by the headcount." She frowned at the hour and the strange question. "Are you sure that everything is okay Ma'am?"

"Yes, it was just a question; it's always good to know these things."

"I see." She really didn't and why was she being asked such a direct question about security. "Is there anything else that I can assist with?"

"No that's it thank you. I just wanted to be sure of well, how things are. I'll leave you to it, thank you Raysmau."

She heard the phone go down as she replaced her own and straightened up her back with a grimace.

She looked forward to the closed door in front of her in thought about what was clearly not a generalised question; the curator was worried and clearly knew something.

She wondered how many more at Loxley knew about these potential developments and hoped that things were not being kept from her. In any event her concern deepened as she looked at the ticking clock.

She really hoped that she didn't have to wear this all night.

For Mildred this was a late night, at least gone 10.30 and it had been some time since she had been up at this hour. Looking out of her front window towards her neighbour's lawn, the badger seemed to have disappeared and no doubt she would hear Mr. Jenkins cursing in the morning at the state of his potholed garden. She sat down on her couch considering this; sometimes people get upset about the slightest of things and matters that are out of their control. Given what she had learned this evening, if any of it were true, getting upset about a lawn would be the least of her problems in Mildred's new world.

Dark forces', 'bad things'; she smirked to herself at the ridiculousness of it all. She shook her head in amusement at whatever planet these people were living on. She stared at the framed certificate on her wall knowing that if she were to remain in the crazy cat cult a new one would now be added alongside it.

Her hands went behind her head as she lay back in the seat considering the obvious differences in *'rank'* that she had witnessed this evening. At the two gatherings before, she had failed to notice the now stark differences between those who were the senior elders and the others (other than their age of course). The seniors dressed differently from her and the other Mildreds, Daphnes and Jessicas; although of course she was not to address the *'Jessica'* she knew as Jessica any further. It was weird beyond belief.

The senior elders seemed to keep themselves to themselves, like they were in a clan of some sort. They had drivers and dresses that were no doubt expensive. Even Jessica, no scrub that, *'Suzanna'*, was showing far too much leg and skin like some of the other elders. Probably something designer, and not from the charity shops, where most of her clothing came from. But at no time was she invited into conversation with the various clusters being made to feel that she was not entitled; she gained some nods after she was *'promoted'* but that was about it. If she did overhear conversation it was never about cats and that was somewhat irregular for a cat membership club or the Horde or whatever it was called.

If people on her street, like the kids at the bus stop, thought that she was oddball, this group were a pool table full of oddballs. And the jewels they were wearing, what was all that about? Like some sort of kings and queens, not that there was a man in sight of course, but the metaphor she was content with. She smiled to herself as a picture came into her mind from some time ago watching television on a Saturday afternoon. She scratched her head. 'What was the programme called?' She gave it some thought, oh yes, 'The A Team'. A couple of them were dressed up in enough jewels and chains looking like the big guy on the programme you didn't want to fall out with. She had forgotten his name as well.

"I love it when a plan comes together!" she giggled to herself but there didn't appear to be any plan here whatsoever, just a collection of crazy people.

Confusion remained.

Nubia's body jolted and her eyes opened looking directly at the ceiling. She put her hands to her head to guide her neck down to normal level and focused on the empty glass of Scotch. With everything going on she couldn't believe she had nodded off.

Rubbing her eyes and blinking a couple of times she could see that the clock informed her that it was only a few minutes before midnight. Her pulse elevated knowing that in a few minutes all of this would be over. The prophecy on this occasion had failed. Her neck was stiff from having fallen asleep and the fact that the first thing she saw was her wooden panelled ceiling; her head must have fallen backwards. With her hands, she guided her neck to the left and heard a little crack. She grimaced although it didn't hurt but the sound was unpleasant to hear. She pushed her neck to the right and immediately jumped from her chair "Nahla.........Nahla!"

She looked at the Shorthair cat that was standing on the window sill with the white of her tail slowly twitching back and forth.
Nubia immediately ran over to Mildred's cat.
"Nahla, you're okay!" She smiled as the cat showed no interest whatsoever staring intently into the night sky. Nubia followed her gaze towards the stars and a shiver immediately ran through her. Her hands started to tremble as she used them to support her body weight as she leant over the couch and leaned against the windowsill.
"Do you know something?" She watched her tail that looked somewhat agitated in its movements. "Nahla do you know something?" Nothing, no change, no sign or response. "NAHLA!" she raised the pitch of her voice and Mildred's cat turned her head slightly to look at her. "Good, so you understand me then. Do you know something, give me a sign?"
She looked into the deep blue eyes of the cat. "Should we be worried?" Nahla looked at her for a few seconds and nodded and returned her eyes back to the August night sky.
Nubia recoiled away shaking and put a hand to her mouth in worry. She spun

around to look at her clock. It was a couple of minutes before midnight as she swallowed and looked back at Nahla. She stepped closer towards the windowsill looking at Nahla whose focus had not deviated from the night sky. Nubia looked across the Welsh skyline and despite the differences in their languages they both were terrified as the midnight hour approached.

Duat had sat patiently as he pulled his hood down and inhaled deeply and closed his eye.

Extending his right arm he flexed his hand a couple of times and felt the power extending through him as his palm deepened in colour. He opened his eye and watched on at the life that moved through it.

He could hear the impatience and movements deep below sensing the anticipation outside of his chamber from others who would consider him as their kind. He wasn't of course but they had uses and would be loyal soldiers for as long as he needed them until the time was right.

Tonight they would do battle with the enemies of old, it had been a long time coming. When the beast is free it would tear through their defences, their Escarrabin were no match for it. He placed his glowing palm to the wall and looked to his right at the two keys resting on the table. He closed his eye again to concentrate. There were nerves above he could feel that but the constant ticking overhead remained. He looked at the hourglass; it was not quite time but could feel that it was very close.

Mildred woke with a startle and immediately sat upright in her bed; she put her hand to her chest and took a couple of deep breaths. She had had the most terrible of dreams and could feel beads of sweat on her brow. She leant over to her bedside table and picked up a hair tie and fixed her hair back feeling dampness at the roots. She sat there in confusion for a moment trying to remember what she had been dreaming about but it was fading away. She winced trying to recollect it, recalling a lake on fire and figures that were faceless or their faces were hidden she wasn't sure, but in any event it didn't make any sense.

She looked around her room in the moonlight that poured through the window as she wiped at her brow. It was far too warm in here, it was August but this was too much, must be that global warming thing she had heard about. She stretched her toes and got up and went to the window to let in some air although very little breeze greeted her as she did so. The skyline was completely clear and silent as she looked at the moon that offered some reassuring light from the darkness of her dream. The first night Missy was away and it comes to this, terrible dreams. She was eager for her return and could not wait until the morning.

A rustling from the bushes next door caught her attention as she looked down to the garden below and had to double blink and rubbed at her eyes. "Well I never" she watched as the badger reappeared but she was more fascinated by the three cats in the garden all looking skyward. She looked up at the stars and leant out of the window to see what they were all staring at. As she looked back down the badger was looking directly at them. It was the strangest of things as he then turned his head upwards following their direction.

She witnessed further movements and could now see a squirrel. *'I didn't think squirrels were up at this hour!'* As she watched a fox also appear as they all looked skyward.

She continued to watch Mr. Jenkins garden zoo fascinated by what she was witnessing. What a strange phenomena as she looked skyward in anticipation with a smile wondering, if Missy were here would she be sat with them as well. It was like they all knew each other.

Her smile was short lived and instantly replaced by concern as two bright lights came into view, falling from above. She rubbed her eyes as they came closer flying some way high above her home, they looked to be on fire and there was a white lit trail coming from behind them. As they passed overhead she looked down and watched the cat's heads following the trail as the other animals did as well.

Both objects still high in the air flew over her home out of sight.

She looked back down to the garden. The other animals moved away but the cats remained and she watched their tails twitch in unison.

Unlike Dr Fennaway she didn't speak cat but she had to concede they looked to be very scared.

Duat's right palm was still pressed firmly to the wall as he focused deeply on what he could hear and feel coming from the above.

His breathing became more intense as he closed his eye and stretched out his fingers. His mouth opened with a hiss as he pushed further and further running his palm throughout the building above when he stopped and opened his eye.

He breathed deeply as the drawl ran out of his mouth and a smile broke out across his face. The smile turned to anger as he removed his hand from the wall as he looked at the hourglass.

The last grain of sand had fallen.

"Nahla, Nahla?" The curator looked at the cat in anguish and then back to the clock again, midnight had passed, her clock ticked but there were no chimes. Her hands were shaking as she climbed onto the sofa and started hanging out of the window looking everywhere that her eyes would take her.
She looked back at Nahla. "Is something going to happen; is something going to happen?"

She looked deep into Nahla's eyes and froze as fear suddenly appeared in them. Her own eyes matched Nahla's fear as she spun around to look outside again.
"Oh no, it can't be!!" Her knees buckled under her tiny frame as she fell against the couch as two bright lights came into view heading in their direction. They both watched the double light trail across the Welsh skyline. Nubia recoiled and put a hand to her face in fear as one erupted into eight separate falling stars that faded away. The one remaining ball of fire streamed overhead past the manor house as Nubia hung out of the window watching it disappear into the distance before a bright flash of light lit up the skyline that must have been seen for miles as the noise of a loud bang travelled towards them.

She collapsed into the sofa holding her chest as Nahla climbed down from the windowsill to the floor and stared at her.

Nubia was shaking all over as tears formed in her eyes "lights from above, a light will come from above!"

She steadied herself to her feet. "CLERIC!!" she screamed at the top of her voice "CLERIC!!"
Her door flung open as the cleric looked on at the curator who could barely stand and was out of breath. "Get me the Reeve."
"Ma'am?"
"Get me the Reeve, **GET ME THE REEVE!!!**" she screamed as loudly as she could as the cleric rushed out of the door and continued screaming even after she had left "**GET ME THE REEVE!!**"
Her voice travelled the length of the mansion house. Clerics and Escarrabin still working looked at each other and in that very instant, as her voice reached the corridor of clocks and the artwork of elders from the past, there was a deep cold echo as every clock within Loxley was silenced.

Time had stopped; they had ticked for their very last time.

The Reeve, in response to the cleric's call, was making her way towards the curator's chambers. With what she knew or suspected from today, to have received an urgent call at this hour was very unnerving.

She was surprised to see that Nubia's door was slightly open as she pushed it forward and poked her head inside.

Nubia was in some sort of catatonic state as the Reeve looked at the bottle of Scotch that was two thirds empty and watched their curator swallow another mouthful from the now empty glass.

"What's going on Nubia?" She looked upon the short stature of the curator who was leant against her desk struggling for composure and breath.
"It's happening again Reeve."
Her eyes looked damp as if she had been crying and she looked terrified. It was

true they did not have a great deal of time for each other but it was worrying to see her in this state of pain and anxiety.

She spoke calmly and quietly. "What is happening Nubia?"

She was nodding repetitively "It's started."

"What has, I don't understand?"

"Well did you not see it?" Her eyes looked in pain and a little bloodshot from the tears.

She shook her head and raised her arms slightly "See what?"

"Light.........light from above, the light fell........fell from the sky." She was highly animated and flapping her hands and pointed out of the open window. "It crashed.........crashed to the ground some miles away."

"What, you can't be serious, what did you see?" She walked over to the window and looked outside.

"The second sign, it is as foretold."

She turned around and saw Nubia pointing at her clock as more tears ran down her cheeks.

Horrified the Reeve looked at the pendulum that had stopped swinging.

"It will be the same in your office and everywhere."

The Reeve pulled back the cuff of her jacket and lifted her left arm up and tapped at her watch. It had stopped at two minutes past midnight.

"I see it in your face Reeve, you know what this means, I have been trying to tell you."

She let her arm fall at her side and without words sat on the couch underneath the window.

"Look."

She followed the direction of where Nubia was pointing, to a black cat with a white tipped tail that was sat quietly on a single seat, until that very moment she hadn't noticed her. Her eyes widened in surprise. "Whose cat is that?"

"Mildred's."

The Reeve frowned and looked at Nubia. "Which Mildred?"

"Mildred from Shrewsbury."

"Is this the cat that was bearing the pain?" She looked at the curator who was now sat on the end of her desk and nodded. "Well what on earth is it doing here?"

"I had to take action, I needed to intervene and I had to do the right thing."

She looked back at Nahla and swallowed whilst shaking her head in some disbelief. "Nubia what have you done?"

"She was going to be taken away, to a vet and not one of our own, I had to take action; you have to believe me."

The Reeve's mouth hung open temporarily, her head still shaking. "I ask you again, what exactly have you done?"

"They would have run tests on her; we can't allow that, it might have exposed us!"

The Reeve pursed her lips with a knowing expression. "Is that why I saw Jessica here earlier today," she looked at the non-ticking clock, "yesterday? I'm guessing her being here again has something to do with this?"

"Her name is now Suzanna as I understand and yes she played a role."

"Nubia, you have to be honest with me, what exactly did she do?"

"Well, I put her on surveillance and she switched the cats with one of her own and brought Nahla here."

Flabbergasted the Reeve slumped back into the couch. "You did what! You put one of our ladies out on surveillance, someone untrained. Well what a fine job I bet she did of that. Security is my department Nubia, are you insane, are you for real!"

"What is that supposed to mean?" she responded in some spite and waving her arms. "Is all of this for real, are we for real Reeve?"

They both sat in silence to gain some composure.

"I remember some of it you know, the last time this happened."

The Reeve looked up at the curator.

"My fear is justified; I know what it did the last time a light fell from above."

The Reeve crossed her arms. "Ridiculous that was too long ago."

She spoke softly in some discomfort "I do Reeve, I really do."

The Reeve smiled and was shaking her head.

"It's not a laughing matter!"

"No, it really is not but no one has memories of those times."

"Well I do and that is why I was selected for this role. You think I panic and you all think I overreact but I remember, I know what happens!"

"That cat is one of us and important and it will have a role to play."

The Reeve looked at Nahla who was watching their every move and she still looked at her as she spoke. "So if I have this right, Mildred does not know that Nahla is here and Jess (she coughed)....Suzanna's cat is now somewhere else?"

"Yes that is correct."

She turned around to look at Nubia. "With another vet?" She nodded in agreement. "Well they may run tests on her cat instead."

"It was an educated risk and besides I had Fennaway speak with her beforehand. Suzanna's cat Khepri was asked to help us."

"Asked or told?"

"We always ask and never assume Reeve, that is the way of things."

The Reeve leant forward onto her elbows in thought. "This changes things."

"Changes what? We need to act and act quickly. The second part of the prophecy has taken place right in front of my eyes and it cannot be a coincidence that it has happened here, right in front of us!"

The Reeve nodded in agreement. "No it can't and there is something else very troubling happening that you are not aware of."

The curator frowned. "How so, what am I not aware of?"

"We need to go upstairs to speak with Lady Safiya."

"Well, yes I agree, she needs to know!"

"She does but that was not what I was referring to."

The curator leaned her head forward hanging on every word. "Well?"

"Something has awoken in the deep of the below. What is now happening cannot be a coincidence, we need to go into the below."

The curator rocked backwards in shock. "You serious?"

"Yes now, right now."

Duat had never been further into the below than where he had needed to. He had given his *'motivational'* talks to the others that dwelled here over the few floors below his own. His talks were full of venom and his words unforgiving; he had done well and could sense their anger at every turn. They bowed to him now quite rightly and addressed him as their master. He had won over their confidence of achieving what they had believed was impossible. Their will to live beyond these walls and chambers was evident and he suspected that many of them had been far below, looking for a means of escape in the past.

Their language of Volemon and their own symbology had been carved into the walls throughout the lower floors; the first floor where the Escarrabin would greet them on a daily basis was left in their old darkened and natural state.

Duat had been presented with facts and knowledge; he did not know about the watchers tunnel when he arrived here and did not care for how far they had progressed with it. But that desire to be free of here gained him their support rapidly, they would do his bidding.

But the facts he did know was at the very bottom of the below was the original home of the Reeve's treasures that they had stolen and was not rightfully theirs. Their original stronghold must have taken many years of digging and carving their way with ancient tools to hide their secrets and wealth. Only on rare occasions would some of this wealth materialise to the outside world that was 'miraculously' discovered in a field or a dessert somewhere, no doubt for a price. Pirates that paraded as protectors; that was their only admirable quality.

He held his right palm up to an unlit torch and breathed upon his palm and watched the flames light up the area around him as he held the torch aloft. Safe in the knowledge that the two keys were in the pocket of his robe he walked towards the stairwell and could hear hisses all around him from the watchers that were seething in anger and ready for change.

The ancient stone steps beneath his feet were worn and uneven and he reached over to the wall on his right and removed another unlit torch and brought the two of them together. The dark void directly to his left of the spiral stairs had no supporting rail. He leant over and dropped one of the torches down. He watched on as the flames became more distant as it fell far and further than he expected. The thud of it hitting the bottom took a couple of seconds for him to hear. He was not the only one to hear it as a roar propelled up the staircase followed by multiple bangs against iron. The size of the beast would be of such enormity that it may struggle to fit up the staircase. He hoped its clumsiness would not bring the whole lot down upon them both.

He descended into the darkness with the torch held above him and his suspicions were correct as he ran his palm over the old watcher's language. The others had the sense of touch but not like him, but the acidic quality of their resin from their right palms had allowed them to leave their marks all over the wall as he progressed further down.

He could see the steam rising in front of his eye as his breathing intensified in the coldness of this place as the banging and noise from below became ever closer.

He passed other doorways as he went down that had not been opened in a long time. He knew what lay beyond some of them but they were not of interest for him right now. Free the beast, free the watchers and in time there would be a new order and that would allow the others to come.

"I'm aware of the lateness of the night Ma'am but it cannot wait. I will also have the curator with me."
Nubia looked on completely confused as she watched the phone being put down. "Well, what is it?"

The Reeve stood up. "I'll explain when we get there; time is of the essence I suspect." She went to walk to the door and spun around and reached for the phone again and pressed in the extension number. "Raysmau, just checking that you are up, has your clocked stopped?"
Nubia looked on watching the Reeve's head nod up and down.
"Yes I understand, stand by your phone I may be calling."
The phone went down and the Reeve ushered the curator to follow. "Make sure you close your door behind you Nubia, the cat needs to stay in here."

Unusually for Nubia she was silent and was struggling to match the pace of the Reeve. The Reeve sensed her nerves and they may be justified and as yet she did not know what else was potentially going on in the below.

They ascended the stairs over two floors passing a handful of clerics; most were resting in their own quarters at this hour. Nubia's head was bobbing up and down as she tried to keep up with the increasing walking speed of the Reeve as they approached Lady Safiya's quarters.

There was no knock at the door, no pleasantries as the Reeve pushed the heavy door open and there was no cleric to greet her this time either.

"Lady Safiya?"
"Yes Reeve, I'm coming" was the voice from behind the door in her sitting room. The two of them waited. The Reeve looked down to Nubia who was puffing a little from the quick late night excursion. Nubia looked up to her, her eyes wider than normal and still a little bloodshot. Their eye contact was broken at the sound of the heavy door being pulled open in front of them.

"Well come in then both of you."

The lady of the house was dressed in slippers and a dressing gown, her hair unkempt; Reeve's phone call had clearly disturbed her.

"Take a seat."

"Yes My Lady." Nubia nodded as they both sat. There were no cats present on this occasion.

"I'm guessing your meeting with me earlier and the ring has led to something then?"

Nubia looked at the Reeve. "What ring?"

The Reeve sat upright with composure and gathered her words. "Yes Ma'am it did and I have troubling news."

The lady sat down supported by her cane with anticipation, she could also see the nervousness of the curator. "I see, well let's hear it then."

"I have had to consult with my head of Order following the news of, shall we say, activities of a watcher who calls himself Duat."

The lady swallowed at the name. "That does not bode well."

"No, quite. I can't go into the fullness of what he may have done but we suspect he has been able to obtain keys that open a gateway or a passage in the below."

Nubia looked in horror. "What?"

"What gate, what passage Reeve?" Safiya enquired.

"Yes My Lady. In truth I cannot be fully sure but we have reason to suspect that my ancestors a very long time ago created a form of shield in the below and behind that shield were kept secrets that have laid in rest for centuries. We suspect this watcher may try to access this shield and free what lies beyond it."

Nubia froze with her mouth open as she heard this.

"This event is troubling enough but this evening Nubia has witnessed what she believes to be the second sign of the prophecy…"

"Yes My Lady, it fell some miles away, it flew right over us!"

Lady Safiya was shaking her head not fully understanding what she was hearing. "What flew over, what was it?"

Nubia shrugged her shoulders. "Well I don't know My Lady, a comet, meteor or something." She lifted both of her hands still shrugging. "My Lady, please look." She nodded at the clock behind Lady Safiya.

Safiya frowned and turned around to look at her clock. It said it was two minutes past midnight and the pendulum was silent. The frowned expression remained as she looked back at them both, leant on her cane, rose to her feet and walked over to her grand old clock. Turning the key she opened the case and touched the static pendulum and pushed it to her left. It swung back to the central position but no further. She re-coiled her hand away from it and gently closed the case and pressed her hand against the cabinet, bowing her head. Her back was still turned to them as she spoke. "Reeve what time is it please?"

"I don't know Ma'am; all of the clocks have stopped. I've not checked our computers to see if they will give us the time but elsewhere they have all ceased to move, it is an undeniable event."

Her head was still bowed. "The last time this happened we lost great numbers." "And there was a light from above then which was described as a comet by others on the outside." She nodded gently "Possibly Nubia but it was a different time then." She walked slowly to her seat and the Reeve noticed shaking in her hands as she steadied herself on her cane and sat down.

"Tell me more of this watcher. How has he obtained these keys to which you refer? I am not aware of such keys."

"No Ma'am, you wouldn't be as with the finger ring you have worn for so long, my Order protects the Horde Of Light but some of our measures are secretive." "I'm aware of that Reeve but it still does not explain how he got them in the first place. I trust the key I gave to you is still safe?"

"Yes Ma'am it is."

Lady Safiya nodded as she looked at the Reeve and lent forward. "What did it open, you need to tell me?"

Nubia looked directly at the Reeve shifting uncomfortably in her seat; she wanted an answer as well.

The Reeve tilted her head down and lifted up her hair and unclipped her neck chain. From between her chest, underneath her tailored white shirt, she pulled at the chain and the final key was revealed to both of them.

As the Reeve held it up Nubia squinted at the perfect circle but could only see the centre piece from behind. "What is that?"

"A Key."

They both looked over to Lady Safiya who had exhaled deeply as she looked at the floor. "The centre piece Reeve, is it of the serpent?"

The Lady looked upwards to see the Reeve nodding; her hand went to her temple in response.

"What do you know of this watcher Nubia?"

Nubia frowned. "I don't My Lady this is all news to me, security is the Reeve's department."

The Reeve lowered the key to her legs and gave the curator an unpleasant stare. "And you haven't answered the question as to how this watcher obtained missing keys 'from somewhere'."

The Reeve did not enjoy the tone of her voice along with the inverted commas gesture.

"The Order Of The Reeves does not concern you."

"But it does me."

They both looked at Lady Safiya. "Tell me what you know Reeve it could be very important."

"It would betray my Order Ma'am."

"Better that than betraying all of us! If the prophecy is coming to pass we need to take action. Tell me Reeve right now what do you know?"

The Reeve looked at the floor and took a deep breath knowing full well that the curator was staring at her. "We have a storage chamber within the grounds only known to my Order. Somehow this watcher we suspect may have gained entry and it is a possibility he has taken the keys for two of the locks of the shield in the below."

Lady Safiya's mouth was opened in shock as was Nubia's. "Oh let me take a random guess, would it be somewhere around the great statue of Salma?"

The Reeve shot an angered stare at the curator.

"I saw you from the window. Ma'am one moment she was there and then she was gone."

The Reeve flared her teeth. "Leave it."

"What do you keep there, hidden gold and treasures I presume?"

"I told you to leave it, something has to pay for all of this. We may be an Order but we still have overheads and costs."

The curator shook her head. "And this watcher knew what neither of us did? Well what a conundrum!"

The three of them sat in silence composing their thoughts.

Nubia started shaking her head. "Oh wait, now it all makes sense. That's why there are no cameras outside, that's why there is no CCTV. It's for her lot to protect their treasure, to make sure we don't know about it!"

"THAT'S ENOUGH both of you! They both looked at the floor in response to Lady Safiya's outburst.

"Both of you need to stop this, although I must concede Nubia, you do have a point there that will be worthy of some investigation."

The Reeve looked up and then at the curator with some aggression.

"When did this watcher get brought here?"

"It wasn't Ma'am as I understand, it appeared outside our gates."

Lady Safiya leant forward on her chair and looked over. "You can't be serious Reeve?"

The Reeve raised her eyebrows together and her eyes and lips twitched over to the right.

"So a watcher appears here knowing our location, knows about a hiding place unknown to anyone on these grounds except for you. And not just that, was able to bypass any security measures that you had in place. I'm guessing that you have some?"

"Some, Ma'am?"

"Security measures in place?"

"Yes Ma'am there are."

The lady of the house shook her head and slumped back in her chair and brought her hand to her mouth in consideration of these facts.

"Timing, timing...everything happens for a reason. He showed up here recently?"

"Yes Ma'am so I understand, a couple of weeks ago. The Escarrabin brought him in and took him below."

The curator frowned. "A couple of weeks ago?"

"Yes why Nubia?"

She held her right hand up in thought trying to process everything and started shaking her head before a very concerned expression appeared across her face.

"Lady Ebonee My Lady."

"Not her again Nubia!"

"No wait Reeve, let Nubia finish."

Nubia put a hand to her temple as she thought; it was known to me that Lady Ebonee had a relationship with Lady Tempest."

"You've been talking to Ebonee?"

The curator nodded. "Yes My Lady, I have her ear."

The Reeve rolled her eyes.

"Lady Ebonee spoke with dear Lady Tempest quite regularly."

"Are you sure Nubia, that's highly unusual, Tempest was only a sixth degree elder?"

"I know but Lady Ebonee told me in confidence that Lady Tempest was investigating something, something that left unchecked could escalate and have severe consequences, for all of us!"

"She's losing her marbles Nubia."

"That's the Keeper's words Reeve, not your own, you don't know her!"

"But I do and very well and she is a friend of mine for that matter Reeve."
Nubia shot a patronising smile at the Reeve.

"So what are you saying Nubia?"

"Well don't you see; Lady Tempest loses her life a couple of weeks ago and suddenly a watcher shows up here, knowing what he knows and knowing more than you and I My Lady."

Lady Safiya looked at the curator with concern.

"She was not knocked down by a bus, how could she be?" The curator spat her words and shook her head back and forth and suddenly froze and looked at the head of the house. "She was murdered Ma'am, she was murdered I'm telling you!"

Lady Safiya put a hand to her mouth in worry.

"She knew something. She was onto something and someone and probably this watcher did it!"

The Reeve spoke softly. "Nubia, Tempest could not have known about the vault and how to access it."

"Well maybe she did, or maybe she didn't but she may have known that this watcher did know and was trying to stop it!"

The Reeve shook her head. "Well then why wouldn't she speak to me, security as you state is my department?"

The curator looked increasingly angry. "Well maybe she thought that she couldn't. It would appear that you have secrets to hide as well!"

The Reeve sat back in her chair and diverted her eyes away; she was not going to rise to this, particularly as the curator may actually be right in some of her estimations.

Safiya held both of her palms up. "Okay, Okay, please let's remain calm, I need a moment with this."

"What are we dealing with here Reeve, and what is that third key for?"

The Reeve chewed at her lip and took her eyes from the wall and looked back over. "My head of Order had to go deep into the ancient archives and her investigation is not yet complete. But in light of events that have taken place here this evening I feel that we need to act."

"You are referring to the potential second sign."

"Yes Ma'am I am."

"I'm aware that one of our own was baring pains of two hearts, do we know of her status now?"

The Reeve looked directly at the curator who gave her a look of pleading not to say anything. "Yes Ma'am we believe that she is now better and that is the added worry that her recovery is as foretold."

Nubia looked gratefully at the floor.

Safiya nodded. "I see," not knowing that the cat was only two floors below her. "So, tell me about the key."

"From what I've been able to establish, the shield below is a wall of iron. The two missing keys need to be inserted at the same time to open a doorway within the wall. However countermeasures are as always put in place and this is one of them." She lifted the circle of bronze from her legs and could feel the roughness of the patterns on the reverse side that formed some kind of combination. It was an assumption but she guessed the unique design would allow the key to lock into the wall and then be able to be turned.

Safiya pointed at the Reeve. "But he does not have that?"

"No Ma'am, he does not and without this being pressed into the iron wall the doorway should not open."

There was the slightest of smiles from the lady of the house but only the very slightest. "You think that he does not know this?"

The Reeve nodded "The doorway was never meant to be opened by one person that is why this key was kept separately and secretly."

There had been a brief moment of silence before the Reeve resumed. "However I am concerned. This key and both of the others are very old. There is no guarantee that they work or any countermeasure in place will work either. We do not know if the doorway will open, we do not know whether the iron shield will hold and could possibly be destroyed. But of course that is not the only reason why we must act."

Safiya nodded "What is it the watcher wants, what is he trying to get from there?"

The Reeve took a deep breath and avoided the curators gaze. "It's what he's trying to set free."

The curator's chin prodded forwards. "What?"

"It only came to my attention today that sounds have been heard from the deep of the below. The sounds are unnatural, something has awoken from beyond the wall of iron."

The curator looked in panic at Safiya who looked down before she spoke. "I asked you before if the symbol on that key was of the serpent. Is it something to do with the enemy of old? Is that symbol a warning?"

The Reeve nodded a few times. "Yes Ma'am I believe it is."

Safiya rested her elbow on the side of her chair and placed her hand to her chin, closing her eyes. "What is it, what is this beast?"

The Reeve swallowed and looked at the curator and then at the lady of the house. "It's possible that it maybe the Hydra."

Safiya's hand moved from her chin and covered her eyes.

The curator's face was in equal measure of terror and laughter. "THE HYDRA, are you demented!"

"It is as I have been informed curator" the Reeve retorted.

She spoke in laughter. "That's ridiculous. How could it possibly be here and why for that matter? Honestly your Order at times is more of a hindrance than help." She was shaking her head in disgust. "The Hydra being here, that was thousands of years ago...."

"Remember that as well do you?"

"Don't you patronise me!"

"ENOUGH!!" They were both silenced by the loud voice that cut over them. "You are both ladies of the Order, now act like it!"

They both looked on as the head of the manor's hands quivered and her voice wavered as she spoke. "There are no other ladies here, they have all been to their gatherings this evening. How many Escarrabin are present Reeve?"

"When they all return from their duties from last night it will be 36 Ma'am."

She nodded clearly in discomfort. "We will need them."

Nubia looked in shock. "My Lady do you believe any of this?"

"Ma'am I believe we need to act quickly. I was going to wait until dawn but in view of what is happening right now, as we speak, I don't think we can."

Safiya nodded and got to her feet and turned to look at her clock.

They both stood up as their senior rose.

The Reeve was looking for a response. "Ma'am?"

"I need to get changed." She turned to look at the Reeve and nodded and headed, with her cane, towards the door.

The curator swallowed as she looked at the Reeve decisively walking over to a desk and reached for the phone.

She waited patiently for a few seconds before it was answered. "Raysmau, this is the Reeve, we are at diligence." She slowly put the phone down and looked at Nubia.

"It has started."

Chapter Twenty Nine:

WALLS OF VOLEMON

Watchers have their own unique smell, a smell that those above may describe as some form of decay, but this, this that he could smell right now was something entirely different.

The thin skin around the two gaps in his skull that represented nostrils, where a nose would have been a long time ago, twitched slightly. He was not immune to this smell as the thin skin over his forehead displayed faint frown lines of nausea.

No-one had been here for a very long time. Even the etchings of the language of Volemon had stopped on the wall next to the stairs some way back.

The chamber was dimly lit from the torch he had dropped from above and the one he held in his left hand. In the coldness of the place Duat surveyed the dark iron wall that was absorbing much of the light. Despite the cold and damp he suspected the smell was coming from the other side, from what lay beyond it. Reasonably encouraged, this suggested that the wall was not as sealed as it probably was when constructed. The beast that lay beyond could not have eaten; the smell of decay must have been from something consumed a long time ago.

He could hear movements beyond the wall and the hissing sound of multiple heads as he looked around the holding chamber. On his left and right he could see two old torches were secured into the rock each held by a large iron ring. He would take advantage of those.

As he lit the torches on both sides of the chamber he wiped saliva from his mouth and focused on the seal of the Reeves now clearly visible and engraved into the ironwork.

He read the two words that accompanied the seal 'Tenere Immortus', words from the old language that roughly translated to 'hold of the undead'. The left side of his mouth turned slightly upwards in amusement of their fickle ways.

He walked forward to the wall and placed his right palm upon the ironwork and closed his eye and concentrated. He waited a few seconds but nothing could be felt and nothing could be heard. He reopened his eye and hissed. He could not communicate directly with the beast, something within the wall was stopping him from doing so. The beast had awoken shortly after his arrival here, why he could not communicate directly with it he could not understand.

He removed his palm and stepped back hearing a large bang against the wall of iron. The roar that followed was deafening as multiple thuds echoed throughout the chamber, it was growing restless. He may not be able to communicate directly but it sensed his presence and no doubt could feel that freedom was imminent.

The wall was strong; there was no doubt of that from the unflinching barrage of weight that was being thrust upon it from the other side. He looked across the length of the wall with some concern; there was no obvious sign of a doorway as he walked its entire length. The temper and noise from the other side was relentless as he waved the torch around straining his eye for something to assist him. He knew the entry point for the keys would not be obvious and he searched as quickly as he could. The beast may well have sensed or heard his immediate presence but he could not be sure of controlling it once free. If he couldn't, he would need to protect himself and that would not be an ideal situation as he needed it by his side, at least initially anyway.

He was drawn to an intricate carving cut out in the rock on the right hand side of the wall as he waved the torch in its direction. Even from a distance he could see that it looked to resemble the head of a serpent.

He moved towards it focused upon the unusually shaped head of the snake whose mouth was open much wider than would normally be possible, even for a snake.

He was trying to concentrate but the noise was becoming overwhelming from the other side of the wall. Why the Reeves would have taken the time to carve out something with so much detail he did not know, presumably as a warning to others.

The multiple sounds of impact upon the ironwork were becoming too intense to focus.
"SILENCE!!!!" he yelled at the top of his voice with no affect. "SILENTIUM!!!"
"SIOPI!!" as the roar subdued to a hiss and the occasional rattle of a head against iron could be heard.

It appeared that he had some form of control after all as temporary as that may be as he studied the rock carving that was rich in detail but he couldn't see any entry point for a key or keys.

The saliva fell from his mouth to the floor below and as he watched it descend he could see lower down to his left hand side a perfect circle was cut into the ironwork. He passed the torch to his right hand and crouched down and with his left he put his fingers into the circle that was only an inch or so in depth. He removed dust and dirt and could feel there were rough abrasions inside the circle. Removing his hand he re-stood and stepped backwards. He could feel the thin skin of his forehead rising again but this time with confusion rather than nausea.

He glanced back at the head of the serpent. The cut out circle could not be a coincidence but it meant nothing to him. However with the Reeves nothing happened by chance, it must have some form of purpose.

There were a couple of large bangs against the wall again. "SIOPI!!" his voice becoming more impatient as the sound of hissing echoed around the chamber. Time was critical and he needed to find the entry points as quickly as he could. The combination of the snake and the carved circle meant something, it must be close. Knowing that the Reeves may have some form of countermeasure in place, he chose to sacrifice his left hand just in case and he started to run his fingers in circles over the ironwork. He re-coiled his hand on a couple of occasions in response to the aggressive banging coming from the other side. The beast was becoming more hostile and he could not be sure if he would have control over it, the longer this took the less likely it would be. The wall was still holding but for all of his powers he would not be able to penetrate it unless the key inserts could be found.

His frustration was growing with the fear that he was losing control. His own hiss of anger was not on a par to the sounds from the Hydra but in that moment that was the only common ground they shared. He watched the steam emanate from his mouth as it moved over the wall and he yelled out in temper and stamped against the floor. He reached for the keys in the pocket of his robe in desperation and held them in front of his eye. As he did so he felt a draft upon him coming from the direction of the carved serpent. He turned the keys towards it and looked over his shoulder to the right and could see that one of the torches fixed to the wall had started to flicker.

Still holding his own torch in his right hand he separated the two keys in his left and held them towards the head of the serpent. There were two turquoise coloured stones in the eyes of the serpent that, until that point, he had failed to notice and they glowed against the flickering light. He placed a key directly over one of the eyes of the serpent's head noticing for the first time there was a tiny jewel carved into the base of the key. He moved the head of the key in a circular motion over the turquoise stone set into the eye and turned to look over his left shoulder. He hissed in satisfaction as he saw the faintest of flickers from a tiny turquoise stone set into the iron wall. He rushed over to where he had seen the light flickering. It was low down on the wall as he crouched down to see the tiny coloured stone but there was no key hole. He dropped the torch to the floor and felt around it and left a key on the floor to mark its place. He ran back to the serpent and placed the other key over the other eye of the snake and saw a similar reflective light flicker above the other one in the wall, just further to the right of the one he had just discovered.

Positive he had cracked the Reeve's code with a stretch of both arms he could feel both of the small stones set into iron and pressed against both of them. Instantly he heard movement coming from within the iron wall and to his right a small opening appeared. He emitted a hiss with his own success.

He grabbed at both of the keys and rushed to the formally hidden key ports. He brought his eye level to the opening and could see two very old key holes cut into the ironwork; he knew instantly they were designed to fit the four sided keys.

He drew a deep breath at the importance of the moment as he felt the wall shudder as the beast hit against it from the other side. "Soon, soon, soon, my friend." He blew the dirt off the key that had lay on the floor and inserted them both at the same time. He took a step back in consideration as he rubbed the saliva from his mouth and closed his eye and with a smile he reached out for them and turned them both to the right. He could hear sounds of old locking mechanisms moving within the door as he reopened his eye and pushed against the keys in anticipation of the parting of the wall of iron.

The echo from the locking mechanism could still be heard but nothing was happening. He tried turning them the other way but there was no movement. The keys were locked into their ports. Grimacing he applied all of his strength to the keys as a breeze drifted over him again. In the stillness of the chamber he could see the torch to his left had started to flicker.

He let go of the keys and turned around to look at the flickering torch. Its movements were exactly the same as the one on the right.

"What, what is it?" he yelled in a temper at the torches as his eye was drawn to the head of the serpent. He swallowed deeply as something glowed from one of the teeth of the open mouth and he rushed towards it. There was another stone which he pressed upon, and immediately a light flickered to his left from the centre of the cut circle.

In anguish he rushed to it and pushed the circle cut into iron, his saliva running uncontrollably.
"NO, NO, it can't be!!" as he hit out at the circle. He put both of his hands to his head as the banging from the other side started again and the chamber was full of the sounds of multiple snakes hissing in angry unison. He spun his head around looking at the torches. There was something else, he must have missed something, there were only two keys he was certain of that. "WHAT IS IT??" His yelling and rage was becoming uncontrollable when all of the noise suddenly stopped within the chamber. In the silence the slightest of sounds

could be heard. He looked at the head of the serpent and then to the flashing of the stone set within the circle in the wall. He stood in the silence hearing his own breathing when the faintest sound started to make its way down to him from the above.

He rushed out of the chamber to look up the stairs and could see shadows moving in the dim light at the very top. This was followed by the sound of watchers in pain as their howls started to make its way down to him. He turned to look at the wall and shook his head in confusion. He had no idea what was happening and then a sound travelled down the stairs that he did know the meaning of.

He looked back up from the darkness of the base of the staircase as the sound became louder. "It can't be...it can't be!" He ran back to the wall and grabbed at both of the keys again. Putting all of his weight upon them to the point that they may bend or break at any moment when he heard sounds of movement from the carved serpent and he stopped instantly. Breathing heavily he could see the light in the circle was flashing and the mouth of the serpent began to move and became wider. He stepped away from the wall hearing the Hydra bellow at full volume as he put his hands to the two holes in his skull that he listened through, and covered them. He stared at the mouth of the snake as liquid began to run from it onto the floor below and a mist started to form within the chamber.

He swallowed and stepped backwards and even with his ear sockets covered he heard an almighty roar of pain from behind the wall and dozens of rapid bangs against it. There was one more bellow that sounded more like a scream and he could hear the beast retreat away, it was gone.
"NO, NO!!" as he put a hand to his nostrils and forced himself against the keys again.

The chamber started to fill with noxious smoke and he could feel his eye was starting to run as he coughed and spluttered and spat saliva and phlegm across the floor. He started to wretch in some pain as he fell against the wall from the poison in the air and looked at the two torches that flicked and immediately went out.

He dragged his way out of the chamber and fell at the base of the staircase and looked upwards at shadows moving quickly above. Coughing he started to pull himself up the stairs, the noise from the above becoming ever closer and more apparent.

Holding his midsection and covering his mouth he steadied himself to his feet and started to climb slowly upwards. He looked behind him; the noxious smoke was not following and was contained within the chamber.

As he ascended he knew he was right about the noise he had heard below, the further he climbed the louder it became. He slumped to the floor trying to regain his breath, still holding his midsection in considerable pain and spat against the wall and looked up from his bloodshot eye. He knew the sound and knew what it meant, it was undeniable.

The general alarm had been sounded as his head slumped against the wall. He had failed, the beast would not be freed and the Escarrabin were coming.

Still partially dressed in her battle armour, Raysmau had put the phone down and walked as quickly as she could to the security control room. The door was slightly open and she pushed her way through. "Escarrabin Layla and Amera we are at diligence, sound the alarm immediately."
They both looked at each other. "Ma'am?"
"Now, that's an order!"
"Yes Ma'am; Ma'am may I ask is this a drill and shall we continue to monitor the cameras outside the grounds?"
"This is not a drill Amera," Raysmau looked briefly at the floor "and no, the problem is already here." She looked back up at both of them. "Use of pulse fire is authorised; issue the instruction through your terminal to the weapons store. The scatterblades on charge make sure they are primed."
They both looked at each other again. "Erm, yes Ma'am, right away."
"I will give a short briefing at the muster point in ten minutes time; make sure all Escarrabin attend without exception."
"Yes Ma'am the security block will be notified immediately however many have not yet returned from duties away from here this evening."
"I'm aware of this" she snapped "send a message to their navigators and phones to return to headquarters as quickly as they can."
"Yes Ma'am, activating now, we are at diligence."

Raysmau pointed her hand forward. "Open the outer door will you."

"Yes Ma'am, doing that now."

Raysmau left the control room and headed through the opening security gate and waited with some irritation for the outer door to open into the main lobby. She was drawing deeply on her breath as the outer door opened. Security measures outside the manor are tested once a month and she hoped that now they were actually being called upon they would work without hitch.

She looked up towards the balconies as the general alarm sounded echoing throughout the building. Only two clerics sat at the main desk at this hour as they looked at each other and lifted their heads with concern towards Raysmau. "Stay at your posts unless otherwise instructed and secure the clerics residence."

"Yes Ma'am."

She watched the fingers of the pale hands direct instructions through their computer terminals locking down and securing the cleric's sleeping area. Only those working would now be within the main part of the building.

As she stepped into the centre of the lobby area the steel shutters slid down over the windows of the lower level of Loxley and she could hear the very old portcullis moving beyond the main doors. She waited patiently for the sound of their closure before moving back into her quarters.

Only a short drive away from headquarters Kassia was in fits of giggles. Shula, the more serious of the two, couldn't help but smile.

"Honestly, she did not know it was ancient wine. In fact it probably wasn't wine at all, was made by monks or something. Far stronger than usual and she thought it would be a good idea to see if pulse mode was working. Destroyed a desk and the tapestry behind it caught fire, took three of the girls to put it out."

They carried on laughing. "She didn't get away with it though."

"What happened to her?"

"I got a message from her not so long back, they sent her to Alaska." Kassia was still laughing.

"Alaska?"

"Yes punishment presumably, didn't think she would like the cold and solitude." Kassia ran a hand through her hair still laughing.

"And does she?"

"Does she what, like it out there?"

"Yeah."

"Says she loves it, views are amazing, goes into the mountains on time off, she's still not allowed a scatterblade of course."

"Ha ha, I bet."

They drove to the bottom of the secluded road towards the semicircle of trees and Kassia held her pin badge up to the scanner as they sat watching the trees move to the sides and the view of the manor opened up in front of them.

"That's odd, look."

Kassia looked forward.

"What are all of the floodlights doing on?"

They drove under the archway towards the house and Shula leaned forward to the windscreen.

"Am I seeing that right?" as she strained her eyes as the house became closer. "Is the portcullis down?"

"Lower level windows are secured as well."

They were both drawn to their navigator that displayed a new message as Shula read it aloud. "We are to return to headquarters immediately." She looked at Kassia. "Something must be going on." "Navigator disengage!" Kassia's coded voice overriding its control and she took charge of the car and sped up. "We'll get to the security block as quickly as we can; I'm not liking the look of this. "No me neither."

After a very brief lull, Shula was back in serious mode again.

Nubia tore into the Reeve's office after finding her main door unlocked yet again "Reeve.....Reeve!!"

She was panicking, the alarm ringing throughout the building for someone who remembered events of the past was becoming too much.

She was not in her office so she pushed her way into her private quarters. She could see the Reeve in her dressing room half dressed in battle armour. "Well don't knock will you!"

"I'm sorry, Reeve do you mind if I stay with you, I don't feel safe?"

"Why, the watchers are below. There is nothing to indicate at this time they have escaped and, as unlikely as that would be, they would run anyway, they have no interest in you Nubia."

"That's as maybe, I'll just feel safer."

"As you wish but you stay behind out of harm's way. When at diligence it is for soldiers, not for curators, clear?"

She nodded fearful of everything happening so quickly. "Yes I understand."

"I've told Raysmau what she needs to know and she'll be giving a briefing in the next few minutes within the security block. Use of pulse weapons has been authorised."

She watched the curator nod in acceptance and could see the worry across her face. "Don't worry Nubia, we are trained for this." She opened her ceremonial cabinet and took out her modified spear. "This spear has never been fired as an act of aggression." She could feel the worry emanating from Nubia. "I'm sure it won't be tonight."

"If the beast has got out things could be terrible."

She stopped dressing and looked down at Nubia and nodded. "It could be but, if my head of Order is correct, that wall cannot be opened without this. She pulled at the chain that hung around her neck. Nubia could see the tip of the secret key appear from under the Reeve's blouse. "The only way anyone is getting this from me is to take it from me, understand?"

Nubia swallowed as her body shook, her head giving the briefest of nods.

"And that is not going to happen." She started to dress again and affixed her upper body armour that proudly displayed the crest of the Reeve in the centre of her breast plate.

She took a hair tie out of one of the drawers of her dresser and tied her hair up at the back.

"Nubia, ring downstairs and have a couple of clerics watch over Lady Safiya until after the briefing, we'll send a couple of Escarrabin to her directly afterwards."

Nubia nodded and headed out of the room to use the Reeve's phone in her office.

She lifted her helmet up and placed it over her head. The red ceremonial mane hung from the back and she dragged the frontage down to protect her jaw and mouth. It would be impossible for her to wear breathing apparatus as well as her traditional face protection so she would have to judge that as things evolved.

Nubia came back into the room. "Front desk are arranging two of the clerics that were still on duty to watch over Lady Safiya. Their sleeping quarters has been locked down so only a few are active within the building."

"Good." She put on her heavy gloves, flexed her fingers and picked up her spear. She couldn't help but notice the curator was looking at her differently. "What is it Nubia?"

She smiled. "You are dressed properly for a change, you look like a Reeve."

Nubia could not see the faint smile that had appeared from behind the mask. "Careful curator, you almost paid me a compliment."

"I won't make a habit of it."

"I don't doubt, let's go to the briefing."

Gamila rushed into the weapons cache and collected her scatterblade from the quartermaster. "What's going on?"

"Just take your weapon Escarrabin, use of pulse fire has been authorised. Move to the muster point immediately."

She looked behind the quartermaster to the clock on the wall that had stopped. "Yes Ma'am."

Alian was ahead of her and she ran to catch up with her. "Alian do you know anything?"

"Not a thing other than Raysmau is going to be giving a briefing very soon."

"Do you think this has something to do with what we told her?"

Alian looked at her and nodded. "I suspect so but why now and at this hour I have no idea, something has happened."

"Did you notice the clock in the weapons store, and my watch, they've both stopped."

"Mine too, it's not a coincidence."

"It looks like everyone is being called. How many of us are there do you think?"

"Don't know, guessing about 15-20 many won't be back from last night yet."

They both entered the canteen to see other Escarrabin talking to each other whilst others were coming in behind them. Gamila looked over to see the familiar face of Kassia entering the room with Shula; both were dressed in what looked like business suits. "Well you don't look ready."

"We've literally only just got back. The portcullis is down, what's going on? Everyone is reporting in."

"Don't know but we had to report to Raysmau earlier that Alian and I had been in the below. There's something down there."

Kassia smiled. "You what, you're joking right?"

Alian shook her head. "Afraid not."

Shula shrugged her shoulders. "Guess we'll find out, about now actually," as she saw Raysmau walk into the room wearing full battle armour.

The quartermaster walked in the room. "Attention!"

The Escarrabin all stood to attention with their scatterblades to their sides.

They looked on as the quartermaster stood on tiptoes and talked into the ear of Raysmau. She nodded. "So this is everyone for now, 19 in total?"

"Yes Ma'am."

"Right Escarrabin at ease."

She watched them all partially relax as she did a quick visual inspection of their battle dress.

"I'll tell you what I know and it's vital that you listen. Firstly this is not a drill exercise."

She could see that she had all of their attention.

"Information passed to me by the Reeve, who will be joining us shortly, is there have been a series of events that we do not determine to be a coincidence. I'm not going to go into all of those right now as this could be time critical and we will be moving immediately. There is a potential and it is only a potential that something in the below, something from the past may have awoken."

She looked on as heads looked at each other. Mumbled speculation was heard and she held her hand up to silence them.

You are all members of the elite Escarrabin Order and you have undertaken your training and studies about the history of the Horde Of Light and why we protect them. Their heritage, their legacy depends on us to ensure that darkness does not prevail. What may be happening here right now in the deep below, you will not find in text or your training manuals. There is a suspicion and reasonable grounds that a carcass may have been buried deep in the below, an area none of you have seen, and that carcass may have awoken."

There were further looks of concern around the room but this time in dignified silence.

"There are actions of what we believe to be a rogue watcher and that he may have played some part in this. How and why we do not know as yet but it is enough to be a concerning development. The creature buried a very long time ago some of you may have heard of it and as such you need to know. It is an old enemy of the past, a serpent creature, and we believe it to be, what it is known more commonly as, the Hydra."

There were immediate audible gasps around the room.

"The snake demon?"
"Not a demon but if awoken it will act with ruthlessness and will need to be destroyed."

Raysmau turned around hearing footsteps behind her and saw the Reeve walk in wearing full battle dress accompanied by Nubia.

Raysmau felt the mood of the room change in an instant, seeing the head of security dressed for battle.

"However, the Order Of The Reeves a long time ago put security measures in place and we believe that this watcher does not have the necessary tools to release it. So that said the objective is, we go into the below as far as we need to."

She paused for breath letting her message sink in among the concerned faces.

"None of us can be sure how many watchers lie below, that will be changing as of this evening. We will conduct a full search and all watchers are to be detained, the rogue called Duat is to be brought before me. But understand this; take no chances, the watchers despite their bloodline are controllable within this secured environment. If this Duat is uniting them we know from history they can change and adapt quickly. All of you will be issued with extra protective gloves. Make sure you and they wear them before you apprehend them. Once in gloves, cuff them and bring all of them up to the central lobby as we need to detail all of them. Security has been too weak here for too long. That changes today.

As we are at diligence the lift down is disabled so, against usual protocol, the door leading to the stairs below will be opened from this side so we can use the stairs down. However it will seal again behind you and you will need to use the scanner to exit upon your return, those functions are not disabled. Watchers are to be brought up the stairs and we will construct a cordon within the lobby for their detention. Are there any questions?"

"Does it breathe fire Ma'am?"

All of the Escarrabin turned to look at Kassia.

"Blimey Kass what have you been watching?" Alian said with a shake of her head.

Kassia shrugged her shoulders. "Well I don't know!"

Raysmau unimpressed frowned. "However, it is said that the breath of the beast and the fumes from it is highly toxic so you will be issued with breathing apparatus and eye protection but I will reiterate, we do not think that it can escape. Pulse fire of the blades are not to be used below unless in an emergency and if so at the lowest level of pulse; ensure your pulse dials are set properly. If the beast is free your blades should be used as their original intended purpose, as a sword weapon. You are trained for both. I will issue an order if sword application is needed. All of you carry out comms checks and that your earpieces are secured. Do so now and any problems report to the quartermaster. Escarrabin, Amera and Layla are in the control room; speak with them if you need but only if you need. Maintain radio silence as much as possible."

Raysmau surveyed the room and nodded. "Well that's it then, carry out your checks and collect the rest of your equipment and don't forget the gloves. I'll meet you in the lobby as quickly as possible. We move immediately."

Raysmau turned to the Reeve, seeing the small stature of the quivering figure of Nubia hiding behind her. "Madam Reeve is there anything you wish to add?" Raysmau watched the iron mask of the Reeve move slowly to its left and right.

"That's it Escarrabin collect your gear and move to the lobby as soon as you can. Shula and Kassia get changed immediately."

Raysmau walked to the Reeve. "Ma'am they will know we are coming now that the alarm has been sounded." She watched the Reeve slowly nod. "Fear Raysmau, fear."

She had no doubt they were in fear but if it had been her decision she would not have alerted them. Going into the darkness when they are most active was bad enough, if they are trying to unite this was going to be a very difficult test.

If the beast had been freed losses were inevitable.

Raysmau depressed her push to talk button on the front of her breast plate and lowered her chin to speak into it. "Control, silence the alarm, I can't think over it."

Their response came through into her ear and the general alarm was silenced. Without the sound of clocks there was an eerie silence within the central lobby. The Reeve looked at Raysmau. "Are you ready?"

She nodded in response without words; her anxiousness was fully justified as she surveyed the assembling Escarrabin.

Raysmau spoke loudly to ensure she was heard. "Has everyone comms checked?"

"Yes Ma'am" was the collective response.

"Ensure your scatterblades are primed and be mindful of our rules of engagement, no one discharges fire unless threat to life is imminent. Sword application will be on my order."

She turned around hearing movements coming down the stairs and gestured with her head to the Reeve to turn around.

They were both looking away from their soldiers to see Lady Safiya coming down the stairs. "I'll speak with her" the Reeve said quietly to Raysmau. Raysmau nodded again and continued to brief the Escarrabin.

The Reeve walked to the bottom of the staircase and pushed her face guard up to reveal her face and looked up to Lady Safiya who had two clerics either side of her. "My Lady, respectfully this is not the place for you right now."

"Oh hush Reeve; I'm not going to miss this. What is happening right now will have to be reported to the Grand Council in any event."

She was now at the base of the stairs and level with the Reeve. "I know what you do is with all of our best interests Reeve and your Order are secretive and wise, but you know that I do not have to take instructions from you." She smiled looking directly into the Reeve's eyes sat between the iron nose protector that came from the Reeve's battle helmet.

The Reeve smiled ruefully back at her. "Very well My Lady but let me insist that two Escarrabin replace the clerics."

"That's fine, thank you Reeve." She turned either side to the clerics and thanked them.

"Clerics your quarters are sealed off at the moment so please wait on the upper landing under the dome for now."

"Yes Ma'am." They both nodded their heads and walked back up the stairs.

"I will also ask that the curator joins you as well as I don't want her below."

"That is also fine; I guess I'll just wait here then."

The Reeve smiled and nodded to the lady of the house and walked back to

Raysmau. "Assign two to watch over Lady Safiya please."

"Soad and Yara come to me."

Both guards came quickly towards her. "Please watch over Lady Safiya, don't leave her side for the duration."

"Yes Ma'am," they responded at the same time.

The Reeve stepped to the right of Raysmau towards the curator. "Nubia I wish for you to remain with Lady Safiya while this takes place."

"I would like to see what happens Reeve!"

"You are not trained for battle. Wait with the Lady, that is non-negotiable. I don't want you going below and besides you are not dressed properly."

"But Reeve…"

"End of discussion please, we have to leave."

She watched the curator sulk off heading towards the stairs and looked back to Raysmau and pulled her face protector back down.

Raysmau had finished speaking to the Escarrabin who were now ready for the order.

"Raysmau, this is your operation, your soldiers, control lies with you unless I deem it necessary to take operational command, is that clear?"

Raysmau pulled down her face protector checking that her night vision goggles were in place on top of her helmet. "Yes Ma'am, that is clear."

"Good, well then let's proceed."

Coughing regularly it was slow progress up the stairs. In pain from his bloodshot eye Duat had no choice but to use the wall for support.

The alarm was still ringing above and as he looked up the stairs the moving shadows were becoming more impatient and agitated. He would need to control the watchers quickly.

He stopped climbing and steadied himself. "BELATOR!!" he yelled as loudly as he could, his voice echoing around the cavern of the stairs. "BELATOR!!" He coughed and spat across the floor. He could hear shuffling above him and looked up to see a dark shadow moving down towards him and then the watcher's face appeared. "Master!"

"Come to me!"

Bellator moved as quickly as he could down the spiral staircase. "Master, what happened?" He put out an arm of support to steady Duat who was unbalanced. He leant against the wall and spat across the stairs. "The Reeves and their countermeasures, I underestimated them. I was not in possession of the facts. I've inhaled something but it will pass."

"Master, where is the creature, the brothers are restless awaiting your command?"

"It is below but it has retreated, that is why you do not hear it anymore." He coughed. "It could not be freed, not now anyway. They have many secrets and much is buried and hidden away down there."

"But Master, the noise from above, are they coming?"

He smiled as saliva ran down his chin. "Oh yes, they are coming" he steadied himself and started to walk up the stairs, "but do not worry, you and I will be fine, the others...not so much."

There was concern in Belator's eye. "But we need our brothers, we need them on the outside."

"We will but this is not over, the evolution of the new realm has only just started. Their prophecy of change is taking place as we speak, it is unstoppable."

"Prophecy Master?"

"Their fears, the stopping of their time; come my friend we must go up to greet them. Follow my instructions throughout and you will not be harmed." He looked at Bellator. "You shall be leaving here tonight."

"Yes Master, thank you but they will be coming in force, the brothers are sure of that."

They both stopped talking hearing the alarm from above being silenced.

"I am more than what I appear to all of you and we are leaving this evening, their vileness I can stand no more."

Bellator bowed his head. "Yes Master."

"Come my friend we must unite the brothers and we do not have much time."

Raysmau pressed her push to talk button. "Control receiving?"

"Yes Ma'am loud and clear."

"Override the door."

"Activating override."

The Escarrabin heard the security locks free and the button outside the door changed from green to red.

"Shula take front, Masika and Suma behind her." She nodded at both of them to do as she instructed. "Massika scan the area once below on your movement tracker and stay close to me." "Yes Ma'am."

"Suma monitor for gases." She raised her voice. "Everyone affix gas masks and eye protection. Other than those on detail up here everyone else goes down." Raysmau nodded at Shula. "Open the door and proceed inside." She watched the Escarrabin sling her scatterblade over her shoulder and with gloved hands she picked up two heavy magnets with handles from the floor and fixed them to the door and pulled. As the door started to open the cold air from below drifted into the lobby and the Escarrabin all lifted their weapons, the silver chrome reflecting from the lighting of the chandeliers above.

Shula jammed her foot against the door to hold it open and reaching for her scatterblade she moved through the door's opening. At the top of the stairs she looked over the drop to her left and pointed her weapons downwards. Masika and Suma followed behind her and they started to move down the stairs in formation.

Raysmau nodded at Lotfia to move through. "Keep a check on your scanner as well until we've found them."

"Yes Ma'am."

Raysmau moved through the door to the stairs, followed by another thirteen of the Escarrabin and the Reeve.

They descended the stairs to the first floor below ground; Raysmau surveyed the area and the darkness of the chamber. "Spread out." She ushered with her right arm for them all to move and separate before placing her arm back to support the weight of her scatterblade.

"Masika, movements?"

She looked into her hand held scanner and moved it to her left and right. "No, negative Ma'am." "Suma, emissions?"

"Negative Ma'am, air is breathable."

"All keep masks on for now."

The Escarrabin moved forward checking the expanse of the wide empty chamber and its cold stone walls.

Raysmau nodded towards the officers at the front. "Proceed to stairwell."

They moved across collectively towards the stairs at the opposite side of the chamber. Shula pointed her scatterblade down the stairs and gave a hand gesture for the others to follow as she started to head down and quickly disappeared out of the sight of the others. "Rashida and Kissa remain up here at the top of the stairs." They instantly responded "yes Ma'am," content in the knowledge that they would not have to proceed further. The Reeve nodded to both of them as she passed by, her finger over the trigger release button; her spear was fully primed for battle should she need it.

As Shula reached the bottom of the stairway she ushered for the others to quickly catch her up. The second floor below was as dimly lit as the one above. Light bulbs hung from old wiring crudely tacked up to the walls. Many of the bulbs were not working and those that were offered only the faintest of light reassurance. She moved across to her left to let the others enter the chamber. This was as far as she had been below ground much like the others. The silence was eerie; the occasional sound of a water drop could be heard from somewhere, probably from a leak above ground.

She waited patiently for the others to fall in line behind her; she could hear the orders of Raysmau behind her speaking to the others.

"Any movements showing?"

"Negative Ma'am, this floor is quiet, there's nothing here."

"Suma readings please."

Raysmau watched her shake her head. "Nothing it is all clear, air is breathable."

"Alian, come to me" she beckoned with her hand.

"Yes Ma'am."

"The noise that you heard before, it was from this floor?"

"No Ma'am the one above; that is as far as we come to collect and return the watchers. The sound would have been coming from down there presumably." She pointed to the stairs at the end of the chamber that Raysmau had to strain her eyes to see.

"Masika go to the stairs with Shula and check for movements below, use your night vision goggles if you need them."

"Ma'am." Masika nodded holding her movement detector out directly in front of her.

The Reeve had now moved up directly behind Raysmau and they both looked around the old chamber that lay in perfect silence.

Raysmau pointed forward. "Proceed" and they all moved to the stairs.

It was not lost on the watchers that Duat has been hurt. He had rushed his instructions as they gathered in silence on the third floor below ground. They stood in a semi circle and he was directly in the middle in front of them. He spoke as quietly as he could his strength returning quickly. "Remember what I told you all, do not resist at first and wait for my command, some of them will be assisting us. It is me they want and I will surrender to them." His smile was ruthlessly fake. "Keep your hoods up and they will probably try to cuff us and make us wear gloves. Remember they will not fire upon you unless they are losing control. It will be me and me alone that will provoke that control."

They heard movements directly above them. Duat looked furious as one of the watchers let out a hiss that travelled up the stairs.

Shula stepped backwards hearing the noise of the watcher and turned to Raysmau. "Contact!" she whispered.

In silence Raysmau lifted two fingers and pointed to her breast plate and indicated with one finger for them to go down the stairs. Shula lowered her scatterblade and took two grenades from her belt and pulled the pin on both of them and looked at Raysmau. She nodded as both of them were released.

The watchers could hear the sound of the two light grenades bouncing down the worn stone of the stairs where both grenades settled directly in front of them. Duat spoke at volume as it didn't matter any further. "Do not look at them, shield your eye!" All of the watchers bowed down looking at the floor. There was a huge blast of white light that sparked throughout the room. The noise of the second explosion travelled throughout the below. "Open!" hissed Duat as soon as he had heard the second blast. The watchers all recoiled at the intense light within the chamber shielding their eye.

"Go, go, go!" Raysmau yelled as Shula rushed at the stairs immediately followed down by Masika and Suma as the rest of the Escarrabin descended on mass to the chamber below.

The Reeve reached the bottom of the stairs looking at all of the drawn weapons pointing at a semicircle of watchers. She could not tell how many of them there were, maybe thirty or so. The chamber was in silence save the hissing that was still coming from the two grenades. She could see the watchers were still struggling against the intense and sudden light that still lit the chamber. She had not been down here before and took in the huge area that had been cut from rock. There were tunnels directly to the left and right and stairs further ahead.

"Suma readings please."

"The air is normal quite breathable."

Raysmau smiled below her mask. The watcher had failed, the Reeves security measures must have worked. "Remove masks." It was an educated risk; if the beast was loose they would have known about it by now.

Raysmau stepped forward to the recognisable skull of Duat. "Is this all of them?"
He hissed as saliva ran from his mouth. "Raysmau, the heart of soul of the Escarrabin" he laughed loudly and spluttered a cough.
"Stop laughing watcher."
"You should address them by their real name, by what they are really called."
"They?"
He continued to laugh. "Slave of the Reeve, that must be her right there." He nodded to the figure behind Raysmau carrying the spear. "All that armour, you must be fearful?" His mouth opened wide as the saliva fell to the floor.
"Shut up watcher. I will ask you again and for the last time, is this all of you?"
"Shut up and you want answers Raysmau? Your arrogance and incompetence is the true value of the Escarrabin."
"Incompetence?" The Reeve moved forward. "It is you that didn't get what he came for."
Duat hissed "you know nothing."
"We know what you tried to free below and failed."
"Failed?" It is your kind whose time has run out. Tell me Reeve, how are your clocks, what time do they tell you?"
There was a little murmuring behind and the Reeve heard one Escarrabin say to the other *'how could he know that?'*
"Enough of this." Raysmau was running out of patience. "On your knees watcher." She pointed her weapon directly at Duat. He looked at the gleaming chrome work of the scatterblade against the dimming lights of the grenades as she moved her finger over the trigger.

"As you wish." He slowly moved down to his knees.
The Reeve watched from behind her mask, she didn't like it, he was conforming too easily.
Raysmau nodded at Shula. "Gloves, secure him first before the others. He is bound to be lying, there will be more."
Shula released one of her hands from her scatterblade and reached to a pocket behind her leg armour and pulled out a pair of leather gloves and threw them in front of Duat's knees. "Put them on." She returned her hand back to her

weapon and pointed it directly at him.

Duat picked them up with an arrogant swagger and looked at Shula with a grin. "Stop smiling watcher, it makes you look even more ugly, if that were at all possible."

He separated them and went to put one on his left hand. "I assure you that I am far from what your kind call ugly, I am beauty."

The seriousness of the atmosphere was disrupted momentarily by a few sniggers from behind where Shula stood over Duat.

"Silence!!" Raysmau instructed.

Shula was not amused in the slightest and when she saw the right hand was gloved she stepped closer to him. "Put your hands behind your back."

Duat surveyed all of the weapons pointing at him as he put his hands behind his back and closed his eye to concentrate. He could feel movements through his right arm down to his palm. Strain lines appeared across the thin skin of his forehead as he focused. He could feel his palm burning through the leather in the glove of the right hand. Bellator standing behind could see flashes of turquoise against the light within the room as the smouldering leather came apart and fell to the floor.

Shula slung her scatterblade over her shoulder. "Do not resist" she commanded as she reached into a different pocket and pulled out a pair of cuffs. Duat turned to look at Bellator and smiled. "Eyes front watcher, or should I say eye?" She crouched down and took hold of his left wrist and put the cuffs around it. She reached for his right hand and immediately as she touched it felt a wave of heat pass through her as he secured his hand to hers and looked at her. "I am ready, are you?" The heat had frozen her movements and he ripped his right hand away from hers and brought it down upon her forehead. Shula shook uncontrollably as deep red blood vessels streamed across both of her eyes.

"Let her go watcher!" Raysmau commanded.

"Let her go." "Drop your hand" could be heard from multiple Escarrabin throughout the chamber.

He pulled Shula closer to him. "SERVATORUS!" he yelled as loudly as he could as spit exited his mouth all over her.

"Watcher let her go or we will fire upon you!"

He let go of her laughing and dragged himself behind her using her body as a shield.

Shula stood up, her shaking had stopped. He stood up to meet her gaze and looked into the redness of her eyes. "Do what needs to be done."

Her mouth was quivering as she turned to look at the Escarrabin whose weapons were all pointed at her. Looking from right to left across the chamber, their yells and words were unheard as she glanced down at her scatterblade.

"Watcher get away from her" yelled Raysmau.

Their yells of command echoed around the room.

"Shula, Shula!!" Kassia was screaming "get away from him." She looked directly at her friend. "What has happened to you?"

"She's not herself" asserted the Reeve.

"Watcher get away from her or we will fire upon you" Raysmau yelled for the second time.

Still snorting his laughter he stepped back a couple of paces with his hands held aloft. "As you wish Raysmau."

The Reeve's eyes suddenly widened. "Look at his palm!"

The Escarrabins gaze were immediately focused upon Duat's right palm and his laughter stopped in an instant. His mouth opened and the saliva fell as the familiar hiss of the watchers came from Duat's mouth.

"SERVATORUS!!"

Time within that moment seemed to pass slowly as Shula's mouth opened in anger as she brought the scatterblade up towards her chest.

"Escarrabin drop the weapon!"

Her face contorted in rage as she looked to the left of the room at two of the Escarrabin. She snatched the weapon up as the white pulse of light left her scatterblade sending the Escarrabin scattering diving for cover. She screamed as the pulse struck the solider on the left sending her tumbling backwards.

"OPEN FIRE, OPEN FIRE!" The command was issued as the chamber lit up with the white pulses of the Scatterblades. Shula continued to fire hitting the solider second on the left. She fell in a heap next to her former colleague.

Stone fell from the ceiling and the blasts impacting against the walls sent rock hurtling around the chamber. Duat crouched down as a blast passed him striking the wall to the side of him covering him in dust and stone. He reached out for Bellator. "WATCHERS MOVE!!" The black cloaks needed no further instruction and they were gone in an instant, scattering in all directions down the tunnels.

"After them, after them!" Raysmau yelled as she shielded her face from an indiscriminate blast from Shula as the ceiling rocked above her and some of the Escarrabin gave chase.

"SHULA!!" she turned to look at her friend Kassia whose hands were shaking. "Drop it, drop it now!"

Shula hissed back at her and was immediately struck across the chest. Shula fell along with her scatterblade.

As she dropped to the floor, a hand stretched out and gathered the fallen scatterblade and that, along with all of the watchers, disappeared down a tunnel. Kassia lowered her weapon her hands shaking in shock and started to walk towards her.

"What are you doing?"

She turned to look at Raysmau. "I need to see if she is dead Ma'am."

"Well of course she's dead. Maintain your focus and get down that left tunnel. Masika join her and continue to scan, we have no idea how many are here."

She swallowed and looked down at her friend.

"She was lost to us."

She nodded a few times her lips quivering. "Yes Ma'am."

"Make sure this doesn't happen to anyone else, now get down that tunnel."

She watched the two of them lift their scatterblades and move to the tunnel on their left. "Reeve, Ma'am are you okay?"

The Reeve stood up brushing the stone from her breast plate. "Yes I'm fine."

"Rashida and Kissa get down to us now." At the top of the stairs of the first floor Kissa and Rashida both looked at each other and swallowed having heard the exchange of fire below.

"Control receiving?"

"Yes Ma'am go ahead."

"Send remaining Escarrabin down to us immediately, who ever can be spared, with a limited cordon around the lobby area and ensure all doors remain secured."

"Yes Ma'am, although most are with you. As others return from last night's duties we will send them down."

"Received."

"Kassia receiving?"

"Yes....pro.....level...."

"Kassia receiving?"

".....dark.....movement....."

The Reeve and Raysmau immediately looked at each other as the sound of a blast came through their earpieces. The sound then travelled towards them from the tunnel. "We are losing comms and control down here."

"Yes we are. Raysmau, look how many tunnels there are and that's what we can see directly. There may be further ahead and we don't have enough soldiers. We can't send them in two at a time, we don't know how many we are dealing with and how many tunnels lay beyond. We have to concentrate on Duat; it looked like he went down there. He is the snake, we need to remove the head of the snake." She pointed at the tunnel behind where Shula fell. There was another sound of a blast from a tunnel directly in front of them.

"Yes Ma'am and the other Escarrabin may not be back for some hours."

"Yes, I know, tell me your thoughts."

"Well Ma'am. I agree, this could be a maze down here. We could be chasing them for hours, we have no idea how deep it goes."

"Agreed and....?"

"And my gut feeling is that we have to call them all back and come here again in the morning with the full accompaniment of troops. We have already lost three." They both looked over to the two Escarrabin that had fallen by Shula's hand.

"Agreed, but we must get Duat tonight, we must get him now. Take him and the others will conform again, he is unlike any watcher I have ever seen."

"Lotfia and Suma get down that tunnel and bring back Kassia and Masika. Rashida and Najla both of you get down there and you two go down there, bring everyone back to this point who gave chase. The rest of you search without going far and detain Duat if you find him, ignore the others for now. The Reeve and I will head down that tunnel, once everyone has gathered and if you have not captured Duat, you all precede down there to catch us up, understood?"

"Yes, Ma'am."

Bellator had the scatterblade in hand but was clueless how to use it. They were moving quickly in the near darkness of the tunnel. Duat turned to look at him and the two watchers that had followed. "Give me cover."

"Master?"

"With the blade."

"Master, I am sorry but I have never used one of these before."

Duat snatched it from him. "It's not complicated. This button here is for the blade that extends at the end to make it a sword; we do not want that so leave it." He held the weapon up to Bellator's face. "This is the trigger; you see here? That is the pulse fire control," as he pointed at a controller. "The cave complex was not destroyed because it is at a minimum setting so you turn it here. Only turn this far when I command, understand?"

"Yes Master, I understand."

"At full pulse it may take a few seconds to charge, it will tell you when ready." He passed the weapon back to him.

"How will it tell me Master?"

Duat hissed in anger and Bellator stepped backwards.

"You will hear it!"

Duat walked away from the three watchers. "Now all of you provide cover for me, they will be following."

Bellator turned around holding the scatterblade awkwardly pointing towards the direction they had just come from.

Duat looked around the tunnel running his right palm against the wall as he walked. To his right there was another passage in near darkness; his vision was good but at the far end it was pitch black. He had not been down this passage before. Stepping back he looked at one of the cloaked watchers not being able to see his face. "You, what is your name?"

"Karawan Sire."

"What is down this tunnel?"

The watcher moved to him and looked to his right. "There are further quarters down there. At the bottom there is a shaft that leads to the floor above but it is sealed from the top Sire."

"Sealed by what?"

"Some of us have tried to leave before Sire; the Escarrabin discovered it some years ago. They came down here with equipment that melted metal, it is a metal seal and strong. You would have walked over it above Sire but you would not know that it was there."

Duat looked into the watcher's eye unnerving him instantly as he looked down. Duat had powers of communication, light and fire but not to break through metal plates by his own hand. He turned around knowing that Bellator could as he looked at the chrome work of the scatterblade. "Come, all of you we go this way."

They had only taken a few steps when Duat stopped and turned to look at Bellator with scatterblade in hand. Full pulse he considered; full pulse may open the iron wall below.

Bellator looked at Duat's gaze as he pushed saliva away from his mouth. "Master?"

Duat lifted his palm slightly for him to be quiet as he considered it. The gas below was deadly and he could not know whether it had cleared; unlikely in a confined space. He chewed with his misshapen teeth, for it would be a risk and this was only the first phase in any event. His thoughts were interrupted from noise in the distance that sounded to be coming closer. The watchers turned to face it. "Leave it, let's go."

They watched Duat walk into the darkness of the tunnel and they duly followed.

The Reeve held her spear in front of her looking down the dimly lit passage. Her body temperature had risen, despite the coldness of the place, from the weight of her armour. She felt at the controls of her spear and pressed the button for illumination. The intense white light shone from her spear and they both watched in silence as she guided it throughout the length and across the walls of the tunnel.

"There are so many tunnels Ma'am, impossible to know where they go."

Raysmau depressed the torch button on her scatterblade surveying the unreadable language carved into the walls and the various offshoots from the tunnel. She had night vision goggles attached to her helmet and they may be helpful but far better to work in 'natural' light if possible.

"Ma'am if we are proceeding down there I insist that I go first."

The Reeve looked at the size of the frame of Raysmau and concluded in an instant that her nobility was just and she would make a useful shield if it came to it. A selfish thought of life preservation rather than cowardice, she decided that it was a good idea. "Please do."

Raysmau stepped forward and proceeded further into the tunnel. "Control comms check." There was no response through her earpiece. "Control comms check, receiving?"

The Reeve stepped forward lighting up the far right hand side of the tunnel as Raysmau lit the left. "Damn walls are too thick, it's just us for now."

They passed other tunnels and cut outs in the rock that were resting quarters of watchers. Now shrouded in eerie silence, Duat could feel the coldness of the place again. "How much further Karawan?"

"The walls curve around to the right, the whole passage is one big circle Sire. We were stood in the centre of it before the Escarrabin opened fire on us."

Karawan was right, the watchers excavation skills were impressive, Duat concluded, as he felt with his right palm the bow in the rock. There was a short flash of light behind them that reflected off some of the dampness of the walls.

"Master!"

"I see it Bellator. They are coming but will not be in numbers, the rest of our brothers scattering saw to that. Karawan move quicker and take us there."

"It's just a little further Sire, up there."

Duat looked at the long nails of the watcher's hand pointing to a gap further up and they rushed towards it. "Bellator stay behind me, if the Escarrabin appear cut them down. They have never showed mercy to you, do not show it to them." Bellator dropped back behind the three of them. "Yes Master."

They approached a cut out area of the semicircle and Duat stopped one of the watchers he had not spoken to before, asking "What is your name?"

"My name is Zuka Sire."

"Go up ahead of us. If this tunnel is a circle they could come from the other direction as well."

"Yes Sire."

The cloaked figure passed by them as Duat stepped into the cut out and looked upwards; he strained his eye looking at the seal of the thin shaft above.

"There are climbing holes cut into the wall Sire," as Karawan pointed at cut outs in the rock for foot and hand placements.

"How could you have escaped through here if it only goes up one floor?"

"Others had a plan before Sire, to lure the Escarrabin down below. In doing so, while they were searching in the tunnels, some of us would climb up and go over the top of them. They found the shaft and sealed it and added the security scanner by the doorway some years ago. The plan was foiled."

Duat shook his head and placed his right foot into one of the cut outs and found a gap above that he could steady himself with and pulled his left leg up. Gripping old stone with his long nails was not easy, as stone chips and dirt fell to the floor as he pushed himself up.

Bellator and Karawan looked up at him making progress as he whipped his left hand away as a broken finger nail fell towards them. The reinforced roof was becoming ever closer as he stretched as far as he could. He took one more lunge upwards and was immediately below the steel plate that had been secured by the Escarrabin.

He put his right palm upon it and felt across it, dirt and small particles of rock fell below as he made a fist with his right hand and gently hit against it. Listening to the noise, he hit it again at three different points; the seal was strong but not immensely thick. The scatterblade would destroy this easily.

He brought his hand down and thrust his right palm against the rock wall and closed his eye. The two watchers below looked at each other as a turquoise glow emanated against the rock face. His face screwed up in concentration and he grinded at his teeth trying to get a connection outside. The grinding was soon to dissipate and he removed his palm from the wall, his eye opened and he started to descend.

"Master is everything okay?"

Duat was still looking upwards. "Pass me the blade, assistance has been summoned."

Chapter Thirty:

FLAMES AT THE LIGHT OF DAWN

Nubia had backed up a couple of stairs having heard the fire exchanges below ground. She looked at one of the two Escarrabin providing security for Lady Safiya and herself. "What are you hearing, what is going on?"

"I'm sorry Ma'am I cannot say other than more support has been requested, there are some communication problems in the below."

"Well many of you are still missing, not back from last night's duties!"

"Yes Ma'am, I know but given the circumstances we need to take you both to a more secure area."

"Rubbish" Lady Safiya interrupted "I'm too old to be hiding; besides watchers can be overpowered.

If that creature was out we would have heard it by now. Someone is resisting."

"Ma'am, we are not in a position to overrule you but it would be prudent advice for us to move from here."

"What is your name officer of the Escarrabin?"

"It is Soad Ma'am."

She turned to look at the other one. "And yours?"

"My name is Yara Madam."

"Look if you both want to go and support your friends I understand."

Nubia looked at Safiya in a state of shock. "I really think they should..."

Safiya's hand lifted calmly to silence her. Your advice is noted and will be on record and whether you go or stay is entirely up to you."

They both looked at each other. "Lady Raysmau's order was clear that we should stay and protect the lady of the house."

"And me!!" Nubia interjected as they both turned to look at her.

"Settled then, we stay unless we hear more pulse blasts that is." They nodded to each other as Yara looked up at the stairs her eyes catching movement and lifted her weapon.

"Yara, it's just a cleric."

She lowered her weapon as the white robed figure descended the stairs towards them. Her head was bowed and no words were exchanged as she passed, both of the Escarrabin looked at each other.

"Cleric where are you going, the manor is at diligence?" Yara questioned.

The figure had reached the bottom of the stairs and turned to them still with head bowed. "I have an urgent message from the Reeve that I need to present to control."

Yara looked down at the cleric with a frown from her elevated position on the stairs. "We have received no such instruction or message, there are comms problem below."

There was a brief pause before her head lifted slightly so the Escarrabin could see her chin. "That is why she messaged me through my terminal. It's important and I must deliver it right away Madam Escarrabin," she said, lowering her head again.

Yara nodded. "Well okay, you may proceed." She looked at Soad as the cleric walked towards Raysmau's secured area. "You think Lady Reeve has her navigator with her or another form of communication?"

She came to her out of earshot of Lady Safiya and Nubia. "It's possible, we don't get told everything, besides they will probably not open the security gate to her anyway." They both turned to look at the cleric as she walked into the archway. From the angle they were at she disappeared out of sight but they could see the right hand side of the security door was closed.

"Well I guess we may get issued with another instruction then?" Yara questioned.

"It's possible I suppose, you want to take point or stand with Lady Safiya?"

"No I'm happy here if you want to go up to her." They both looked up the stairs to where Lady Safiya stood. Nubia was peering from behind her staring down at both of them, her face a bag of nerves.

"Still nothing."

"Keep trying. Three life indicators have flatlined but I'm losing readings on the others, just intermittent blips. The below is too deep and signals are not coming through."

"Escarrabin report your status, this is control receiving?"

Amera nervously looked at Layla with a shake of the head. They both leant over their monitors waiting for signs of something positive.

A buzz was heard across the room and instinct tilted both of their heads to the monitor above, not that there was any CCTV to assist them.

"It could be one of ours wounded or with orders, go check it will you?"

Amera reached for her scatterblade. "I'll go look, back in a mo, keep trying comms."

As Amera left control she could hear Layla behind her still trying to raise any response with the team below.

She was shaking her head as she walked towards the gate. It's times like this I really wished we had CCTV in this place.

She pressed the speaker button. "Control identify yourself please."

"Cleric, Madam Escarrabin, I have an urgent message from the Reeve for control."

Amera let go of the button frowning, looking at the push to talk button. How could she have a message? "Tell me the message cleric, I am control."

"It's a written message Madam, I have to show you."

"Amera took a deep breath. The Reeve must have been wounded to write such a message; the cleric must be a message runner. She entered the code for the outer door to open. The robe of the cleric with her head bowed came into view. "Come towards me, approach the gate."

The cleric walked towards her. "You don't need to bow cleric, pass me the message; what is it written on?"

"My palm."

"The Reeve wrote a message on your palm! Is she okay, is she wounded?"

The cleric nodded.

"Come closer, open your palm."

The cleric put her right hand through the bars of the gate and opened her palm. "Do you see?"

The Escarrabin looked at the palm in confusion. "No, where is it written?"

"Look more closely!" The tone of the cleric's voice deepened as she lifted her head.

"I see nothing, I can't see..." Amera looked up into the cleric's face and froze looking at her red eyes that were bloodshot with rage. "Do you see?"

Amera looked down. Movements were inside the hand of the cleric and turquoise patterns were running across the lines of her palm. She let out a gasp and went to move away as the cleric reached for her arm. Immense pain immediately shot through her disabling her movements as her scatterblade fell to the floor. Her mouth opened to yell out as her body shook and the cleric brought her palm down upon her forehead. The cleric's mouth opened but made no sound as the Escarrabin tried bringing her arms up but she was powerless, all of her strength was draining from her as her eyes rolled and filled deep red in colour. The cleric pushed harder with her palm as the Escarrabin spluttered and fell to the floor. She looked behind her and no-one had seen anything as she lent through the gate with her left arm and hit the control button to release the gate. The gate moved instantly and she stepped through dragging the Escarrabin's body out of the way so the gate would open fully. She was dead but she had no use for her anyway. She glanced behind again and picked up the scatterblade and headed towards the control room.

Further ahead she could see the doorway for Raysmau's private quarters and brought the weapon up to her chin and wrapped her finger around the trigger. She knew control was the next door on the left and, steadying herself, she tilted her head to the right to see that the door was open. She could hear a voice inside talking but only one voice.

With weapon raised she pushed through the door to see one Escarrabin attempting communications.
"Cleric what are you..."
"Drop it, drop it now."
Layla saw the scatterblade pointing at her and dropped the comms set on the desk.
"What is the meaning of this cleric, what are you doing?"
The cleric pulled her hood down and it was the first time she saw her eyes; she froze in fear with the exception of her arms that she had voluntarily raised.
"Raise the barriers!!" she spat in anger.
Layla did not realise it but her head was shaking. "What has happened to you cleric and where is Amera?"
"I am no cleric and your friend is dead. I will not tell you again, take us out of diligence and raise the barriers."
Layla went to move her hands to her terminal.
"Slowly!"

Hands shaking she tried to speak calmly. "There is no escape from here whether they are open or not."

The weapon was moved closer to her head but it was not close enough to try and disarm her. She pushed at the keys on her pad and a flashing button appeared on the screen that said 'Diligence'. She pressed enter and the flashing stopped and bowed her head in resignation as the portcullis started to move upwards and the shutters over the windows on the lower floor started to lift exposing their glass.

The cleric took a couple of steps backwards towards the exit and listened for the sound of the security shutters withdrawing. Satisfied with what she heard, she went back towards the officer of the Escarrabin and raised her weapon again.

The two Escarrabin on the stairs turned around hearing the noise of the portcullis being drawn up and could see the security shutters moving from the ground floor windows.

Soad who was stood to the side of Lady Safiya looked confused and stepped towards Yara. "Diligence could not have been lifted with the others below?" Two other Escarrabin, who had been guarding the doorway to the below, stepped forward into view and looked up the stairway to them.

"Something is not right." Soad pressed her push to talk button. "Control receiving, control receiving?" There was no response.

"Try one more time." Yara couldn't hear any response in her ear either.

"Control radio check over?"

Nubia stepped forward. "What is happening Escarrabin?"

"We've lost communication with control Ma'am."

Nubia looked up to Safiya in worry.

Soad looked at her fellow Escarrabin shaking her head. "Something is not right." She nodded her head down in thought and her eyes sprung back upwards. "Did that cleric come back, the one who said she had a message?"

The look in Yara's face said enough as she spun to look at the entrance door to control. Even at the awkward angle from where she was stood on the stairs it looked like it may be open. She lifted her scatterblade. "I'll go check."

"Ma'am I really think that we should move upstairs to a secured area."

Safiya looked into the face of her security guard considering her opinion this time.

She could hear them calling for her in her earpiece but the pointed scatterblade was stopping any response. The cleric was breathing hard staring at her.

"What is that?" The weapon was drawn closer.

"What is what?"

She heard the muffled noise again. "Take that out of your ear! What are they saying?"

"They are asking for me as I would if I were in their position."

"Take it out and put it on the table now!"

The weapon was drawn closer as she slowly brought her left hand up to her right ear and glanced to the side of the desk at her own scatterblade that was propped against it. She knew that if no response was forthcoming from control it was protocol for it to be checked immediately and others would be here soon. Her movements were slow as she removed her earpiece and brought it forward towards the cleric and let go of it as it bounced on the edge of the desk and fell to the floor.

The cleric hissed in anger. "Not clever!" and stepping forward with her left foot, she stood on the earpiece, glancing down to check it was destroyed. The weapon was now only a couple of feet away from her head as Layla lashed out with her left hand disabling the grip of the cleric and moved the weapon away from her face. The right hand went into a fist and punched the cleric across the bridge of the nose splitting it open. The blow dazed her as she let go of the scatterblade that fell upon the desk. Layla's left arm went straight for her throat and gripped firmly forcing her to lose balance as the cleric fell backwards to the floor. Layla could see the bursting red in her eyes. "Enough of this!"

The cleric's right palm was bursting with turquoise veins as she grabbed the gloved hand of the Escarrabin and pushed down.

"You are under arr..." Layla immediately felt uneasy as heat passed through her glove up her arm and she started convulsing. The cleric could see the fear in her eyes as the grip lost purchase around her throat as her arm flopped. She rubbed the blood from her nose and brought her palm down on Layla's neck. As the cleric leaned over her Layla could see the anger in her eyes but she couldn't fight back as the pain inside her deepened. Turquoise veins came to the surface of her neck from where she was being held, as the colours moved quickly towards her skull. "SERVATORUS!!"

The Escarrabin's legs were shaking as her eyes turned colour. "Servatorus!" as the cleric let go of her and stood over the fallen body and reached for the scatterblade on the desk. "Get up servant!" A thin line of blood fell from the right eye of the former officer of the Escarrabin as she looked up at her. "On your feet NOW!"

She stepped back and watched Layla try to get to her feet, her body shook as she steadied herself against the desk. She pulled herself up. The smell of burnt leather was in the air from the smoking glove as the cleric passed the weapon to her. "Get out there and kill the Escarrabin". Layla took the weapon. "Yes Master."

She watched Layla pass by her with weapon raised. "It's Ma'am" she hissed as she leant over the desk to study the security controls.

With her Scatterblade raised to a defensive position Yara descended the stairs and made her way across the floor of the lobby. She stepped to the left of the doorway of the secured area and brought the weapon up to her chin. She heard movement from the other side as she turned into the archway and could see Layla had her weapon raised. "Control, why are you not at your p…" as she looked down to see the deceased body of Amera next to the gate. She glanced back up seeing the anger in Layla's face. "Drop the weapon, drop the weapon now!"

A white pulse of light came towards her striking her in the torso and throwing her body backwards into the lobby.

Nubia screamed seeing the fallen Escarrabin.

"Escarrabin Contact!!" Soad yelled as she dived over the body of Lady Safiya forcing her to the floor. She looked down at the exchange of fire from the two Escarrabin below her and saw one fall. "My Lady, cover there now!" and pointed at a pillar to their right on the first floor balcony as she gathered her to her feet and unceremoniously dragged her to it where they both hid behind the pillar with Nubia shaking in a ball behind them.

Soad's weapon was aimed at the security entrance as she watched the archway and door being ripped apart from pulse fire scattering stone and wood over the unmoving body of her friend. The surviving Escarrabin officer below had taken cover now engaged in a fire fight. Unless the shooter responsible was cut down by the officer below, sooner or later they would come out and Soad was certain of one thing – that when they did she would not miss.

She stepped back from the control terminal hearing the pulse fire outside and concentrated. Her deep red eyes started to flicker as she placed her right palm against the wall and waited.

Duat felt the positive sign of warmth run through him and recognised its meaning immediately. He rushed to the wall of the shaft and placed his palm on it and closed his eye. Somebody was trying to get through to him but it was weak. He climbed halfway up the shaft, when, confident of his footing, he tried again and looked upwards as his palm received knowledge.
He let go and climbed back down. "Karawan get Zuka back here, it is time. Bellator give me that."

Bellator passed the weapon to him and watched Duat adjust the pulse control. The adjustment was slight, he didn't want the whole shaft collapsing. He stepped inside the shaft and looked at the seal above. Crouching down he lifted the weapon to his shoulder and took a firm hold of the trigger.
He drew in a breath, his hands and body were steady as he pulled his finger backwards. The shaft was instantly illuminated in white light. As the pulse rose he rolled out of the way as the explosion above echoed through the shaft and raced around the tunnels around them. The metal plate was blown off its securing bolts and the blast hit the ceiling above. Rubble started to fall down the shaft creating a dust cloud that covered them both.

Duat passed the weapon back to Bellator and leaned into the dust. He wiped his eye waiting for it to clear, in any event the shaft had held. The other two watchers had rejoined them as he looked at them. "Now, we are leaving!"

The sound of the explosion stopped the Reeve and Raysmau in their tracks. "It came from above!" "Yes it did Ma'am, watchers and probably Duat must be above us, we must go." The Reeve nodded at her as they turned around. "Control receiving?" There was just static noise. "Escarrabin receiving?" She received muffled and indiscernible words from others below. "All Escarrabin if you understand this message report to the first floor below immediately." Raysmau and the Reeve raced towards the third floor chamber as quickly as they could.

Duat reached the top of the shaft and cautiously looked across the stone floor, it looked to be clear. The occasional rock had struck him on his way up and he looked at the hole smoking in the ceiling above. He looked down to Bellator who was climbing behind him. "Move now, it is clear," as he stepped out of the shaft and looked at the steaming metalwork that had previously covered their exit path.

He walked forward looking at the stairway. The Escarrabin must have heard the blast; consequently it would not be long before they were here. He turned to see the figure of Bellator emerge from the shaft; the scatterblade was over his shoulder. "You provide cover and we'll need that," as he pointed a long fingernail at the Blade. The other two were soon to emerge as he looked to the stairs that led up towards the exit and nodded at Bellator. "Proceed up, we don't have long."

Raysmau could not be sure if the others had heard the Reeve's radio call as they entered the chamber of the third floor with caution. The bodies of the Escarrabin lay as they had fallen but they were alone. "Ma'am we must investigate above." The Reeve held her spear in front of her, the light source showing them the way to the staircase to take them up. The light grenades from earlier had long since died as she nodded and Raysmau took the lead.

Raysmau switched her torch off and crouched at the bottom of the staircase looking up with her Blade raised. She couldn't hear any movements above. She looked at the Reeve and gave her a silent signal for her to deactivate her torch and ushered her to join her at the base of the stairs. They ascended in silence and could smell something burning from the upper floor as they reached the top. Raysmau stepped forward and visually swept the room. Her eyes were drawn to a smoking metal plate and the cloud of dust that was still spreading throughout the chamber; she could see small shards of stone falling from a hole in the ceiling. She gave a signal for the Reeve to join her as they both looked around the chamber. On first inspection, within the silence, they appeared to be alone as they swept every corner and curve of the cold room.

They both immediately looked up hearing movements above and Raysmau gave an instruction to the Reeve to proceed to the stairs that would lead them to just one floor below the manor.

Bellator had reached the first floor of the below and looked across the familiar room that the Escarrabin would collect them from for 'duties'. The stairs were at the far end and he could hear pulse fire above. "Master listen!"

"We are not alone my friend."

The saliva ran from Duat's chin. "We have help above," and beckoned the other two watchers to move with them. "The door at the top of the stairs will be secured; the blade will make short work of that."

"But the outer doors Master?"

Duat looked at him and he spoke with a hiss of satisfaction. "They are already open."

"Master. But then what? Where do we go?"

"We?"

Bellator looked confused. "Yes Master, our brothers."

He leaned forward to him. "We are leaving this evening but not everything has been completed, the others will be freed in time."

Bellator turned to look at the backs of the other two who were looking in the direction of the stairs that led below. Duat's words were unheard to them. One turned to them. "Master, movements below."

"They are coming, quickly to the stairs."

Soad looked down the stairs to where the other member of the Escarrabin was pinned down; pulse blasts had caused considerable damage behind her. Crater damage was in the ceiling and had blown away some of the elaborate panelling. One window had been blown outwards and a chandelier hung delicately but mostly destroyed. Her weapon was still pointed towards the arch; whoever was firing from the other side was a terrible shot. She looked down to Ana, the Escarrabin, who had been returning fire, as she removed a grenade from her belt and held it upwards to inform her to be ready. She adjusted the strength dial of the grenade and spoke to Nubia and Lady Safiya without looking at them. "Don't look at it." She stepped towards the top of the stairs and put her scatterblade on the floor and brought the light grenade behind her and threw it as hard as she could towards the archway. Hearing it bounce upon the floor she reclaimed her weapon and turned around to shield her eyes.

The sound of the blast rang through the chamber shaking the chandeliers and artwork fell from the walls. Soad turned around pointing her weapon at the archway and noticed that Ana was doing the same. A figure fell through the arch shielding her eyes. Soad shook her head in disbelief as one of her own came into view. "Ana hold your fire!" but the command was too late as she was sent reeling backwards crashing against the door where she fell.

Lady Safiya looked on in horror at the downed Escarrabin. "What the bloody hell is happening?" Soad looked down from the balcony to see that Ana's weapon was still raised but she had moved forward to check upon the Escarrabin that had been hit earlier. She checked and found no pulse and moved towards the body of Yara and checked that the Escarrabin she had just shot had been killed; she kicked the scatterblade away although she knew that she had passed. She stepped backwards towards the stairs to be greeted with Soad pointing her weapon at her.
"Soad what are you doing?"
"You just shot one of our own."
"I'm telling you that was not one of us. She was the one that was firing at me and killed Yara and Ruon!"
Soad received the comment with a face of incredulousness. "WHAT?"
"Ridiculous!" was heard from behind them as they looked at the tiny frame of the curator. "Never heard of something so unbelievable."
"I'm telling you the truth Ma'am whether you like to hear it or not." She looked at Soad, her hands were shaking. "Others have fallen below and we need to go down."

The Reeve and Raysmau had reached the base of the stairs as the sound of footsteps on stone was heard from behind. They spun around as quickly as they could, turning their weapons towards the staircase, and were somewhat relieved to see the faces of Alian and Gamila appear.

Raysmau beckoned them over and pointed with one finger upwards as Gamila crouched to look up the stairs. She had seen the smouldering metal on the floor below with some concern. "Looked like a heavy pulse blast." Raysmau put a finger to her mouth to silence her.

Raysmau moved first, stepping forward onto the stairs whilst the other three followed closely behind her. As they approached the top they all crouched down, with Raysmau indicating to Alian to move straight across the floor to provide cover. She looked into her eyes and spoke quietly. "Ready?"

She nodded and took a deep breath and brought the weapon up to her chin. "Go!"

Alian stepped up and ran across the floor to the far wall, Raysmau moved at the same time to cover the near side. They could immediately see moving shadows in the distance of the far set of stairs. Alian gave a hand signal to move forward as all four of them moved to the stairs with their weapons primed.

Bellator was ascending the stairs and felt a hand on his shoulder. "Wait!" Duat turned around. Shadows in the dim light of the chamber were moving towards them and noise underfoot could be heard. "They are here! Bellator come back, come back." Duat pulled him to the bottom of the stairs. "Don't get close to those doors."

Duat looked at Zuka. "Come closer to me."

"Yes Master?"

The watcher walked down the steps to him. "We have to go Sire."

He glanced towards Bellator and resumed looking into the face of Zuka. "Yes, WE ARE!" Duat pushed against him as he fell backwards down the last two stairs onto the floor of the chamber.

"Watcher on your knees!" screamed Raysmau as the falling cloaked figure came into their line of sight.

The watcher fell on his side and looked back up the stairs towards Duat. His mouth opened bearing the nubs of his stained teeth as his hiss of anger filled the room. "Traitor!" he spat at Duat.

"WATCHER, ON YOUR KNEES!"

Zuka flicked his head instantly towards the Escarrabin and with rage stood up and came towards them aggressively.

The pulse blast from Raysmau's scatterblade sent him backwards. He fell, his dead lifeless eye looking towards the stairs. Duat hissed as saliva projected from his mouth. "Bellator, full pulse NOW!!"

Bellator turned the pulse control as far as it would allow and looked at Duat who was pointing upwards ahead of them. "Destroy that door!"

He held the weapon upwards waiting for the sound of notification that the weapon was ready; a double bleep was heard and he pulled at the trigger.

The recoil from the huge release of energy from the blade sent him backwards against the wall as the pulse light travelled up the stairs.

Having heard Duat yelling the order for full pulse, Raysmau turned screaming at the others. "Take cover, take cover!"

Duat crouched down and shielded his eye as the pulse struck the doorway above. The door bowed on impact. There was silence for a fraction of a second as time appeared to freeze. The whole building shook as the door was blown from its fixings as the lift shaft to the right collapsed. The explosion and wave of fire blew across the lobby and carried down the grand walkway. Chandeliers were torn from their holdings as the downstairs windows blew outwards one at a time as the passage of fire passed them. Artworks on the wall were instantly ablaze as the dust made its way through the flames engulfing the floor above.

Duat opened his eye feeling the heat soaring towards him as a ball of fire raced down the stairs at him.

Bellator and Karawan also saw the oncoming blast of fire and threw themselves over Duat to shield him as the flames raced over them into the chamber. The ball of fire impacted Karawan's back as his cloak was immediately set alight. His scream was heard throughout the chamber as the fire blast raced down the tunnels of the below. The blast was lifeless and quickly extinguished against the dampness and cold of the walls.

From Raysmau's order the four Escarrabin had scattered for cover shielding themselves behind pillars and rock. The fire ball had passed by them or over them causing minimal damage to their battle armour. The Reeve moved from the pillar she had hid behind to see the flaming figure stumbling around the chamber. She looked on in anguish as her ears rang with the noise of his pain. She raised her spear and brought it upwards to her chest and pressed the button for the trigger release that dropped down from the spear. Wrapping her index finger over the trigger she pulled back. The pulse of light struck the screaming watcher sending his flaming body backwards. The screaming had stopped as the lifeless watcher fell to the floor. She lowered the spear looking upon the flames that still continued to burn the remainder of his cloak.

Duat had instinctively protected his right palm as the fire raced over him. Using his cloak with his left hand he thrashed against Bellator trying to put the flames out on his cloak. His own minor burns were not of significance but that could not be said for Bellator and he could smell the thinness of the watchers seared skin. He pulled Bellator's head back as Duat looked into his eye. He was burnt and hurt, to what extent, as yet, he did not know. "Get the weapon, we are leaving!"

Duat had seen Karawan fall from the pulse blast of the Reeve and looked up at the remnants of the doorway that was still burning; the stonework that had held it was long gone scattered above.

In some pain from the amount of skin he had lost on his hands, Bellator reached for the scatterblade and gingerly rose to his feet as his cloak smouldered.

Duat helped pull him up. "Now let's go!"

They both ran up the stairs towards the flames. A pulse blast raced by them, striking the wall, covering them with stone, as Bellator fell through the former doorway. Duat moved through shielding his right hand from the flames. Bellator had fallen on stone that had covered the corridor and the grand lobby. He looked up among the flames and dust to see Duat moving forward "Master!" Duat turned to him and pulled his hood down. His saliva was frothing around his mouth, his eye bloodshot. "Get up!"

He reached for the weapon and in some pain stumbled to his feet as a chandelier crashed to the ground to his right. He was surrounded by fire as artworks burned and parts of the ceiling above him were still ablaze.

Duat paused in the fire and dust looking towards security control as the figure of the cleric emerged and she started walking towards the opened gate. With a scatterblade in her arms Duat beckoned her forward.

Nubia's hysteria had momentarily paused as she hid behind Lady Safiya. Soad's heart rate was still far from where it should be, following the explosion and fire blast that had ripped across the lobby blowing the main outer doors partially open. She looked down through the flickering light of fire and dust at what appeared to be a figure coming into view on her right hand side. At the same time a figure appeared at the entrance to Raysmau's archway as Soad raised her weapon.

"Wait." She felt an arm on hers and looked at Ana. "Let her get closer." They both crouched behind the balustrade of the staircase and looked on as the pair of them appeared to be communicating.

As the cleric stepped into the lobby they could see for the first time that she was armed.

"That's close enough!" They both stood up from the stairs. "Drop your weapon!"

"Drop it now" Soad screamed.

Quite disinterested by the threat, the cleric casually turned her head to look up to the stairs to see two Escarrabin had their weapons trained upon her. She looked back to Duat and he nodded and stepped backwards out of view of the others on the staircase. Knowing the other Escarrabin would be on their way, time was short. "KILL THEM!" he yelled at the cleric.

She whipped the weapon around and fired striking the wall next to the staircase completely missing the two Escarrabin.

They both ducked for cover behind the balustrade as fragments of stone from the wall came hurtling towards them as the cleric quickly stepped back into the archway. Pulse fire was immediately returned striking the walls either side of her covering the cleric with multiple stone shrapnel.

Alian could hear noises from behind her as two other Escarrabin tore into the chamber and she stepped forward out of hiding to greet them.

"What the hell just happened Alian?" Rasida said as Kissa looked on in stunned silence as they moved forward. "A fire blast just raced by us down the tunnel."

"No time to explain."

"Proceed forward" yelled Raysmau as the six of them passed the two smouldering cloaks of the watchers and made their way up the stairs.

"Alian how many went through the doorway?"

"I only saw two Ma'am."

Duat stood next to the damaged lift shaft looking at the thick caballing ablaze and the smashed remnants of the lift below. He turned to Bellator. "Can you run?"

"I can try Master," as he reached for the weapon.

Duat focused knowing they had little time, his appearance as a watcher was drawing to a close.

Bellator stumbled towards him. He was in pain and could feel the burns underneath his cloak and could see where some of it had bonded with his skin.

"The slave will protect us." He pointed towards the main doors. "That is our exit."

"Slave Master?"

Duat turned to him. "She has opened the doors for us."

He gestured towards the cleric that they were heading for the doors, as her dust and stone strewn cloak moved forwards again to the front of the arch.

Duat stretched his right arm out. "Pass me the blade."

Bellator passed the chrome weapon to him as Duat communicated with the cleric showing her where the dial for the pulse control was.

A pulse blast struck the wall next to her and she fell having been hit by heavy stone and Duat froze momentarily looking at the fallen cleric. Her hood had fallen as she steadied herself back to her feet; her pale face that rarely saw sunlight had blood running down it from a head wound. But the blood that coursed through her veins was strong and determined as he watched her moving the pulse control dial.

"Be ready my friend."

"Yes Master," although he had no idea where they were going or what they would do once there.

The cleric stumbled forward with her weapon raised. They both watched her depress the trigger as the huge pulse blast left the weapon, taking her from her feet as she crashed against the battle scared wall to her side.

The noise of the pulse emission sent the two Escarrabin diving to their right to cover Lady Safiya. The pulse was nowhere near them as it struck the other end of the balcony with an almighty blast of light and fire. Nubia was screaming as the balcony crumbled and fell to the lobby below. The blast of fire soared upwards scorching the balcony above. Stone and dust raced over their huddle impairing their vision but the fire was short lived. The pulse control had not been fully turned; if it had they would certainly have fallen as well.

The fallen figure of the cleric was unmoved. The noise of falling masonry from the balcony filled the central lobby and Duat sensed the opportunity. "Now!" as they both rushed for the remains of the grand entrance doors. They pushed their way through, the weight of the heavy oak doors with iron fittings were still ablaze. Bellator glanced around hearing screams from above but they were not being fired upon. They felt the air of the outside move over them as they ran across the gravel driveway at the front of Loxley.

"Stop where you are!"

Bellator turned to see the Escarrabin moving through the doors surrounded by flames, their weapons trained upon him. He counted six of them but more were bound to be behind. "Master, they are here!"

Raysmau indicated for them to move forward as she glanced over the heavily damaged frontage of the manor house. Glass and stone were scattered as far as she could see and pockets of fire burned all around.

Soad lowered her weapon relieved to see the arrival of some of her fellow soldiers moving across the lobby. She glanced down at Alian who beckoned her to follow them. She turned to Lady Safiya. "Are you okay my Lady?"

"What, are you serious, I'm far from okay," as she gingerly rose to her feet leaving Nubia wrapped in a ball behind her. She looked at the collapsed balcony and the flame scarred walls and the bodies below. "Get down there and finish this, whatever this actually is!"

"Yes Ma'am." Ana looked at Soad and nodded towards the open doors below as they raced down the stairs.

Safiya looked around at the burning picture frames, their canvases had long since gone. She shook her head and looked down to the shaking curator who was still curled up in a ball. "Nubia, what on earth has happened here?"

Her eyes were watery, tired and scared as she looked up. "The prophecy, it is happening, it can't be stopped."

"But he didn't get what he came for."

"No...not yet."

"I must see this with my own eyes. Come Nubia and be careful of falling masonry."

Nubia struggled to her feet watching Lady Safiya without her cane slowly weave her way through the rubble on the stairs. She was shaking all over and could feel the heat of the multiple fires as she moved down the stairs behind. She didn't have the confidence that Safiya did but knew that she had to see what was happening.

Duat passed a flaming statue dragging Bellator with him ignoring the calls from behind. He glanced around to see some of the downstairs windows were still ablaze and smoke was pouring into the sky above them.

The Escarrabin poured across the gravel giving chase with weapons lifted. "That's enough!!" commanded Raysmau. "Stop where you are right now!"

Bellator hanging on the back of his master was looking at them as they stopped moving. The blade was still in his hand but he didn't have the initiative to know what to do next. He let go of Duat who was still facing the other way, his palm was alive and restless as he flexed his fingers.

The Escarrabin surrounded both of them in a semi circle. "Turn around Duat and get on your knees and you watcher, drop that weapon." Duat recognised the voice of Raysmau and smirked as he ran his hand across his mouth flicking the saliva to the floor.

"Escarrabin are dead, watchers are dead, all attributed to you. You have plenty to explain and you will do at the highest order."

The Escarrabin could hear a deep laugh from the cloaked figure who still had his back to them. "Raysmau, warrior of the Escarrabin, you have no idea of what the highest order is," as he turned around to look directly at them. His bloodshot eye reflected the flames burning behind the Escarrabin.

"All of you and your ceremony, your uniforms and your armour did not save all of this!" he hissed at them. "Your security failed at every level, you are beaten, ill educated and incompetent."

"That's enough!!"

He looked at the Reeve who stepped forward with raised spear. "Watcher drop your weapon now." Duat looked at Bellator and nodded. "We do not need it my friend."

The Reeve watched it fall to the floor. "On your knees both of you."

The salvia from the smiling mouth of Duat hit the floor first as he moved down to one knee.

"Both knees and you, do the same, now."

Bellator did as instructed.

"Both knees Duat!"

He looked up to the spear pointed at him and into the eyes hidden behind the mask.

"We all wear masks Reeve."

"Last time and I will not ask again, both knees now, or you will be fired upon!"

He watched the other Escarrabin move closer to him.

"NO."

"What?"

He laughed as he spoke "NO!!"

He whipped his right palm towards the Reeve as a blinding white light burst came from it. They were all instantly defenceless and shielded their eyes. The heat from the light became more intense as they were forced back as the light started to burn. Bellator shielded his eye and moved backwards putting his burnt hands over his face.

"Master?" He looked at Duat who had stopped laughing now, instead making noises of intense pain. Still partially shielding his eye his master turned to look at him. His body was shaking as he watched thin folds of skin fall from his skull. "Master!"

He looked in horror at Duat's eye as it split in the centre and moved across his skull to form two eyes as the cuffs that he been fixed to his left arm fell to the floor. The two holes in his skull that were formally nostrils broke as a snout started to appear. His cloak split down the back and he fell to the floor as his back arched.

Yells of pain from the Escarrabin could be heard as they protected their eyes from the light and heat as Safiya and Nubia appeared at the door and immediately covered their eyes.

In complete fear Bellator yelled as loudly as he could, "MASTER!!" as he watched the back of Duat split in the centre as two black veins appeared that separated and grew outwards. His terror intensified as the wing like veins split into different sections and grew downwards flanked with skin and blood vessels. The light from Duat's palm was shaking and starting to fade, his voice had changed as it spat with anger, "Come to me!"

Bellator shakily got up and walked towards him as he felt a claw grab hold of him as the light from the palm went out.

There was immediate silence as the Escarrabin lowered their hands that had been protecting their faces; all that could be heard was the heavy snorting of a creature breathing. They looked at the two bright red eyes staring at them and froze; the other watcher had a huge claw wrapped around his torso. One of the Escarrabin said in fear under her breath, "what the hell is that?"

The Reeve, with hands shaking, slowly started to raise her spear again as they heard a deep roar that almost sent them backwards, as the two veins extended and a cracking noise of bone could be heard from the creature's back. Bellator felt a rush of air over him as he was dragged upwards.

"OPEN FIRE, OPEN FIRE." Pulse fire entered the silence of the night as a huge black tail whipped over them as it climbed up into the sky and flew away out of sight.

An order of cease fire never came and it didn't need to, as the Escarrabins' weapons were lowered as they looked into the clear sky as the light from the full moon shone across the Welsh landscape.

Raysmau turned hearing gravel move behind her to see Safiya standing there looking upwards.

Alian was the first to speak. "What the bloody hell was that, I've never seen a watcher who, well, could do that!"

Safiya could see the fear in the soldiers faces as she turned to the quivering figure of Nubia; she knew that Nubia understood what had just happened as she looked into her watery eyes.

"I'm telling you that is not...."

"Enough." The Reeve cut Alian off and looked at Lady Safiya who in turn looked at Raysmau as she pursed her lips. "I never thought my day would see this, what has happened here this evening," as she looked down at Nubia again. "Ma'am?" the Reeve responded and removed her helmet. "That was no watcher."

"No, no it wasn't." Her response was softly spoken as she considered her words and looked at the nodding head of the curator.

"No Reeve that wasn't," as she looked forward again, "that was a gatekeeper."

"MASTER!!" They all turned around to see the cleric run out of the doors waving an arm in the air. She was unarmed as far as Raysmau could see. "Lower weapons." She was running towards them not caring or paying any attention to them. "MASTER!!" she was screaming as loudly as she could as she ran past all of them and started running down the driveway. The floodlights were still on as Raysmau looked at Rasida. "Strike her down."

"Ma'am?"

"Put her down. You saw her eyes, she is lost and a danger to us all. She is possessed by him, now put her down."

Rasida looked at the Reeve. There was no counter command as she lifted her scatterblade and brought it to her chin. The white robed figure was now in the distance as she lifted up her sights and closed her left eye and took aim. She breathed in deeply and held her breath as she pulled at the trigger.

All of them watched the white pulse of light travel down the driveway as it struck the cleric in the back. Instantly she fell upon the gravel. Rasida lowered her weapon and they watched the cleric's right leg lift slightly as she pushed herself upwards to her knees. She looked up to the sky muttering something as the turquoise veins faded and she breathed her last.

Rasida swallowed as she looked at the others in silence.

"Leave her there." The Reeve didn't question this instruction from Raysmau. The others looked amongst themselves and back down the driveway at the fallen cleric on her knees.

Safiya closed her eyes and looked upwards taking deep breaths as she felt her hand being taken by Nubia. She reopened her eyes and looked at the Reeve. "He will be back, but not tonight; the gate has been opened. What happened here this evening is just the beginning."

She looked down at the curator. "Come Nubia, let's get you inside. We will all reconvene in the morning."

They watched the two figures walk back towards the destroyed frontage of the mansion. Safiya didn't turn to them as she spoke and it was almost nonchalantly as she did. "Raysmau, please have someone put the fires out will you."

"Yes Ma'am" she responded but her words were so quiet no-one else would have heard as she looked at the Reeve, but there were no words they could exchange.

A gate from another place had been opened and this had been a failure on every level.

Saturday 5am

Raysmau was deep in thought and for the benefit of the Escarrabin, for those who remained, it was important that order was shown. She had removed the ill-fitting upper assembly of her body armour but the rest remained as she surveyed her office. Her door was still intact but closed and she had slumped into her chair. Much would be asked of her but more so of the Reeve who, as the commander of security, had failed. Escarrabin had died, watchers had died, a cleric had died, the building frontage was partially destroyed. There was no walking away from this, they would all be summoned.

They would have to go below again later to recover the bodies and this time carry out a controlled search and round up all of the watchers. With Duat, or whatever he was really called, gone, she hoped for little resistance. Maybe normality would resume but she knew that it would be brief.

She looked at the artwork on her walls depicting glories of battle from a former age; there would be no painting hanging anywhere in the future portraying what happened a few hours ago she was sure of that. Her clock had not regained life and still read two minutes past midnight.

She cracked her neck back and forth and with composure got up and headed to her door. Reassurance was what was needed now. Other Escarrabin who had since arrived from their duties last night wanted answers and she knew that answers as to what she had witnessed would be in very short supply.

The other side of the door from the tranquillity of her office was difficult to take in. The corridor was destroyed from pulse fire. The main door had been blown apart and the gate had come away at the top from the wall. She looked to the floor and could see blood on stone shards, the blood, presumably, having lived within the cleric.

She moved to the right to security control and an Escarrabin officer went to stand up upon her entry into the room. She waved her arm. "Save it," as the officer resumed her seat. "Anything outside, have you seen anything moving out the front?"

"No Ma'am. I've been watching the CCTV and the road outside is clear, all is quiet."

She nodded. "Good, please keep watching," and turned to leave.

"Ma'am, excuse me, but should we be expecting something, will something else happen?"

Raysmau stopped and didn't turn around to the question. "After last night............yes, I think there will be more to come and much will change from now, this Order has been dormant for too long."

She left the room and stepped between boulders of rock to look at the flame scarred door that lay in pieces.

Central lobby was a singed shadow of its former self, not destroyed and fixable, but it would take some time. The bodies had since been moved as she looked to the floor as the pin of one of the fallen Escarrabin caught her eye. Bending down to pick it up she looked at the collapsed balcony to her right, the scorched artwork on the walls that was irreplaceable, chandeliers in pieces, marble now discoloured from soot and dust; it smelt of death in this former peaceful place.

Two Escarrabin were staring at her from next to the fallen lift shaft. She walked through puddles of water to them and looked down into the deep hole that fell below. "Any movements?"

"No Ma'am, nothing has come up the stairs nor have we heard anything."

She nodded. "They lie now in peace. They will be scared but I suspect we will have to round them up tomorrow."

"And of the other Ma'am?"

"Other?"

"The beast, what lay below, what will become of that?"

She didn't know the answer and nodded at the two security officers. "I'm sure the Reeve has that all in hand." It was a lie but the best she could offer.

She walked away from them knowing that talk would be rife amongst them and that it would spread to others in the Order all over the world. She looked to the sunlight of the morning coming through the open doors and the windows that had been destroyed. The fires were now out but the window frames smouldered. She could still see the fallen cleric on her knees down the driveway. This night would make the history books for all of the wrong reasons. Judgements would be made and it would not be forgotten for a very long time. Everything was about to change.

Chapter Thirty One:

THE SCARRED COMET

CATURDAY 7.36 am

Mildred woke with a start and quickly opened her eyes, instantly squinting, as the rays of morning sunlight made her put a hand up to her face. She had had the strangest of dreams, quite apocalyptic really and most unusual for her. Already the memories of whatever she had been dreaming about were being to fade as she pushed sleep from her eyes. She opened and closed her mouth a few times "aarrgghh" as she chomped up and down. Her breath was offensive even to her, as she licked at her teeth and ran a hand through her tangled hair.

Blinking a few times, a smile appeared over her face and she kicked her legs a couple of times under her duvet. "Missy is coming home today, Missy is coming home today....Yay!!"

She had no idea what time it was and didn't know if she had overslept. Her alarm hadn't woken her as yet, it must be early. She neglected her toothbrush and dived down the stairs to her kitchen.

She was horrified as she looked at her clock. "Two minutes past twelve, it can't be!!" How she had slept in till midday she had no idea as she looked down at her cat pyjamas. Missy will be here soon she thought to herself, I can't greet the vet dressed like this. She launched herself back up the stairs for something to wear. Her best and, quite possibly, her only friend in the world was coming home and she couldn't wait.

Nahla lay curled up on the couch as Nubia looked down at her. "Quite how you can sleep I have no idea. You saw it, you saw it fall from above. Nahla…Nahla!" She bobbed her head up to look at the curator. "Are you not fearful, do you not feel our anguish?" She put her hands on her hips. She knew that Nahla understood what was happening but there was little she could do about it. She chewed on her teeth and looked at the phone, then back at Nahla. "I guess it's time you went home" whatever time it was of course. Without the constant reassurance of time Nubia felt lost. She made a judgement call from looking out of the window at the height of the sun and reached for the phone. The phone rang at the other end but took longer to be answered than she would have liked. "Yes, who is this?" a very sleepy voice spoke with a cough clearing her throat.

"Get up Suzanna, there is work to be done!"

Jessica scratched at her head, still coming to terms with her new name and coughed again. "Yes My Lady, what time is it?"

"I have no idea but I'm going to be sending Nahla back to you, she has made a full recovery from the pain she was in."

"Well that's amazing news My Lady," as she put a hand to her mouth and breathed into it and brought it up to her nose and squinted.

"About the only thing that is…"

"I'm sorry My Lady, what was that?"

"Never mind Suzanna, you'll find out in due course as I'm sure everyone will I suspect. Look I'm going to have a security driver bring Nahla over to you so be ready to receive her in just over an hour and a half or so."

"Yes My Lady, although I have no idea how to switch…"

"Just do it please, it's very important Suzanna."

"Yes My Lady, I will do my best.

"Yes you do your best, please do let me know when it is done."

The phone went down at the other end. Suzanna stared at her phone and shook her head. "That woman is so rude!" Still at least Khepri was coming home; she had been worrying about her. She rubbed at her eyes but unlike Mildred, went straight to the bathroom for her toothbrush.

Saturday Morning 8.58 am

Looking at the new quarter light on her car Sarah pouted her lips in annoyance; the other woman should be paying for that really. She still had her details, undecided whether to chase it up or not. She had had enough hassle in her life recently and didn't really need any further.

She breathed out and looked upwards to the sign outside of her work place, 'Castle Hollow Veterinary Practise' and she could see movements inside reception. Sarah suspected that she had been the subject of gossip after yesterday's events. She would have to shrug it off; it was as simple as that, as she headed towards the main doors.

"Good morning Sarah" Samantha said with a smile.
She nodded and spoke quietly. "Good morning. Have there been any calls for me? My personal phone has been quiet, well as far as work goes that is." She put her work bag on the floor.
"Oh, you still getting hassle from him?"
"I seem to attract them," she nodded as a clipboard was passed to her with some notes on them. Do you know if the shorthair cat called Missy has been okay overnight?"
"Fine, no problems at all as far as I know."
Sarah nodded. "Do you know if any testing was done on her, bloods taken or anything else?"
Samantha shook her head. "I'm not aware of it as she appeared to be perfectly well when she got here according to David."
"Mmm."
"Any reason why you would ask?"
She shook her head. "No, no, was just curious that's all. I'm glad she is doing well, I have to return her in a bit."
"Well the kettle is on if you want a cup of tea before you start."
Sarah smiled, and picked up her bag. "Thank you, a cup of tea is in order I think, do you want one?"
"No, I've just had my second already."
Sarah's smile continued as she let herself through the doors behind reception and looked down the corridors. All seemed quiet as she passed by the kitchen area and took a pair of gloves out of her pocket. She went to the back of the building to the kennelling area and looked through the small piece of thick glass in the centre of the door. It looked like no one was in there as she let herself in, closing the door behind her. She put her bag on the side and took out what she needed.

She passed by dogs, rabbits and reptiles before she got to the back of the large room where the cats were kept in their own area, a part time cattery of sorts. She saw Missy immediately. The handwritten name above her cage she didn't need to read to know that it was her. "Good morning Missy and how are you?" Khepri blinked a couple of times but never lifted her head that was resting on her front paws. She turned around to check she was still alone and gathered a warm towel and took a needle from her pocket and unlocked the cage. "I'm truly sorry to do this but I know what I saw." She ran a hand of reassurance back and forth down what she believed to be Mildred's cat and wrapped her in the towel exposing a hind leg.

With clippers she removed the smallest amount of hair that she hoped would go unnoticed. "I'm sorry, this will take just a second," as she depressed the needle into the cat's leg and watched the small vial fill with blood. She felt Missy tighten under her hand that gently supported her. "There you go, all done," as she sealed the vial and put it into her pocket. She cleaned over the injected area and applied a small temporary dressing. "Mildred seems like a lovely lady, you have a good owner and she cares for you, I want to make sure we do right by her. You're going home soon after I've had a cup of tea." She smiled as she spoke.

She reclosed the cage, locked it, went to the exit door and peered through the glass. The coast was clear and she reclosed the door behind her and removed her gloves. She knew what she saw yesterday was a phenomena and it required further investigation.

Saturday morning 10.05 am

Suzanna sat in her car staring at the old Polaroid camera. Just push the button and click I guess, she thought to herself. She put it on the passenger seat next to Nahla who had been swiftly returned by a lady who had very little to say for herself. She wore a strange type of uniform and seemed anxious to get away.

She started the car and headed in the direction of Mildred's home. How on earth she would carry out a cat exchange for the second time she had no clue. Quite why this had been put upon her she had no idea. Much didn't make sense and the vet woman who has Khepri thought she was some sort of private detective!

It didn't take long before she was only a road away and pulled up again outside the shop from the land that time forgot.

Sat there looking at the frontage of the old building and the faded paintwork, she clicked her back teeth together for inspiration.

"Mildred comes here all the time doesn't she?" She looked down at Nahla. She didn't have the gift of the cat language apparently but she was confident that Nahla understood what she was saying. She ran a hand across the back of the cat that stayed at Mildred's. "It's really good to see that you are better though, you had us quite worried."

She pressed down on one of the controls on her door panel so the window came down slightly for some air. "I won't be long, just need to figure out what to do." She stepped out of the car in her gleaming heels, straightened her pencil skirt and pressed the remote to lock. The windows of the shop looked like they could do with a good clean as she went over to look at the assembled items that were displayed in quite a disorderly fashion. There were posters all over the windows advertising concerts and postcards that people had added for their missing animals 'have you seen...' etc.

She peered inside between the posters needing to make sure that Mildred was not in the shop. The man behind the counter immediately saw her movements and looked up at her. Her eyes flipped to the right to read a karaoke night advert at the Futility pub that she knew was at the end of the road.

There was no sign of Mildred so she entered immediately hearing a tinkerling of a bell ringing above her head.

"Oh hello again," the man rasped, "you like Karaoke do you?"

Suzanna turned to look outside the door when she realised that he was speaking to her. "I'm sorry?"

"Karaoke! I saw you reading the advert. It's a good night out, doesn't matter if you can't sing!" He chuckled away to himself and she watched him adjust his trousers as he breathed out heavily.

"Oh no, I'm not really interested in that." She smiled and exited the conversation to look around the shop.

"Oh, right you are." He shook his head and continued reading his newspaper.

She wandered around the shop with no clue what she was looking for. It may be from years of protecting cats that her eyes were drawn to tins of cat and dog food stacked on an old shelf when she paused with an idea.

She walked over to the counter. "Erm do…"

"Farming paper is it today?"

"I'm what, sorry?" She had a confused expression on her face.

"You came in here yesterday, left with the Shropshire Farmer paper."

Her head tilted forward with puzzled frown lines across her forehead. "Oh, yes, no I wasn't very interested in that."

The man's face was reasonably perplexed.

"Did read something about the sheep diving contest though."

"Oh yes" he rasped "that's quite the scandal, everyone's talking about it." He leaned forward to her. "Apparently the use of anabolic steroids or something, makes the sheep jump higher supposedly." He leant back and gave a satisfactory nod having provided her with the local gossip. "Don't know what the world is coming to?"

"Erm, yes, well er, tell me do you have a cat lead?"

His right eyebrow raised. "Cat lead?"

"Sorry I meant to say dog lead, for a small dog, with a collar."

"Right you are." He spoke in a soft but confused tone, "wait right there." He walked to the other end of the shop murmuring something to himself.

He returned to the counter with a bright pink lead with a collar. "That should fit any small cat, I'm sorry, I meant to say dog."

She looked up at him and smiled and took what looked to be a very expensive purse out of her jacket pocket. He noticed the notes inside it and the gold symbol on the outside, probably from some exclusive fashion house.

"How much is that?"

"I'll take eight pounds please."

"Well here is ten, keep the change."

He picked it up. "Thank you, you can help yourself to another farming paper if you wish?"

She picked up the lead and headed for the door. "No thank you, not much of a farmer."

The bell tinkled overhead as she wobbled on her heels and went through the door.

"You're not kidding" he muttered and looked down and continued to read.

She quickly got into the car and threw the lead onto the floor in front of the passenger seat and started the car. "Nahla, we are going for a walk!"

The car moved away from Mr Frank's shop heading in the direction of Mildred's house.

Stockings, brown skirt, blouse and her home made cat sweater were adorned as she looked out of her bedroom window with some curiosity. She frowned looking up and down the road as it seemed very quiet for midday on a Saturday in the height of summer.

She looked at her alarm clock on the side and walked over and picked it up, two minutes past twelve? That seemed kind of odd as she must have spent ten minutes or so getting ready. She brought it to her ear but there was no sound of ticking coming from it as she placed it back down. She shook her head reasonably certain that she had wound it up yesterday. Oh well it was a strange day after all so she probably did forget. She should switch the kettle on just in case the vet wanted a cup of tea; it was the very least she could do.

She walked down the stairs into the kitchen and picked up the kettle and took it to the sink to fill it with cold water. The minute hand of the clock had not moved as she put the kettle down and took the clock off the wall. There was no ticking coming from that one either. She flipped it over and took the batteries out that she had only replaced a few days ago. "Bet they had passed their sell by date as well" she scoffed knowing that she would be taking those back to Mr Franks later.

Clock was put down on the side as the kettle went on the gas ring and she walked into the front room and switched on her television. Maybe that would be able to tell her the time.

She could see a reporter speaking at a fast pace as she bent over to turn the volume up. It looked like an important news item, as in bold letters, 'BREAKING NEWS' was at the bottom left of the screen.

"Well that's a good question Mary. The safety record is still intact to the very best of our knowledge but authorities here are being very tight lipped as we await some form of official announcement. There is still a 100% safety record that no one has been killed from falling debris or what is sometimes referred to simply as space junk."
Mildred cocked her head back. "Eh?" as she took a seat.
"But early reports say that these were functioning satellites?"
"Well yes we believe so and experts are doing some head scratching today as to how they didn't fully break up within the atmosphere. I'm not an expert Mary, but from those who do know about these things, usually as satellites near the

end of their life, they perform a burn or an orbital manoeuvre and are sent into what is called the graveyard orbit. Apparently this movement takes less fuel than to bring them back to earth. For those that do, and from as early as 1971, over 260 craft have been directed to the South Pacific to an area often called 'Point Nemo,' the oceanic pole of inaccessibility which is not easy to say quickly. I had to practise it a few times Mary and that area, the Point Nemo I refer to, is over 1,600 miles away from land."

"So why do they do this?"

"Well this is done with safety in mind along with sending satellites into the graveyard orbit to try and minimise satellite collisions. But in any event that would appear to be what has happened here in the early hours of this morning."

"Do we know when there may be an official announcement?"

"As I say Mary, everyone is being tight lipped here and the whole area is sealed off, but many are saying that events like this were not likely but probable. I spoke to Professor Morgan Stephens from Lochnagar University on the phone earlier and he informed me that there are over 170 million pieces of so called space junk flying around us overhead. Many granted are very small in size but observers here said there were two balls of light that fell. One disintegrated, breaking into many pieces that are scattered over 50 miles but the other did make land contact behind me here in North Wales."

Mildred's mouth fell open; it must have been what she saw last night as she put her head into her hands and rested them on her knees.

"As you can see behind me Mary, many have gathered here and you can read some of the banners they are holding up welcoming what they believe to be alien spacecraft. Henry Hubbard is here with me, who has driven over from Welshpool and saw the falling lights. So tell me what did you see Henry?"

"Well I was outside right, it was a beautiful evening, having a couple of bottles of cider as you do, well quite a few actually. It had gone midnight I think when this bright ball of light flew over my house and I saw a ball of flame erupt in the distance. I hid under my garden table just in case it was a nuclear bomb. It obviously wasn't or I wouldn't be here now would I, ha ha ha? Anyway, so I finished my cider and asked my mate Barry next door to give me a lift over here, I was a bit pissed you see."

"Right, well, thank you Henry and so..."

"This is the new Area 51 this is."

"Thank you Henry."

"They are here I'm telling you, this is Wales's Area 51!"

"Yes thank you Henry and we do apologise for the use of bad language."

Mildred could hear that Henry was still talking in the background as the reporter cut him off and security moved him off camera. She could see there were people waving signs in the background saying 'Government Cover Up' and 'Aliens Welcome' and other stuff.

"In any event Mary, the Space Lawyers are going to be rubbing their hands in glee. According to Professor Stephens the actual collision would have happened maybe as long as 24 hours beforehand."

Mildred was distracted by the kettle whistling in the kitchen as well as the clock on her television screen saying it was only 10.47 am

----

It was quite late in the morning when Sarah was given her full itinerary for the day. As she worked through her notes it would appear that she had a few calls to make in the afternoon. Knowing that she had said to Mildred that she would return Missy around midday there could be no doubt of how much she loved her cat so maybe an hour earlier would be welcome news.

She walked into reception with a carrier in hand and waited for Samantha to finish her phone call. She lifted the carrier up. "Just to let you know that I'm taking Missy from out the back if you could check her out."

"Okay bear with me," as she tapped away at the keys of her computer, rolling her tongue as she read the screen. "Okay, Rocke Road belongs to Mildred, does that sound correct to you?"

"It does."

"Okay no problem, I'll check her out."

Sarah nodded to her and headed out the back as David the senior partner appeared from his room. "Sorry I haven't seen you so far today Sarah, how are you feeling?"

"I was feeling fine yesterday David, just going to take Missy back to Mildred."

"Oh yes, the cat with multiple heart beats," he grinned.

"That's not funny, I know what I heard and saw David."

He still had a teasing smile on his face. "Okay, well anyway I'm sure her owner will be glad to have her back."

"Yeah, I think she will, catch you later."

She headed through the door with a little scowl on her face 'make fun of me, we'll see' as she went to the back and unlocked the kennel labelled 'MISSY'.

"Come on now, time to get you back home. Hope you are not going to cause me any more trouble Missy."

With surveillance experience under her belt and now prepared, Suzanna parked her car just a little way before Mildred's house on the opposite side of the road. It would be a waiting game as she tapped at her expensive watch that seemed to have stopped working, but it was commonplace that she would forget to wind it up.

"Guess we'll just have to sit and wait Nahla." She crossed her arms looking down the road and adjusted her rear view mirror to see cars approaching her from behind.

She picked up the camera that fortunately had a strap attached to it and put it around her neck. "Suppose we had better get you ready then," as she adjusted the collar and placed it around Nahla's neck. "This has been quite the security operation Nahla to get you back home. I do hope Khepri is okay," Nahla met her eyes, "and that they haven't done any tests on her." She chewed at her lips at the thought of it. "That could cause complications." She picked up the lead and attached it to the collar. "Let's hope not."

She ducked down to look out of the windows. There was no Church with a clock in sight and the time on her phone seemed temperamental. It would have to be guess work and especially, no matter what, do not get seen by Mildred. *'Before midday she said, the vet would be back before midday.'* She shook her head knowing that she should have asked the time from the strange man at the shop.

Fifteen minutes or so must have passed when she saw in the rear view mirror what she thought was the vet's car approaching. She ducked as it went passed. "Well that was quick work Nahla, she's replaced the car light already!"

She picked up Nahla and checked no one was driving by as she got out into the road and crossed over to Mildred's side of the road.

The car ahead's break lights were still on with the engine running, as she sped up her steps, which wasn't the easiest to do with the footwear she had selected. "Right Nahla, I'm going to let you go, please do play along." She lowered Mildred's cat to the pavement. "Keep up with me," as they approached the vehicle as its engine was switched off.

426

Sarah got out of the car to see the very unwelcome face that she had first seen yesterday. "Oh you again?"

"Well what are the chances?"

"Yes indeed, what are the chances in an area you claimed not to know. You owe me a hundred pounds in damages as well."

Suzanna pondered, "I do have some money in the car, let me get that for you."

"No, that is not necessary just please leave me alone and stop following me or I'll report you to the Police."

Suzanna's head recoiled back in shock. "The Police! Why?"

"I've told you I want nothing more to do with him and he must get over it, he..."

She looked down at the floor with some surprise. "What are you doing?"

"What do you mean?"

"Why is your cat on a lead?"

"Well I'm taking it for a walk."

Sarah's eyebrows rose. "You are taking your cat for a walk?"

"Well yes, don't you?"

"No." She shook her head and crossed her arms. Her body was ridged with exception to her tapping foot. "You really are the worst private investigator ever, just leave me alone."

"Honestly, I have no idea what you mean but look I must pay you, here, hold my cat." She stepped forward quickly picking up Nahla and forcefully passed her into the vet's arms. "I'll just be a moment."

"I told you that..." Sarah sighed as the strange woman moved away from her so quickly she didn't have a chance to stop her.

Suzanna opened her car door and hid behind it and reached for her purse that was already in her pocket and took out some notes. She looked up through the glass to see the vet staring at her and clicked the camera on and closed the car door.

Sarah glanced down at the beautiful cat. "Well you are very pretty, you look just like Missy." She gave her own comment a moment's thought.

"Oh well now, don't you both look beautiful together, I must take a picture."

"No, I don't think so thank you, here please take your cat."

"No, I insist."

"You insist! I insist that you do not."

"Nahla close your eyes!!" as Suzanna pressed the button and an almighty flash lit up the vet who instantly froze.

Suzanna puffed and panted and took a step back in shock. Not just because the vet's mouth was frozen open clearly about to speak with her arm raised. It was more to do with the woodpigeon that fell from the tree above and bounced on its back on the pavement with its little legs twitching in the air.

"Bloody hell!"

She looked quickly around. No one seemed to be watching. She let go of the camera that fell on the strap around her neck, dived at the car and opened the door. "Hello Khepri!!!" She flipped the catch on the carrier and took her out holding Khepri under one arm. "Right you go there as she switched the cats, disconnected the lead and placed Nahla into the carrier, closing the door.

"Khepri just stay there a mo." She was starting to panic as the vet wasn't moving, frozen to the spot. "Blimey, I hope I haven't killed her." She looked behind again to see if anyone was around. She watched the woodpigeon on the floor's legs start to move and it righted itself. The vet blinked and wobbled, clearly disorientated, as she put a hand to her head which she shook a couple of times. "That's odd, I feel a bit queasy."

Suzanna's hands were shaking; the pupils of her eyes were as wide as they could possibly go. "Are you okay?"

"I'm not sure; here you'd best take your cat."

"Gladly, thank you."

The woodpigeon shook its wings and, making a funny sound, flew off straight into the side of the vet's car, creating a small dent on the driver's door.

Suzanna, watching the pigeon and the vet at the same time, held her arms out as she received her cat. Sarah noticed the weird stranger was holding the cat lead and frowned. "Wasn't that…"

"Wasn't what?"

She stepped forward to Suzanna and snatched the Polaroid from the bottom of the camera. "I told you not to take pictures of me!" She walked to her car and tossed the Polaroid onto her car seat, "and if I see you around me again no ifs no buts, it's the Police!"

Suzanna nodded and lowered her head. "Okay well goodbye then."

The vet put her hands on her hips and watched the lady wobble in her heels as quickly as she could back to her car and she shook her head in disgust. "Honestly!"

She went to the rear of the car and opened the door. "Hello Missy, you are back at home, come on now." As she picked up the carrier she was immediately distracted by a pink object on the cat as she held the carrier up to eye level and paused. "Were you wearing a collar before?" She was thinking it over, and was fairly positive that Missy didn't have a collar. She looked over at the car in front of them doing a three point turn in the road, as it sped off at some speed. She looked back into the carrier as Mildred's cat looked back at her. 'Maybe all of this business in her personal life was getting to her,' she was forced to consider.

"Khepri high five," as she held her hand up *(that was not received)*. "Job well done, Lady Nubia will be most pleased," as she felt the money in her pocket and released she hadn't paid the vet, "and it only cost me a dog lead ha ha!" She hit the gas and continued to giggle away as she looked at the dog lead on the floor that was minus a collar. Her giggling immediately stopped as she looked at Khepri's collarless neck and looked forward to the road. "Oh bugger!"

The car sped away all the same.

Mildred bobbed at her window like a demented meerkat when she heard someone outside and rushed at the front door. "MISSY!!! Sarah please do come in."

She beckoned the vet into her front room. Mildred turned down the television as Sarah looked at the screen. "What is going on?"
"Mmm?"
"On the television, looks like a news story."
"Oh aliens have landed in Wales or something, anyways how's my Missy?"
Sarah blinked, her nose twitched with the fishy smell and frankly already wanted this day to be over. "Erm, yes, she is fine Mildred, quite strange, in fact one may say quite peculiar all in all."
"Can I have her?"
Sarah smiled at seeing the excitement in Mildred's face. For all of the weirdness there was no doubt how much Mildred loved her cat. "Yes of course." She placed the carrier down on the sofa and unclipped the cage and took Missy out. "Here you go" and passed Missy to her.
She watched Mildred cling to her cat like a mother to a newborn as her eyes became watery. "Missy I have been so worried about you!" Sarah suspected that Missy would have a lot of hugs and loving today.
"Would you like a cup of tea?"
"No thank you Mildred I really must go I'm afraid, I have a busy day."
"Well that's okay, not a prob...Oh, you've given her a collar?"
Sarah swallowed. "Er, I, er really can't explain that, call it a present from us," as

she shifted her body uncomfortably.

"Well okay, thank you, are you sure she is okay?"

Sarah nodded without words; she didn't know what to add.

"Well, if you are sure but thank you ever so much for what you have done."

Mildred looked at the very simple smile across the vet's face as she picked up the carrier and headed for the door and opened it herself.

"Mildred if there are any more problems, anything please call me personally on my mobile."

"I will of course and thank you for bringing back my friend."

She smiled. "You're welcome, I had best be off."

She watched the vet walk down towards her gate as she closed the door and looked at Missy. She was ecstatic and clapped her hands together. Her friend was home and she was not lonely anymore.

Life was good.

Sarah lent on Mildred's gate trying to think everything through. Something was sorely amiss but she was struggling to figure it all out as she went to her car and took her keys out of her pocket.

Unlocking the car she rubbed at her eyes and noticed the Polaroid on her seat and picked it up. She was still rubbing her eyes when a noise of shock emitted from her mouth. The carrier fell to the floor with a crash as she held the picture to her face with both hands. Her mouth fell open with horror as she looked at the picture of her skeleton and what looked like a skeleton of a bird falling out of a tree behind her. She looked upwards to see a woodpigeon wobbling on a branch above her as she let out an audible gasp.

She swallowed and stumbled backwards a couple of times feeling queasy and looked back down the quiet road to where the other lady had driven off.

Her breathing was audible as she reached into her pocket for her phone and went into the picture files and brought up the photograph she had taken of the strange lady. She closed her eyes in thought. "Jessica!" as she remembered what the lady had said her name was. She continued to stare at the photograph of Jessica as she brought the Polaroid closer to her face to look at the cat.

She was shaking her head in shock. Unlike herself and the bird wobbling in the tree above her, the cat's image was solid, not transparent and not skeletal.

It also looked like the cat's eyes were closed.

She lowered the Polaroid and put a hand to her heart trying to gain composure as a frown etched across her face. Blinking she looked down. "Is that a bloody dent on my car?" as the woodpigeon flew away.

Two hours or so previously

The Reeve sat with her head in her hands dwelling upon the lost Escarrabin as well as the part she played in events only a few hours beforehand.

It was a disaster. Security penetration, lost soldiers, killed watchers and who knows how much costs in terms of damage to the manor house. She knew that she would be called upon to give her account of everything and of course the realisation that they may have witnessed the presence of a gatekeeper who had actually dwelled for a short period at Loxley. She shook her head 'where do you even start?'
She would need to consult with her head of Order but she didn't want to as yet. She needed to think everything through and she was nervous about making the call. She looked up at the clock and wondered if the clocks had stopped in other parts of the world as well. If so it may well be her that will be hearing from her head of Order very soon.
She took a sip from her glass of water and returned it to her desk.

The security measures in place were not fit for purpose, that was a fact. She collapsed back in her chair, the one she had assembled herself, not the old heavy chair on its side next door.
She would need to consider it step by step. Firstly how that watcher, or whatever it was, got below the statue, that would be a good place to start. How he could have known about the chamber and, even more so, how he was able to penetrate it using the hand scanner?

She went to pick up her glass again and noticed the prints of her fingers on it; her eyebrows came together as she held it to her face and let out a very audible sigh and put it down and walked quickly to the side to look at her other glasses.

She held up a large wine glass that had not been washed and closed her eyes seeing her whole hand print on it. She also noticed that one was missing…the cleric had taken it.

She stepped back and shook her head and smashed it against the wall. Well that was one question answered, many more to go.

47 minutes later...

She was dressed back in her business suit. The clerics, who usually had their heads down with work, were now looking upwards at the slightest sound. They were unnerved and had every right to be. She had been summoned to Lady Safiya's quarters; no doubt the curator would also be in attendance. Protocol would dictate that her head of security would not be present but she would have preferred it if Raysmau was there for support. Difficult questions would be coming her way; a Reeve would not have been tested like this in generations. It would be of no surprise to her if she were summoned before the Grand Council. Being demoted or expelled was the least of her worries.

Lady Safiya's cleric greeted her and there was no waiting around as she was shown straight in to the sitting room. Sure enough Nubia was standing there with her arms behind her back and not a cat in sight.

She nodded. "Ma'am" and looked at the nervous short figure in front of her and acknowledged her with a nod of the head "curator."
"Please sit Reeve."
"Yes Ma'am, thank you." She perched herself on one of Lady Safiya's expensive antique single seater chairs.
"Much to discuss Reeve."
"Yes Ma'am, there is."
"Yes Reeve there is!"
She flicked her eyes towards the slightly shaking body of the curator whose demeanour was a mixture of anger and resentment.
"Come now Nubia, we are friends here let's keep as calm as we can."
Nubia looked at the floor. "Yes My Lady."
"Reeve, our clocks have stopped, our home destroyed and friends lost and in the middle of all of this your Order had an unimaginable creature buried right below us, something so terrible that potentially something may have crossed from the other side to claim it or release it. So my question is why?"
The Reeve knew this would not be easy as she swallowed knowing that the question in the scheme of things was a fair one. "It is difficult to explain the actions of the past Ma'am and I am not aware of the facts, but I'm sure they can

be established in time."

"Well how much time do you think we have Reeve before that monster comes back?"

"Nubia!" Lady Safiya raised her arms, "please let me ask the questions."

The curator's head went down again looking in the direction of the floor.

"We need to know these things Reeve, members of your own security Order have been killed. The one who came, who appeared as a watcher, had power to communicate and convert and he obviously knew some of your secrets, starting with your hidden chamber right here in these grounds!"

The Reeve chose not to look her in the eyes as she spoke.

"For too long there has not been enough transparency between your Order and ours and after events of the last 24 hours that will need to change and we need to work together. Somehow that thing got to one of our own clerics and poisoned her, the rest of the clerics are terrified. We need to know what we are dealing with here. We need to know what is hidden away here and that's just for starters. I have to report directly to the Grand Council who are highly alarmed and that's an understatement!"

The noise of small shuffling feet came from the right hand side of the Reeve. "It just doesn't add up."

"Nubia please!"

"No My Lady please hear me out." She composed her thoughts and coughed to clear her throat. "That creature may have failed but we lost one of our own in Lady Tempest and a chain of events happened very soon after. This watcher practically hands himself to us and now we know why but to what end, what did he want, to overrun this home? He clearly hoped to free the beast below to destroy us and our way of being, but others would come from the Order to protect us. The watchers are in numbers and many more are bound to still be out there but between him and them, what do they hope to achieve, the end of our kind, to take over the lands outside of this place, outside of our Order?"

The curator stepped forward. "So I will put it to you Reeve, your Order put that thing down there a long time ago for a reason that is now undeniable, but we need to know why. I think it was there to protect something else, something that you have not told us."

The Reeve looked up as she stepped back to her original place as the room fell silent.

Safiya twiddled at her thumbs considering what the curator had just said and nodded her head a couple of times. "I think Nubia has a credible point Reeve. Before now we have asked about simple measures such as CCTV to be added not just outside but inside this house. The world has changed as we do not feel as protected as we once did by your Order; last night is an example of that."

"My Order has protected the Horde Of Light for thousands of years, don't you…"

"Reeve that is enough! Know your place within this room as you address me!"

The Reeve's face had reddened in anger as she looked at the slight smirk on the curator's face.

"No one is dismissing what your Order has done for us Reeve and I and the Grand Council never would. We will always remain thankful but the secrets you keep now need to come out. The prophecy is happening right in front of us, right in front of our very eyes. How can we fight if we do not know the facts! The third part of the prophecy has not materialised as yet but I feel it is only a matter of time."

After a short pause and much to the Reeve's dismay Safiya was not done quite yet.

"Let's face it, there has been such a reluctance to go into the below and we didn't even know how deep it was as well as how many watchers were down there. It's too disorganised and, from what I hear, the whole area may now need to be sealed off and they will need to be housed elsewhere."

"Or we kill them off," Nubia mumbled under her breath.

Safiya's eyes widened in alarm. "Curator don't ever speak like that, we are not murderers!"

Her previous smirk had disappeared. "But what purpose do they serve My Lady? They are vile and poisonous, they have no place here!"

"Everyone and everything has a place Nubia, we do not kill because we do not like. That is what the others outside of this place do in their world and it is not an example that we intend to follow."

Safiya sat back in her chair and took a deep breath and looked at the Reeve. "What if what Nubia is saying is correct. Is there something down there, something we need to know about?"

The Reeve shook her head. "Ma'am I am not aware of it, I was not aware of any of this until yesterday."

"Maybe your own Order do not trust you then Reeve."

She scowled at Nubia "I am well thought of Nubia, I suggest you remember that!"

"ENOUGH, enough, both of you please! I know you have your code Reeve but I have to ask you again is there anything we should know?"

"No Ma'am, I am telling you all I know but I need to speak to my head of Order and maybe a trip to the archives must follow. But rest assured we will get to the bottom of this and changes will be made."

"That thing Reeve, that creature, came here for a reason and I don't think any of us has the full picture including you." She leant forward on her chair to address both of them. "But we can be clear on one thing, it will be back and that is inevitable."

There was no response from either of them as they considered Safiya's point of view. The Reeve took in a deep breath knowing this was just the start of the questions that would be coming her way. Her thought process was suddenly distracted by a knocking at the door from behind her. She turned with a frown across her face to see the cleric had appeared at the door.

Safiya looked up "What is it?"

"Ma'am Lady Fennaway is here."

The curator's head bobbed up with some concern. "Fennaway is here?" as she looked at Safiya.

"I was unaware of her coming here Nubia; well please do show her in."

Kamilah Fennaway walked through the open door into the centre of the room with her work bag in hand to see the Reeve staring at her and instantly recognised the confused face of Nubia.

"My Lady," as she nodded at Safiya.

"Fennaway what are you doing here we are somewhat in the middle of a crisis?"

"Well I couldn't help but notice Nubia, what on earth has gone on here?"

"Have your clocks stopped Kamilah?"

She turned hearing the Reeve's question and nodded a couple of times.

"So the stopping of time has affected more than just here." Safiya shook her head a couple of times. "Kamilah this is an unexpected visit, pray why are you here?"

"Well do you not know my Lady?" She looked at the three confused faces. "The Keeper is on the way here. She contacted me well over an hour ago, not sure of the exact time of course as nothing works but she said it was vitally important that I was here."

Nubia stepped forward. "The Keeper is coming here?"

Kamilah nodded a few times looking as confused as the questioner did and shrugged her shoulders slightly. "She should be only minutes away I would have thought."

Safiya squinted her eyes as she thought. "Reeve were you aware of this?"

"No Ma'am I was not." She stood up. "She must be greeted."

"I don't think she needs pomp and ceremony Reeve."

She looked at the curator. "All the same. Ma'am may I use your phone?"

Safiya nodded, "yes, please do."

The room was silent as she pressed at a button on the phone that was shortly answered. "Raysmau, the Keeper is arriving in a moment, please greet her and escort her to Lady Safiya's quarters."

The others could not hear what was being said in response. "No, no, just what you are wearing, there is no time and it doesn't matter in the scheme of things. Please post some guards outside the rubble so she can be guided in."

She put the phone down and placed her hands on her hips as the curator voiced another opinion that hadn't been requested. "Something must be serious if she is coming here?"

"Indeed" nodded Safiya, "the new cats are due here today but she never delivers them herself, something else has made her feel the need to be here."

Raysmau had received the radio call that the Keeper's car was heading down the driveway. In the short time frame she dressed as best as she could but there would be no mistaking the tiredness of her eyes as well as her reasonably unkempt appearance.

As she stood outside on the summer's morning looking down the now relative calmness of the driveway it only took the briefest of glances behind her to see the damage to the front of the grand old mansion house. The smell of smouldering wood and crushed stone was still in the air. The building would take time to repair but much had been lost that could not be replaced.

She took a deep breath to greet the important, unexpected visitor as her car weaved around fallen stone on the driveway. The body of the deceased cleric had been removed a couple of hours ago as she looked down momentarily dwelling on it. As the car stopped, she nodded to the officer of the Escarrabin on driver duties that did her best not to stare at the front of the house, as she left her driver's seat to open the door for the Keeper.

She saw the familiar cane exit from the car door as she was supported by her driver and got to her feet.

"Morning Ma'am, I was not aware of your coming."

"I notice you did not say good morning but I guess there is nothing good about this."

Raysmau watched her look over the front of the house and the fallen brick, glass and debris that was strewn all over the grounds; she could see that she looked very upset.

"It's worse than I feared. What has happened to this beautiful place Raysmau?"

"It's difficult right now to know where even to start but we will get to the bottom of this."

"Your Reeve will have some questions to answer you can be sure of that!"

"Yes Ma'am she has my full confidence and answers will be gained."

"Is Lady Safiya okay?"

"Yes Ma'am, as well as can be expected. She waits for you upstairs."

She shook her head. "I'm glad that part of the building hasn't been destroyed as well! Here, give me a hand with this will you Raysmau."

The Keeper nodded at her driver to open the door on the other side of the car. The security officer walked around the car and took out four large ceremonial carriers that were draped in black cloth; there was a carrying handle on top of each.

The driver carried two in each hand and she brought them around to her. "Pass those to Raysmau will you."

"Yes Ma'am."

Raysmau took the four square carriers that were not exceptionally heavy for her from the security officer. "We need those upstairs, show me the way will you."

"Yes Ma'am. You will need to navigate through some of the block work and stone that has fallen but the stairway up remains relatively intact."

"For now," as she propped herself on her stick and started shuffling forward noticing other Escarrabin outside looking over her.

Raysmau turned to the security officer who was aghast looking at the damage, no doubt aware that some of her own Order had lost their lives some hours before. She nodded at the driver. "Please return to your duties."

"Yes Ma'am," as she closed the car doors and drove the car around to the back of the house.

The cleric opened the door to let the Keeper into the room where she was greeted by the Reeve, curator, the Lady of the house and their veterinarian. "Do follow me Raysmau."

All five of them turned to see the large stature of Raysmau enter the room holding four carriers which they all recognised instantly. Upon seeing them, Kamilah knew instantly why she had been summoned, as a look of worry was etched across her face.

"Raysmau, would you please put those on Lady Safiya's desk."

"Yes Ma'am." She nodded and glanced at the Reeve, who did not show it, but was pleased to have her presence there.

She placed the carriers on the desk and turned and nodded. "Will there be anything else Ma'am?"

"No, thank you Raysmau."

Raysmau headed towards the door offering a slight smile of reassurance to the Reeve and leaned towards her speaking very quietly. "I'll just be outside the door." She sensed the Reeve's nerves as her smile was reciprocated. "Thank you." The Reeve nodded as her head of security exited, closing the door behind her.

The Keeper turned to confirm Raysmau's exit, instantly upon seeing the door close. "Well this is a fine bloody mess isn't it!" She shook her head in anger. "Whatever happened here last night will be examined thoroughly. I'm advised that some of our own soldiers were lost, watchers killed, the building destroyed and a cleric that was somehow overpowered or seduced. Is this all true Safiya?"

Safiya was still on her feet as she had risen to greet her old friend, but resumed her sitting position with just a few words. "I'm afraid so my friend."

She shook her head in disbelief.

"It's always good to see you but you were not expected today. What brings you here other than the events of last night?"

"I needed to be here Safiya as I needed Kamilah to be here."

Kamilah was looking directly at her.

"Did you bring your equipment with you?"

"Yes Ma'am, as you instructed."

"Good." She put her left hand on her hip and balanced on her stick with the right. "I'm not going to go into the process of how our kind are brought to me, but I am greatly concerned by something this morning, something of the like that I have never seen. Nubia please go to the carriers on the desk and read the label on the one on the left would you."

Nubia nodded with some concern as she approached the desk and saw Lady Safiya stand back up.

"What is going on here?"

"Safiya, in a moment I think we will find out."

"What does the label say Nubia?"

She looked up, "Daphne, Housman's Rise, Stafford, Staffordshire."

"Now read the one next to it."

Nubia fumbled with the tag tied to the handle of the carrier. "Suzanna, Porthill Crescent, Shrewsbury, Shropshire."

"And now the one on the far right."

"Daphne, Crosshouses Road, Much Wenlock, Shropshire. The new lady, the one that Mildred from Shrewsbury will be the elder for."

"Yes that is correct. These are their new cats but it is that one that concerns me" as she pointed at the one whose tag had not been read out yet. "Nubia please remove the cover."

She frowned looking at the Keeper, as her shaking hand hovered over the carrier. Her tongue was slightly out to the side of her mouth as she took hold of the jet black cloth cover and pulled it back, lifting it away from the container. She recoiled in shock as the cloth fell to the floor from her hand.

Safiya shook and swallowed as there was an audible gasp from Kamilah.

"Now please remove the covers from the other three."

Nubia looked at the Keeper. Her eyes were full of fear as she pulled the cloths from them one by one and placed them on the table. She stepped back and put a hand to her mouth as her eyes welled up fearing the worst.

The room was silent as they looked at the three gold caskets and the one the colour of turquoise.

"I've never seen anything like it!" Safiya was horrified as she looked at the elaborate and familiar carvings upon the gold caskets. She was not familiar with the one that had the serpents head engraved into it directly in the centre.

"Open it!"

Fennaway looked alarmed. "Ma'am are you sure?"

"That is why you are here. As you know I never see the contents of the caskets, I just arrange their delivery after they are presented to me, but given the events of last night we need to be sure. I don't need to see the other three opened but that one, the one that bears the enemy of old I do. Kamilah if you please, open the casket."

Kamilah's hands were trembling as she picked at the catch to open the door. The Reeve stepped forward as the curator took two steps backwards. Kamilah took a deep breath as she put her hands inside and brought out a small moving bundle that was wrapped in multiple cloths. She pulled at one of the cloths that exposed the beautiful head of a tiny kitten. She nodded. "Her eyes are already open," but that was not unusual. She smiled as a tiny paw exposed itself to stretch and the kitten's mouth opened with a yawn. "You are very beautiful."

"Never mind that Kamilah does it bear markings?"

Kamilah looked at the Keeper and refocused as she pulled away the layers of cloth to expose the body of the kitten. She swallowed as she ran her fingers over the heart of the cat and closed her eyes as her head went down.

Nubia was practically panting. "Well?"

The vet opened her eyes and solemnly looked at the curator and spoke so quietly the others struggled to hear. "Yes Nubia, she does."

"Oh no…it can't be!"

They all watched as Nubia started to crumble as tears ran down her face.

"Nubia please! Kamilah, we need to be sure."

"Yes Ma'am." She lifted her arms forward to Lady Safiya. "Would you mind, I need my bag."

A speechless Safiya held her arms out and brought the kitten into her chest looking at the marking on her side. She hoped hair would grow over it in time.

The Reeve looked on in silence. The only sound in the room that could be heard was Nubia's sniffles as Kamilah reached into her bag and removed her signifier and switched it on.

Safiya held the kitten forward. "No, you hold it please My Lady," as she watched the screen display whilst running the device gently along the kitten's midsection. The unnamed kitten's legs twitched as the signifier rested over the heart. The vet froze, closed her eyes and stepped backwards switching the device off. She turned to the Keeper. "It is unmistakeable, she has two heart beats." The Reeve let out a loud breath as Safiya sat down. The noise of Nubia's tears became more audible as the vet wrapped the kitten back up.

For the first time during their meeting, the Keeper shuffled to a chair and slumped down as her cane fell to the floor. They all watched the vet return the cat to the carrier and she recovered it with the cloth and stepped backwards.

"So, it is as foretold, the one bearing the mark will come." She looked to the floor. The Keeper had little else to say.

"But this is the end, the end of our kind!" Nubia's words echoed within the room. If she were looking for support she didn't find any. She dragged her hand over her nose in a wiping motion. "Reeve, say something."

The Reeve looked up with nothing to offer.

"But the prophecy has now come to pass, we have to do something!"

"And we will Nubia." Safiya moved her eyes to the vet. "Kamilah who is this cat bound for, where is it going?" Kamilah, who had just zipped up her work bag, looked over at Lady Safiya and let out a sigh. She walked to the casket and lifted up the tag. "Mildred, Rocke Road, Shrewsbury, Shropshire."

"What!!" practically spat Nubia. "Are you serious, she's a...she's new...she's only just been made an 8th degree elder!!"

The room was quiet. "She can't have this responsibility; she won't know her backside from her elbow!"

"THEN SHE WILL LEARN!"

Nubia was instantly silenced by the tone of the Keeper and she stepped back further.

"I don't know who this Mildred is but she had better be ready and she had better be worthy." They all looked at the Keeper. "For the time may come when we all have to look to Mildred. The future of our kind may well depend on it and for all of those on the outside of this place and our Order as well."

"But...but Madam Keeper, she knows nothing, she barely even knows about us. Can it not go to someone else?"

The Keeper shook her head. "No Nubia it is as foretold, this is the way things are done. I do not know why she has been selected; these matters are not explained to me. I don't know why this is happening now, in time we will discover these things. But let us all not forget that the one that bears the mark may be for good and it may also be for evil. This Mildred, this one of whom we speak, is now our highest priority and the time will come when she will be tested in the most difficult of circumstances." She turned to the Reeve. "This will fall under your jurisdiction."

The Reeve was biting at her lip and nodded in silence.

"The cat will need to be delivered and taken away from here as soon as possible; given recent events I think it would be wise to expedite that immediately."

"I'll take her."

They all looked to the Reeve.

"I'll take her to Mildred."

"Protocol dictates that an elder passes the cats down Reeve you know that."

"Whilst that is true Nubia, I think this changes things and I'm comfortable that the Reeve is assigned with this." Safiya nodded in agreement as Kamilah remained speechless. The Keeper had spoken and Nubia knew the subject was now closed.

"Nubia would you inform Mildred's elder that there has been a change in process this time. Just make something up, we do not want to cause alarm down the ranks when it is not needed."

Nubia reluctantly nodded.

"You shouldn't need me to tell you Reeve, but take others with you."

She nodded to the Keeper. "Yes Ma'am."

"So it is settled," as she balanced on her cane and stood up. Her face of usual steady calmness was full of emotion. "I fear for our time and what has transpired here and I must report to the Grand Council as will you Safiya. There will be great changes ahead that will affect all of us."

She turned to leave and headed towards the door. "From now on we will all have to believe in Mildred. Look after her Reeve or the time of the watchers will be upon us all."

With the exception of Nubia's sniffles, the room fell into silence again.

She screwed her nose up upon opening the fridge door. "Wow wee that's a bit ripe," and slammed the fridge door closed again. She ran her tongue over her lips considering whether Missy would want to eat some of the sandwich leftovers. The larder was a little empty as usual as she looked for tinned cat food. "Guess I'll have to go and see Mr. Franks, Missy, I need some new batteries for the clock anyway."

She turned around. "Missy?" as she heard the cat flap close. "Oh well now, how do you like that!" as Mildred put her hands on her hips in disappointment alone in her kitchen again. "You've only been back five minutes!"

Nahla never heard the words as she bounced down Rocke Road, there was much to discuss with her friends. She was moving fast, faster than ever, surprised with her own new found strength but she knew exactly where she was heading and that a meeting would need to be called.

She hopped up on the fence and then it was only a short step onto the new shed roof that belonged to Mr. Ablett. The inside of the shed sounded quiet as she looked around his garden and towards his house. She could see there was a new addition to the shed roof that was fixed at the other end of where she stood, that pointed down over the door, but she paid it little attention.

"Right, there's that damn cat," were the mumblings and grumblings inside the Ablett household. He was looking at his CCTV monitor, not that it told him anything new. He could see the cat sitting behind his camera from out of his downstairs windows. "I know you are up to something!" as he walked towards his sliding doors.

"NAHLA!!! You're back!!"
Nahla looked down from the shed roof to see that Scamper had appeared through the undergrowth.
She nodded. "Yes I'm back, been away for a little while."
The cat of no home or 'owner' looked ecstatic to see her. "But we've been worried about you, what happened?"
"It's a long story; did you see the lights above last night?"
"We all did, we sat out and watched it. Do you know something about it? We know it's not a good sign."
Nahla looked forward to see the Ablett man watching them both.
"Call the others will you, I must speak with you all."
"Right, I can do that, everyone?"
"Yes everyone as quick as you can."
"You sound different Nahla, you sound a bit more leader like."
Nahla turned to the scruffy cat. "I have purpose."
"Not sure Said will like this challenge to leadership Nahla."
"Well, there are going to be a lot of changes around here."
"Oh, okay. Can I just confirm, when you say everyone do you mean the badger and the fox that eats too much?"
"Yes them as well."
"They'll be sleeping at this time, especially Freddie. His digestive system needs at least eight hours of recovery."
"Well wake them my friend. You should also start using your real name as well."
"But I like Scamper, it suits my outdoors lifestyle."
Nahla smiled. "If that's what you call it, anyway we can discuss. Can you go and find them please?"
"Righty-oh and off I go."
She watched Scamper dart away as she turned her attentions to Mr. Ablett, as

her tail started to twitch.

There was a noise below her as she looked back down.

"Sorry when you say everyone, do you mean that fool of a squirrel as well?"

She smiled, "yes and the squirrel."

The undergrowth rustled again as Scamper headed off at warp speed level 5.

Her tail twitched as the patio sliding doors opened and Mr. Ablett stepped forward.

"Go away, how many times!"

He stepped forward again as Nahla's tail began to twitch further in a rhythmic motion. As he came closer, she moved closer to him along his shed roof.

"I'm telling you!"

Nahla lifted up her front right paw and swiped at the camera that now pointed towards the house next door.

"Why you!!"

"Andy Ablett what on earth do you think you are doing?"

He was still looking at the cat and did not turn around to greet his wife. "What is it now dear?" as he shuffled backwards a couple of steps.

"That!! That, that's disgusting!"

"What are you..." He turned around to see his CCTV monitor was now displaying the bedroom of the lady next door. He watched on the screen in horror as she lifted up her t-shirt. "Oh my God!!" as he held his hands up. "Dear I can promise you I have done no such thing." He turned around to see the cat walking away and he could have sworn it was smiling.

Nahla jumped onto the fence, away from the escalating noise coming from the Ablett household and surveyed the quietness of Rocke Road, enjoying the moment of silence.

For a lot was going to be changing around here.

The navigator informed her that she was now on the road of Mildred's home. The car headed to the far end to find number one. She glanced into her rear view mirror to the two Escarrabin dressed in plain clothes in the car behind her. Their small arms weapons were sealed away in an untraceable compartment hidden within their car. Being stopped by civilian law enforcement and having to explain their advanced weapons technologies could lead to some tricky outcomes.

The navigator flashed and her right hand indicator signalled that the car was pulling in to park. As the engine stopped, she put her arm over the two carriers that were still covered on her passenger seat, as she released her seat belt. With her arm still over the carriers she looked into the mirror again. She could see that one of the Escarrabin was looking back down the road as the other watched her. Glancing to her right at the old gate that was directly next to her car she couldn't help but stare at the unkempt state of the garden.

She stepped outside next to the gate and looked further down the road. A couple of young boys were making a noise at the bus stop but that was about it. She looked up, hearing a noise from above her to see a very unstable looking woodpigeon in the tree but other than that it all looked to be reasonably quiet for a Saturday afternoon.

She looked forward to the house again, at the state of the windows and the general condition. Protecting this property would take a lot of work she considered as she closed her car door. Looking around again she signalled at the two Escarrabin to stay in their car as she walked around to the front passenger door. She took both carriers out and placed them on the ground, closing the door. Feeling quite exposed, she checked one last time looking behind her and further down the road. She locked the car and picked up both of the carriers and proceeded to the gate. With her hands full she pressed with her backside against the gate, that freely opened, and moved up the weed strewn path.

The gate didn't close properly behind her but it didn't really matter. As she reached the door, she lowered her right arm to place one of the carriers down on the floor and gave a firm knock of her knuckles on the door, picking the carrier back up again as she waited.

Mildred's ears twitched to the sound of knocking and, like an auto response, looked at her un-ticking clock, as if knowing the time would tell her who was at the door. She scratched her head not expecting anyone but that was hardly unusual. She looked around the kitchen floor for Missy but to no avail, she hoped she wasn't stuck up a tree again or worse. Through the frosted glass of the front door she could see a tall dark shadow was waiting for her the other side. Pulling at the catch and poking her head around. "Yes, may I..."
She froze instantly as the tall lady in a black suit that looked half hit woman and

half lawyer stared at her wondering if she had done something wrong.

The stranger spoke gently with a smile. "Are you Mildred?"

"Well, I don't know, it depends who is asking?"

Her question was met by a little smile. "Please do not worry Mildred, I am from the Horde Of Light."

"Oh another one of those crackpots!"

"Excuse Me?"

"Well I..." Mildred glanced down to see that she was holding two containers. "Are they cats?"

"Yes Mildred they are."

The door flew open and Mildred's face was beaming. "Well you didn't say! Come in, come in, excuse the mess I wasn't expecting anyone."

She stepped in past Mildred, who held the door for her, as the nostrils in her nose felt like they had jumped up to her forehead as her eyes watered. 'What was that smell?' She instinctively went to raise a hand to her face to cover her nose, when she realised that she couldn't and coughed. The door closed behind her.

"Are you okay, you seem troubled?"

She spluttered. "Yes I'm fine, thank you; I'm just used to the clear Welsh air."

"You've travelled from Wales. I've never been to Wales, I would like to."

"I expect you will in time Mildred, the border is not far from here after all," as the Reeve stood there not sure where to go next.

"Good, good, then follow me," as Mildred unintentionally knocked her to the side in her excitement, as she was clapping her hands and led her through.

The carriers were placed on the table as the guest looked around at what she guessed within the mess resembled something that may be a kitchen.

"I'm sorry; you didn't say your name?"

Not used to being asked this question she was taken off guard. With a faint smile as her back was to Mildred she turned to her. "My name is Kiya but most call me the Reeve."

Mildred, with her hands on her hips laughed. "Well why on ever would they call you that?"

The Reeve clicked at her teeth with what to say. "It goes back to a long time ago and we've been called different names in the past. It's a shortened term of sorts for the word sheriff."

Mildred was in fits of giggles. "Like in the Wild West, pistols at dawn, that sort of thing?"

"No, not really," was the short response.

Mildred's laughter faded away as her kitchen fell into an uncomfortable silence.

"Oh, I see, erm well would you like a cup of tea or a fish paste sandwich?"
The Reeve looked at her surroundings as well as now guessing what the smell
was. "No, I'm fine thank you."
"Well, okay, so then...cats, cats, cats!!"
The Reeve watched Mildred bobbing up and down like a cork on water.
"Yes, of course." The Reeve walked to the table to look at the two containers
and peaked under the cloth of the one on the left and removed its cover to
reveal the gold and elaborately detailed carrier.
"Oh my!" My Missy was not delivered in one of those!"
"No, this delivery is a little different this time Mildred," as she unclipped the
door and reached inside and lifted out a tiny bundle and unwrapped the kitten.
"Oh my again!" Mildred was practically jumping for joy. "She's beautiful, well I
say that, is she a she?"
The Reeve froze. "Trust me it's a she Mildred," as she passed the kitten to her.
"Oh, I love her!"
"I trust you have a carrier for her?"
"Erm, what, why's that?"
"Really? I've presumed these things have been explained to you?"
Mildred was holding the kitten with as much care as could be possible. "How so,
I do not understand?"
"Well that cat is not destined for you." The Reeve looked at the tag on the
carrier. "I understand that you are the new elder for Daphne, this is her cat and
you have to deliver it to her."
"Oh." Mildred's face fell as she clung to the kitten. "Well what if I want to keep
her?"
The Reeve turned to her. Her body became ridged and her face became serious.
"You must never say words like that Mildred. Your path is clear and that cat is
not for you, it is to be protected by another."
Mildred stepped back a little as the stranger suddenly looked more hit woman
than lawyer and she felt intimidated within her own home.

There was silence between them as it dawned on the Reeve that she had just
unnerved the lady with the unusual dress sense that stood in front of her. She
drew a breath and smiled and looked at the other carrier. "This one is for you
Mildred."
Her smile had returned with some curiosity. "Well please show me!"
"Mildred I have to explain something to you. This, this cat is special."
"Well all cats are special Kiya."

The Reeve, unused to being addressed by her real name, closed her eyes but offered a passive smile. She spoke with a soft tone in agreement with what Mildred had said. "All cats are special, the ones that are brought to you, the ones outside, the ones you see on television. Never forget Mildred that all cats are special." She stepped forward to her, "but this cat, this one that is being presented to you for safe keeping is very special, you must look after it at all times."

Mildred still holding the kitten not meant for her felt a little confused. "Erm... okay."
She watched as Kiya removed the cover exposing the box of turquoise.
"Oh, the box is a different colour from that one!"
The Reeve paused as she went to open the catch. "Yes quite."
As the Reeve removed the kitten, she pulled away at the covers that had kept her warm, as Mildred's face lit up. "But she's beautiful," she smiled, "it's a she?"
The Reeve's lips pursed. "Yes," as she passed the kitten to her.

The Reeve stepped back and looked on at the joy in this relatively new member to the Order as she held both of the cats; it looked like tears were in her eyes. "This one is for me!"
The Reeve smiled and was surprised as she felt an unusual wave of emotion run through her. "Yes she is for you Mildred and only you."
"Well, I can't believe it; I don't know what to say."
"No words are necessary. Just please look after her and the other kitten needs to go to her rightful owner."
"Oh yes, of course, I have no idea what to say to her though," she giggled to herself. "I'll need to work that out. I remember when Daphne came to me for the first time I thought she was a lunatic."
As Mildred held both of the kittens, she brought her own one up to her face and did a double blink. "There looks like some sort of a mark on her?"
The Reeve was prepared for the observation. "I wouldn't worry, probably a birth mark, it can happen." Mildred looked at her face as the Reeve lied to her looking directly into her eyes. "Quite common really."
"Oh I see. It looks like some sort of burn?"
"Like I say, it's quite common really."
Mildred's face was radiant as if she had won the lottery as they both turned around hearing the sound of the cat flap. "Well there you are Missy, come look you have a new sister." She still held the kitten that did not belong to her and

placed the one (with the unusual marking) down onto the floor.

Nahla looked directly at the Reeve as they acknowledged each other, something that Mildred did not spot in all of the excitement.

The Reeve smiled "Well, I'll leave now to let them get acquainted." She picked up both of the carriers and instantly covered the one that bore the head of the serpent somewhat thankful that Mildred hadn't noticed the markings on them.

"Shall I see myself out?"

Mildred looked at the suited lady who called herself the sheriff, now with three cats in her presence, thinking it could be her happiest day for a very long time.

"Erm, no I can help."

"That's really not necessary."

Mildred watched the intimidating suited lady head towards her door but she stopped and turned to speak to her one last time. "Mildred, I have a strong suspicion that we will be meeting again, please do be careful and protect the newborn." She stepped forward and paused. "Oh and one more thing, please be careful around those who have strange glasses."

She looked at Kiya, the Reeve or whatever she was called with kitten in hand while the other two were on the floor getting to know each other. "Well of course," having no idea what the last comment meant.

The suited stranger smiled briefly and left and finally Mildred was alone with three cats, albeit it three was to be a temporary arrangement. But she felt happy, she felt content and Missy was better so therefore she was thrilled. This club, whatever they were, was filled with lunatics but you know they have just given me another beautiful cat so I guess I should be thankful for that as she looked at the two cats on the floor that she could now call her own.

The Reeve made sure the front door was closed and bent down to pick up one of the empty carriers and moved down the pathway, but she couldn't help but peek into the window of the kitchen. She looked through the dirty glass as Mildred innocently played with the cats. It had been a long time since she had seen someone so happy. In Mildred's blissful ignorance the Reeve felt momentarily jealous of her happiness but she knew that it would not last. For Mildred this was a happy day, hopefully one that she would remember in the bad days to come as she bonded with her new cat; the one that none of the Order knew whether was for good or for bad.

As she looked up to the sky and took a deep breath, and quite unbecoming of her, she thought that she may have felt a tear welling in her eye but was quick to dismiss it. Lives had already been lost, the prophecy had come to pass and evil was here. The image of the stranger through the window playing harmlessly with the cats was mesmerising to watch. "You have no idea Mildred, you have no idea and the time will come when you will play a great part for all of us." She stepped closer watching her happy face as she picked up her new kitten. "Much will hang on your shoulders Mildred and many will have to believe in you." She watched her kiss the new kitten that had been prophesised for hundreds of years. "I will believe in you Mildred."

The Reeve stepped back and gathered her thoughts and drew a deep breath. There had been many emotions racing through her over the last 24 hours and she had many pressures to face, as her composure was regained and she headed towards the gate.

She unlocked her car and placed both of the empty carriers on the back seat and walked over to the car with the two Escarrabin in it.

The window came down. "Everything okay Ma'am?"
She nodded. "In the circumstances," as she crouched down to speak to them both through the window.
"Listen I need you both to stay here and blend in, observe everything, do what the others here do."
"Like get a dog?" one of the Escarrabin suggested with a slight smile.
The Reeve, with everything that had gone on, did her best to conceal her smile. "No, don't get a dog." It was a nice feeling to have a smile again, as brief as it was.
"Look if a property comes up for sale or rent I need to know. This road is now a major priority, every person who lives here in this road I want to know about them, what they do, where they go what their routines are. I'll speak to Raysmau to arrange a shift rotation but this property is now immediate priority. Security measures will need to be added without her knowing; this place needs to be fortified."
She stood back up. "I need to get back to headquarters; it will take us some time to rebuild."
"Yes Ma'am," they both responded "we'll log everything."

The Reeve nodded and looked at them with some concern. "Also keep an eye on the sky."

The Escarrabin both looked at each other as the Reeve departed.

Mildred did not like calling her Missy by the name of Nahla, it didn't feel right and she was still very unsure about it; but she watched with curiosity as the tiny kitten wobbled on her feet as the bigger cat looked on at her with playful eyes.

"Missy." There was no response as she coughed slightly. "Nahla!" She had to confess that her cat looked up at her and she didn't know how she felt about it. She was still holding the kitten that didn't belong to her. "So what do you think about our new friend?"
The tiny kitten blinked and then yawned offering little assistance to the question.

Nahla placed a paw over her new sister in a protective way as they began to get to know each other. Mildred wondered how such a young kitten would cope away from her mother but much did not make sense in recent times.
Mildred jumped along with the kitten she was holding. "Nahla, she needs a name!" as her smile broadened.

With one hand Mildred scratched at her head and her dishevelled hair trying to think of a suitable name for her new family addition. She brought the kitten up to her face and sighed knowing that 'apparently' she could not keep that one as well. "Well what do you think?"
She looked around the kitchen trying to think up a suitable name as the two below her played and appeared to be happy. 'Spatula...no...forks...no... blade...no...oh hang on.' She reflected on the earlier news story and remembered the falling lights from the night before.
"Comet, I will call you Comet!"

Mildred was satisfied with the name and nodded in glee and put the kitten on the floor to join the other two. She took a deep breath and in happiness she looked out of her kitchen window with a smile.

If truth be told Mildred knew that Comet would only be a temporary name of course as the Order had told her that every cat had a real name and that's all cats of course, not just the ones in her kitchen right now, cats everywhere the world over. She smiled as she watched them play as noises resumed outside of her house of the bustle of daily life with the comings and goings of people.

As life carried on outside of Rocke Road it would be some time before Mildred would discover her new cat's real name but the time would come when she did and when she did she would be told that her new cat's real name was Tempest.